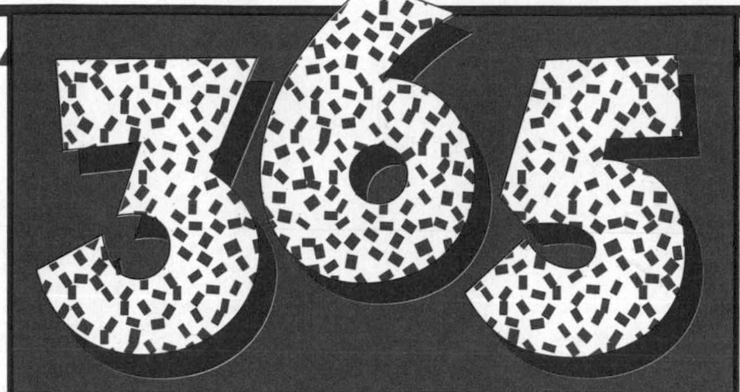

Crafts & Activities

Year-Round Holiday Fun

Contributing Writers
Lisa Lerner
Kersten Hamilton

Cover Illustrations
Kate Flanagan

Illustrations
Susan Detrich

Publications International, Ltd.

Louis Weber, CEO
Publications International, Ltd.
7373 North Cicero Avenue
Lincolnwood, Illinois 60712

Manufactured in U.S.A.

8 7 6 5 4 3 2 1

ISBN: 0-7853-4719-4

Lisa Lerner is a teacher and educational writer. Over the past eighteen years she has written and edited several textbooks and picture books for students of various grade levels and skills. She has completed several children's books, including *Bugs!* and *The History Nook*. Ms. Lerner is inspired on a regular basis by her niece and nephew, Jenna and Matthew Gabriel, and her godson, Jake Lester.

Kersten Hamilton is the author of eleven children's books. She has also written curriculum for public and private schools, literature guides, story tapes, articles, games, and children's songs. Her publication *The Butterfly Book: A Kid's Guide to Attracting, Raising and Keeping Butterflies* was cited as "educationally outstanding" by the Parent Council. Ms. Hamilton lives in New Mexico with her husband and three children.

Cover Illustrations: Kate Flanagan

Illustrations: Susan Detrich

CONTENTS

INTRODUCTION

Dear Parents and Teachers—

We know that most kids will be able to make the projects with little help, but there will be times when your assistance is needed. If the child has never used a glue gun, explain that the nozzle and freshly applied glue are warm, even for a cool-temp gun. Have a glass of water nearby just in case warm fingers need cooling.

You know your child's abilities—craft knives are very sharp and stoves can be very hot. You should judge whether your child is able to handle a knife or a hot pan safely. Even if the child is able to handle those things, you should be present to prevent accidents or injuries! Occasionally instructions direct the child to ask for adult help. Be sure everyone understands the "Important Things to Know" section in this introduction.

Also, there are a few projects that call for plaster of Paris. Children will need help when using this product. Plaster of Paris should always be disposed of in the trash—never pour it down a drain. It could cause permanent damage and clog the drain!

We give some basic information about holidays, but this is a great opportunity for you and your child to learn more about historic events and other cultures. If you have a computer, there are many Web sites you can explore together about holidays and world events. Of course, the library is always a good place to find more information.

Most important, this should be an enjoyable, creative experience. Although we provide specific instructions, it's wonderful to see children create their own versions, using their own ideas. Encourage their creativity and interests!

Hey Kids—

With *365 Crafts & Activities: Year-Round Holiday Fun,* you can make every holiday fun—even some holidays you didn't know existed! This book is filled with exciting games to play, great gifts to make for family and friends, terrific projects to decorate your rooms, and even some fun recipes to make.

This book was made with you in mind. Many of the projects are fun things you can make by yourself. With some projects, however, you will need to ask an adult to help. Not only can an adult help you with the projects, but they can also admire your wonderful results!

It's a good idea to make a project following the instructions exactly. Then feel free to make another, using your imagination, changing colors, adding a bit of yourself to make it even more yours. Think of all the variations you can make and all the gifts you can give!

If you're curious about the holidays mentioned in this book, do some exploring to find out more. Ask an adult to help you research—try the Internet (with adult permission, of course) and the library. Having some information makes you want more information—expand your world with knowledge!

The most important thing you need to remember is to have fun! Think how proud you'll be to say, "I made this myself!"

Key—

Each project is rated as to its challenge level. The chart below shows you the key to the levels. (Each chapter has different symbols, but it is the number of symbols that reflect the difficulty level, not the symbol itself.) Look for the number of symbols beside the title of each project.

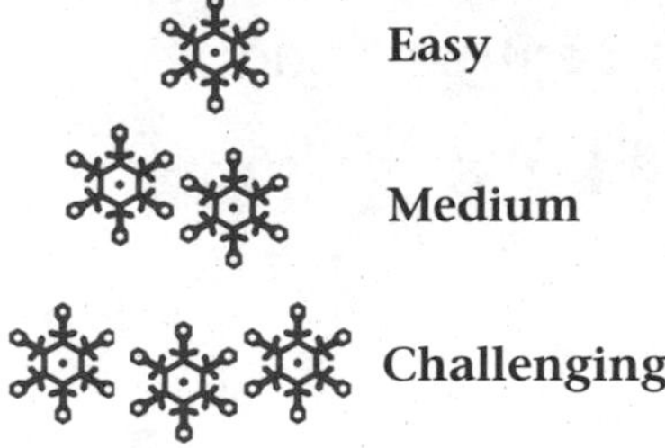

Important Things to Know—

Although we know you'll want to get started right away, please read these few basic steps before beginning.

1. For any project or activity you decide to do, gather all your materials, remembering to ask permission first! If you need to purchase materials, take along your book or make a shopping list so you know exactly what you need.

2. Prepare your work area ahead of time. Clean-up will be easier if you prepare first!

3. Be sure that an adult is nearby to offer help if you need it. An adult is needed if you will be using a glue gun, a craft knife, the oven, or anything else that may be dangerous!

4. Be careful not to put any materials near your mouth. Watch out for small items, such as beads, around small kids and pets. And keep careful watch of balloons and any broken balloon pieces. These are choking hazards—throw away any pieces immediately! Small children should not play with balloons unless an adult is present.

5. Use the glue gun set on the low-temperature setting. Do not touch the nozzle or the freshly applied glue; it may still be hot. Use the glue gun with adult permission only!

6. Wear an apron when painting with acrylic paints; after the paint dries, it is permanent. If you do get it on your clothes, wash them with soap and warm water immediately.

7. Cover any surface you work on with newspapers or an old, plastic tablecloth to protect it. Ask an adult if you're not sure whether to cover the kitchen table—but remember, it is better to be safe than sorry!

8. Clean up afterward, and put away all materials and tools. Leaving a mess one time may mean that Mom says "No" next time you ask to make something!

9. Have fun and be creative!

WINTER

Winter is a very special time of the year. Many important religious holidays happen in this season, such as Christmas and Hanukkah, and other important events are remembered at this time also, such as Martin Luther King, Jr.'s birthday. Look through this chapter; you'll be sure to find something fun and exciting to do indoors on a cold, snowy, or rainy day. And you might even learn something!

1

Hanukkah

STAR OF DAVID BOOKMARKS

Latkes are not the only use you'll have for potatoes this Hanukkah!

What You'll Need: Firm potatoes, knife, paper towels, marker, paintbrush, paints, construction paper, scissors, hole punch, ribbon

Have an adult help you with the cutting in this project. Choose and wash a firm potato. Cut it in half. Pat the potato dry with a paper towel. Using a marker, draw a star of David on the white part of the potato half. Carefully cut the potato away around the star outline. When you finish you will have a raised star. Cut 12-inch-long rectangles from construction paper to make the bookmarks—cut them a little wider than your potato star shape. Brush a thick, even layer of paint onto the star shape. Carefully press it onto the bookmark where you want a star. Lift the potato straight up—don't wiggle or drag it when you lift it. Print a row of stars along the bookmark. Try painting half the potato shape with one color and the other half a different color! When the paint has dried, write messages on the bookmarks, such as "Happy Hanukkah" or the person's name you are giving the bookmark to. Punch a hole in the top of the bookmark, and thread the ribbon through the hole. These Hanukkah gifts can be enjoyed all year long!

2

Hanukkah

DANCING DREIDELS

Not all dreidels are made of clay!

What You'll Need: Thin cardboard, scissors, ruler, pencil, colored tape, paint, paintbrushes, tape, markers, chocolate Hanukkah gelt

gimel	shin	nun	hey
ג	ש	נ	ה

Cut a 12 × 3-inch rectangle out of thin cardboard. Measure and mark the cardboard at 3, 6, and 9 inches. Fold along those lines to make a box shape. Tape the ends together. Cut out two 3 × 3-inch squares of cardboard, and tape them onto the ends of the box. Paint the cardboard in bright colors. When the paint is dry, draw a Hebrew letter on each side (see art above). Stick the pencil through the top, down through the bottom of the driedel. Tape the pencil in place with the colored tape. To play, everyone puts a chocolate coin (Hanukkah gelt) into the pot. Players then take turns spinning the dreidel. If the dreidel lands with the *nun* facing up, the player gets nothing. If the *gimel* faces up, the player captures the whole pot. If the *hey* faces up, the player takes half the pot. If the *shin* faces up, the player puts a coin into the pot. The letters *nun, gimel, hey,* and *shin* stand for the first letters of the phrase *Nes Gadol Haya Sham,* which means "a great miracle was here."

MANY WAYS TO SPELL IT

Hanukkah has only five letters in the original Hebrew; the word means rededication. Because we have to transliterate (change from one alphabet to another) the word into English, there is no definite right way to spell it. But there are over 16 different ways the word can be spelled in English!

Hanukkah

EASY I.D. BRACELET

This personalized bracelet is a unique Hanukkah gift for the jewelry-lover in the house.

What You'll Need: Paper towel tube, scissors, paint, paintbrushes, markers

Running out of gift ideas this Hanukkah? Make a dozen of these, and everyone will love them!

1. Cut 2 inches from a cardboard tube. Cut a slit down one side of the cylinder so that it can be worn on a wrist.

2. Paint the bracelet however you want. When the paint dries, write a friend's or family member's name in large letters on it. Find out each person's favorite colors and use them. Decorate around the name with tiny polka-dots, squiggles, hearts, or any other design. If your friend has a nickname, you can make a nickname I.D. bracelet!

1.

2.

Hanukkah

4 CHOCOLATE HANUKKAH BALLS

If you like chocolate, you'll love these fruity treats!

What You'll Need: Clear glass jar, blue sand, white sand, blue or white ribbon, seedless grapes, wooden skewers, semisweet chocolate chips, saucepan, spoon, saucer of blue and white sprinkles

These chocolate Hanukkah balls will make a beautiful table decoration, but it won't be long before they turn into dessert! Prepare the base by washing and drying a large clear glass jar. Pour alternating layers of blue and white sand into the jar until it is full. Tie a blue or white ribbon around the neck. Wash and dry a bunch of seedless grapes. Push each grape onto a wooden skewer. Ask an adult to help you melt the chocolate chips in a saucepan over low heat, stirring constantly so the chocolate doesn't burn. When the chocolate is melted, dip each grape into it with a twirling motion so the entire grape is covered with chocolate. Before the chocolate cools, twirl each grape in a saucer of blue and white sprinkles. Poke the wooden skewers into the jar of sand you prepared earlier. Make a whole bunch and arrange them like flowers. Place the jar on the table for a delicious centerpiece.

Hanukkah

WISH GIFTS 5

One picture is worth a thousand smiles!

What You'll Need: Old magazines and catalogs, scissors, cardboard, glue, white bag, markers

Why not give someone a castle, a giraffe, or a Ferris wheel for Hanukkah? Let someone you love know you're really thinking of them this holiday with this special Wish Gifts bag. Cut out pictures from old magazines or catalogs of presents you'd like to give. Lay them on cardboard, trace around the edges of the pictures, and cut out the cardboard shapes. Glue each picture onto its cardboard shape. All the pictures can then be put into a white paper bag that has been specially decorated for whomever it is for. Write "I Wish I Could Give You . . . " on the outside of the bag. Does your sister want a sports car? Would Dad like a new camera? Even if you're a little short on cash this year, you can give your loved ones just what they really want.

6

Hanukkah

LUSCIOUS LATKES

These sweet potato latkes are a twist on traditional Hanukkah pancakes.

What You'll Need: 4 sweet potatoes, 1 onion, 4 eggs, 1 teaspoon cinnamon, juice of ½ lime, 1 teaspoon salt, ½ cup flour, ginger (optional), butter, oil, grater, knife, measuring cup and spoons, mixing spoon, bowl, skillet, sour cream, applesauce

Have an adult help you grate the potatoes and chop the onion. Then beat the eggs. Add the onion, eggs, cinnamon, lime juice, salt, and flour to the potatoes. Mix well. You can add a teaspoon or two of powdered or freshly grated ginger for spice. Have an adult melt several tablespoons of butter in a skillet. Add a little oil to the skillet so the butter doesn't burn. Shape a smooth, flat pancake. Have the adult fry it. The pancake is done when both sides are crispy brown. Serve your sweet potato latkes with sour cream and applesauce!

Hanukkah

SHINING TIN MENORAHS

7

You can't light this menorah, but its shine will dazzle you!

What You'll Need: Tinfoil or heavy-duty aluminum foil; cardboard; newspaper; tape; knitting needle, spoon, or nail; glue; markers

You don't need special jeweler's tools for this beautiful engraving. Double a large piece of foil—the doubled foil should be several inches larger than your piece of cardboard. Cut sheets of newspaper the same size as the cardboard; cut enough newspaper to make a pad (7 to 15 sheets). Put the newspaper pad on the cardboard, and center the foil on top. Fold the excess foil over the edges of the cardboard, and secure them with tape, making sure there are no wrinkles in your foil. Use a knitting needle, spoon handle, or small nail to draw the menorah shape onto the foil. Press firmly but not hard enough to break the foil. Work slowly; once the lines are drawn it isn't easy to erase them. Draw with long, smooth strokes, and don't lift your tool until you have finished a line. When you have finished engraving, glue the back of your menorah onto a slightly larger piece of cardboard to create a frame. Color the cardboard around your engraving with markers. Celebrate a shining silver Hanukkah this year!

8

Hanukkah

FESTIVAL IN LIGHTS

Here's a really different kind of Hanukkah candle!

What You'll Need: 8 empty milk cartons, scissors, blue or white paper, glue or tape, thin cardboard, pencil, colored tissue paper, 8 small flashlights

1. Wash and dry the milk cartons, and cut off the tops.

2. Wrap the remaining base with blue or white construction paper, and secure it with glue or tape.

3. Draw a candle template on thin cardboard, and cut it out. Lay it on the front of each milk carton base and trace around it.

4. Carefully cut out the candle shape. Glue a square of colored tissue paper inside the carton to cover the candle-shaped hole.

5. Line up the cartons, and place a small flashlight inside each. When the flashlights are on, the "candles" glow in soft colors. Light one candle for each night of Hanukkah!

1.

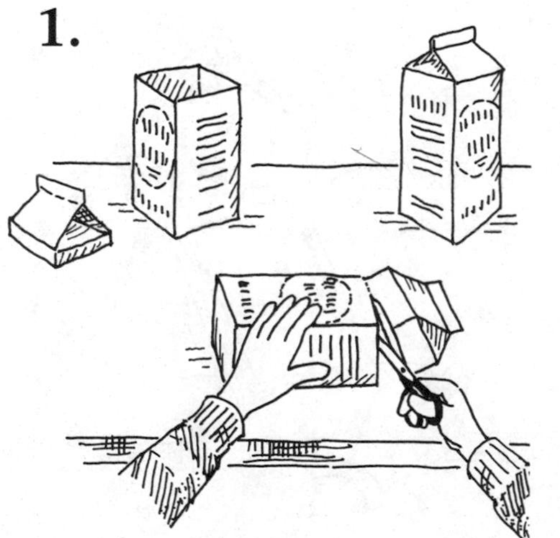

2.

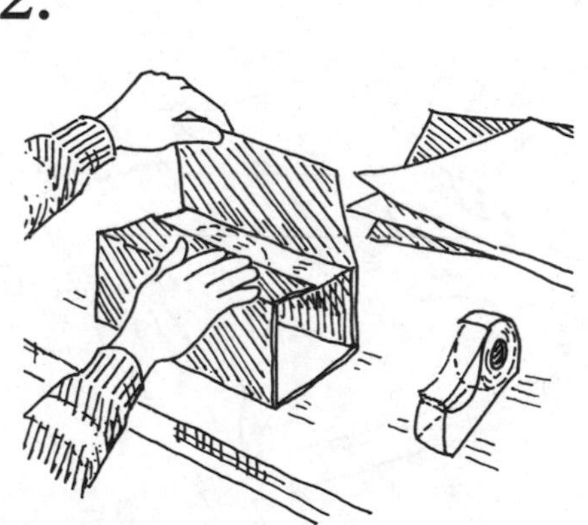

4.

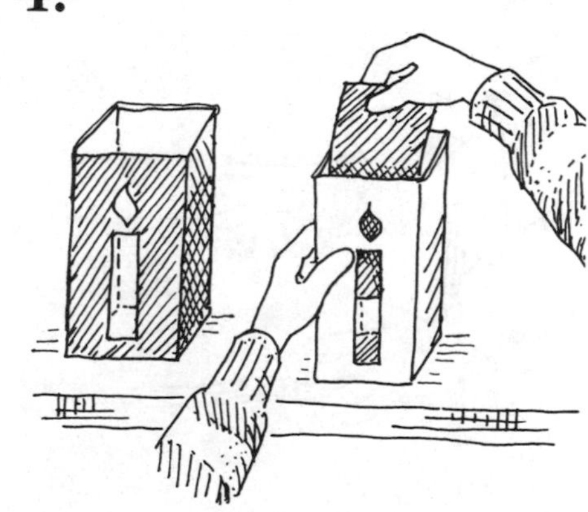

St. Nicholas Day (December 6)

9 ST. NICK STORYBOOK

Put your friends and family in a story about St. Nick.

What You'll Need: Construction paper, scissors, pencil, ruler, stapler, thin cardboard, colored tape, markers, glitter, glue

1. To make a homemade book, measure and cut 6 to 10 pieces of light-colored construction paper into 8 × 6-inch rectangles. Fold the sheets in half. Staple the sheets together in the fold.

2. Cut out 2 pieces of cardboard, 4 × 3 inches each, for the front and back covers. Use a strip of colored tape for the spine of the book. Place the tape sticky side up, and press the cardboard covers down on it, leaving a gap for the pages of the book. Then open the stapled pages flat on top of the covers, and press them onto the tape.

3. Add another thin strip of tape down the center of the pages, and press the tape around to the spine. You are ready to write the story of St. Nick!

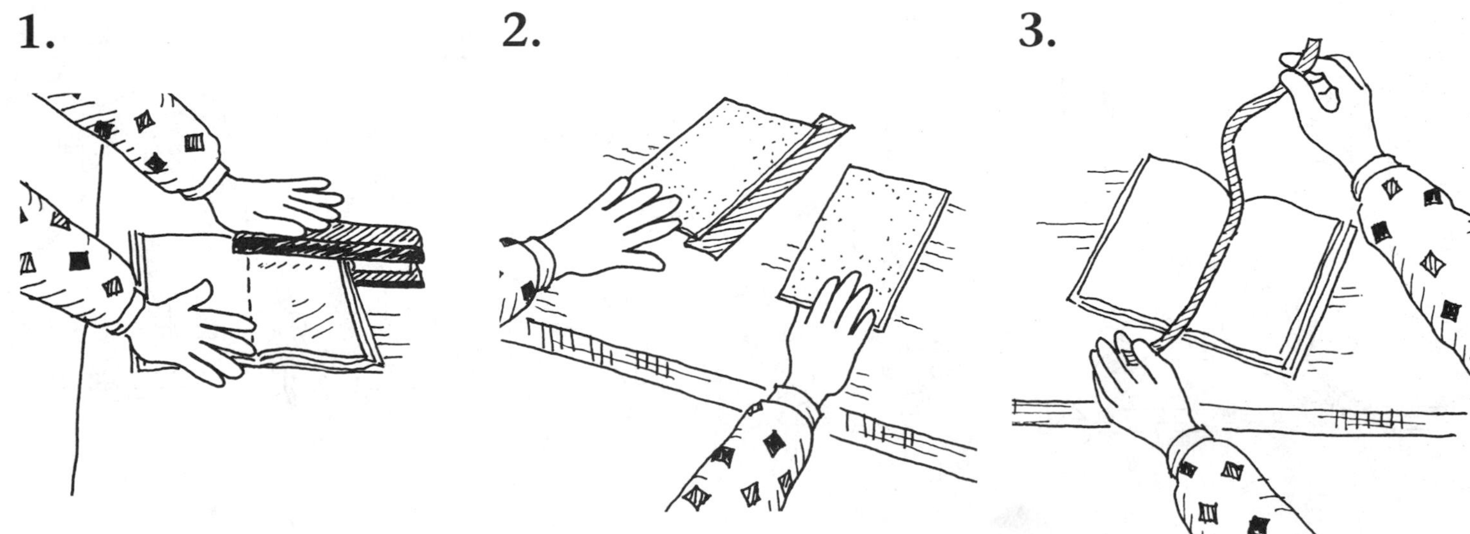

10

St. Nicholas Day (December 6)

ST. NICK CHARM

Give someone a St. Nick charm for safe travels!

What You'll Need: Salt, hot water, flour, measuring cups and spoons, mixing bowl and spoon, rolling pin, drinking glass, cookie sheet, markers or paints, pencil, thin cord

In Italy, sailors put the symbol of St. Nicholas on the prow of their ships for a safe voyage. See page 20 for instructions on how to make clay. Ask an adult to preheat the oven to 300 degrees. Form a 3-inch ball, and roll it out with your rolling pin on a floured counter. Press the rim of a drinking glass into the clay to cut out a circular shape. Cut out as many charms as you want. Use a pencil to poke a hole near the top of each circle. Bake the charms on a cookie sheet for 30 minutes. When they cool, use paint or markers to make St. Nick's face. Thread cord through the hole in the charm. Happy Trails!

Christmas Card Day (December 9)

CHRISTMAS CARD PANORAMA

11

Use old Christmas cards to make a festive scene in a box!

What You'll Need: Shoe box, construction paper, glue, crayons, scissors, old Christmas cards

Decorate the shoe box by gluing squares of construction paper onto the sides and drawing and glueing shapes onto that. Cut out pictures from Christmas cards to make a scene inside one box. It can be a realistic setting with trees and stars or a fantastic scene where toys float through the sky and a tiny Santa looks up at a giant child. Use your imagination! For a three-dimensional panoramic scene, cut out a tab on the bottom of some pictures to make them stand. Save this year's cards to make a new panorama next year. Make one each year, and stack them together to make a really spectacular Christmas display.

Christmas Card Day (December 9)

CHRISTMAS CARD MOBILE

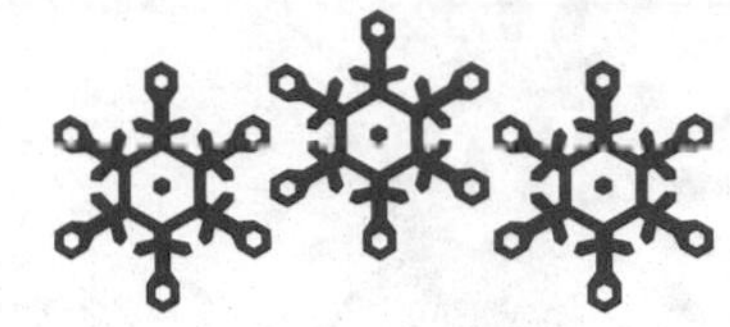

Display your Christmas cards high above the crowd!

What You'll Need: 2 wire hangers, red or green colored tape, plastic drinking straws, hole punch, Christmas cards, red or green colored string, artificial mistletoe, streamers, ribbons, ornaments, scissors

Ask an adult to help you make the base of this mobile. Insert one hanger into the open part of another hanger so that they form a cross shape. Twist the tops together so that they form one hook. Wind colored tape around the base (and the rest of the hangers, if you like). Tape the straws to the base, so they jut out from the base. Cover the straws with the colored tape. These will be the arms of the mobile from which you hang your decorations. Punch holes at the tops of your Christmas cards. Thread string through the holes and tie them onto the arms of the mobile. You can also tie on mistletoe, small ornaments, ribbons—use your imagination! Vary the lengths of the string, and alternate cards with other decorations. Ask an adult to help you hang your mobile.

13

Winter Solstice

RAINBOW IN THE SNOW

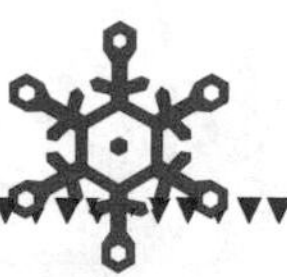

Spray paint a rainbow in the snow!

What You'll Need: Spray bottles, water, food coloring, bucket, brushes

Are you tired of everything in your yard looking colorless and white? Put some life back into your yard! Fill up empty spray bottles with water. Add a tablespoon of food coloring to each bottle, and shake well. Make at least 4 or 5 colors. Then dress warmly, and spray paint a nice, big arch in the snow. Add a second arch next to the first one, and keep adding colored arches until you have a giant rainbow. You can also use paintbrushes to paint other things around your rainbow.

Winter Solstice

PEANUTTY PINECONES

14

Help feed the birds this winter with an edible tree decoration.

What You'll Need: Pinecone, string, scissors, waxed paper, peanut butter, butter knife, birdseed, ribbon

Not all birds fly south for the winter! You can help feed them when they might be having a hard time finding anything to eat. This project will not only feed the birds, it makes a pretty decoration hanging from a tree. Cut a length of string 1 to 2 feet long. Tie the string around the base of the pinecone so that the narrower end hangs down. Place the cone on a sheet of waxed paper. Hold the cone down while you use a butter knife to spread peanut butter over it. Try to cover the whole cone but not the string! Sprinkle birdseed on top of the peanut butter. Roll the cone around on the waxed paper to get all the birdseed. Tie the ribbon into a bow where the string meets the pinecone. (Try not to get peanut butter on the ribbon.) Holding the pinecone by the string, take it outdoors and tie it to a tree branch.

15

Winter Solstice

SNOW MOBILE

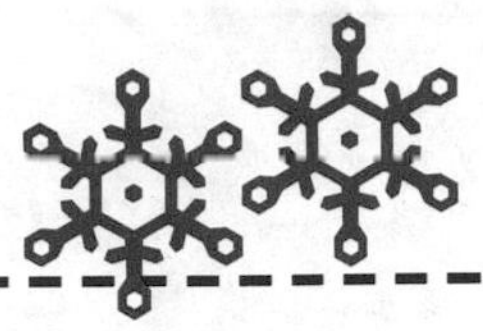

Bring a little winter inside the house with a sparkling, snowy mobile.

What You'll Need: Silver or white glitter, clear adhesive vinyl, scissors, hole punch, white string or fishing line, white plastic-coated hanger, tape, flashlight (optional)

1. Spread silver or white glitter onto the sticky side of a piece of clear adhesive vinyl paper.

2. Smooth another piece of paper over the top, and press out the air bubbles.

3. Cut the glittered adhesive paper into snowballs, snowpeople, and snowflakes.

4. Punch a hole near the top of each shape, and thread different lengths of fishing line or white string through each. If you use fishing line, your shapes will look like they are floating mysteriously in the air.

5. Tie the other end of the fishing line or string to the coat hanger. Make sure some shapes hang lower than others to make your snow mobile more interesting. To hold the shapes firmly in place, tape the tied ends of the string to the hanger. Hang your mobile in a dark room, and shine a flashlight for some sparkling fun.

Winter Solstice

INDOOR SNOWPERSON

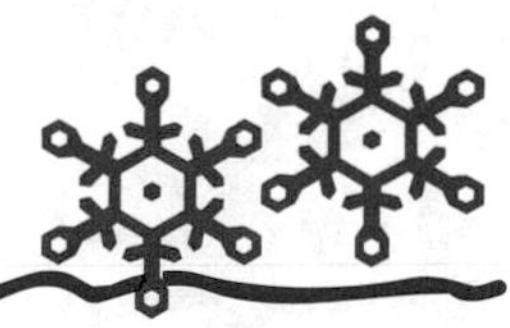

This jolly snow creature can actually live inside the house!

What You'll Need: Old newspaper, black marker, scissors, stapler, old plastic bags, white paint, paintbrush, construction paper, glue, old hat and scarf

1. Fold 6 double sheets of newspaper in half. With a black marker, draw the outline of a large half circle on the paper.

2. Cut out the circle, and unfold the papers. Do the same for a smaller circle, then another circle smaller than that one. You now have the snowperson's base, body, and head.

3. For each stack of circles, staple the sides together a ¼ inch in from the sides. Leave about 3 inches of the circle unstapled so you can stuff the circle.

4. Stick your hand inside the circle—there should be 3 sheets of paper above your hand and 3 below. Stuff the inside of the circles with old plastic bags. Staple the openings closed, and staple the circles on top of each other.

5. Paint the snowperson white, and let it dry. From brown construction paper, cut out "branches" for arms, and staple them to the body. Glue on black paper "coal" eyes and mouth and an orange paper "carrot" nose. Place an old hat on its head, and wind a scarf around its neck.

2.

4.

Kwanza

BAROTSE BOWL

Make this traditional craft of the Barotse tribe of Zambia to hold holiday treats.

What You'll Need: Round, shallow plastic bowl with lid, newspaper, liquid starch, large bowl, paper towels, sandpaper, dark brown paint, paintbrush, clear varnish

The Barotse people make beautiful carved wooden bowls to use in the home. To make one for your home, tear newspaper into 1- to 2-inch-wide strips. In a large bowl, soak the strips in liquid starch for 10 minutes. Take the lid off the plastic bowl, and turn the bowl upside down. Paste the strips one by one onto both the bowl and lid until they are entirely covered. Let this layer of newspaper dry. Add three more layers of newspaper strips, letting each layer dry before applying another. Each time you add a layer, change the direction of the strips to make the bowl strong. Use paper towels soaked in starch to form 2 bird shapes. Attach the birds to the top of the lid with more starched paper towels. Let your bowl and lid dry for a couple of days. When ready, lightly sand the edges of the bowl and lid. Paint them dark brown to resemble dark wood. When the paint is dry, paint the bowl and lid with the varnish to seal them. These bowls make lovely gifts.

Kwanza

TIE-DYE PARTY NAPKINS

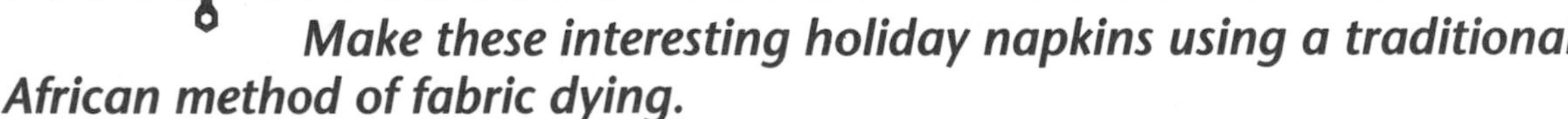

Make these interesting holiday napkins using a traditional African method of fabric dying.

What You'll Need: Wooden clothespin, seeds, stones, glue, white cotton napkins, string, vegetable dyes in bowls, scissors

Glue seeds and stones onto a wooden clothespin. When dry, wrap the clothespin with a white napkin and wind string around it. Secure the ends of the string with a knot. Leaving the tip white, dip and dab your napkin in bowls of different-colored dye. You can wait for each color to dry before redipping if you wish, or let the colors blend. When the entire napkin is dry, cut away the string and open up the napkin to see the design. Each one will be quite different!

19

Kwanza

EGG-CITING SAFARI

Put the animals of Africa into a beautiful Kwanza centerpiece.

What You'll Need: Eggs, long hat pin or toothpick, bowl, cardboard egg carton, markers, paints, construction paper, scissors, plate, cellophane grass

An adult may need to help you with the first part of this craft. To make a blown egg, stick a hat pin into the top of a raw egg and carefully dig away small bits of shell to make an opening ⅛ inch wide. Use the pin or a toothpick to stir the egg inside to break the yolk so it can be blown out. Make a tiny hole in the other end of the egg. Blow through this hole so that the egg's insides will come out the other side. Make sure you are holding the egg over a bowl while you blow! When the egg is empty, put it under the tap and run water through it. Dry the egg, and put it back in the egg carton until you are ready to use it. Cut apart the egg cups of the cardboard egg carton. To make each animal, glue one blown egg on top of one upside down egg cup. Color each egg carefully with markers or paints. When dry, paint on the faces of your favorite African animals—elephants, giraffes, hippos, rhinos, zebras, lions, and mandrills. Cut out construction paper horns, ears, trunks, tusks, and manes. Carefully glue them on. When the animals are dry, they can be arranged on a plate with cellophane grass for an egg-citing Kwanza centerpiece.

Kwanza

20 AFRICAN GOLD WEIGHTS

This ancient form of African money makes a nifty, glittery Kwanza gift!

What You'll Need: Salt, hot water, flour, bowl, mixing spoon, craft stick, spatula, oven mitts, gold paint, paintbrush

Before European coins or paper money reached Africa, gold weights were used. These weights were in the shape of different animals: goats, chameleons, birds, porcupines, snakes, and frogs. To make the clay, mix 1 cup salt into 1½ cups hot water. Ask an adult to help you so you don't burn yourself. When the mixture cools, add 1 cup flour, and mix until smooth. Add another cup of flour and continue to mix with a spoon. Add the last 1½ to 2 cups flour by kneading the clay with your hands. If the clay is sticky, add more flour. If it is dry, add a little more water, a few drops at a time. Ask an adult to preheat the oven to 300 degrees. When your clay is ready, roll it flat with a rolling pin on a floured counter. Use a craft stick to draw the outline of each animal—each should be 3 or 4 inches long. To make a snake, roll a rope and coil it around. Use a spatula to lift the animals off the counter and place them on a cookie sheet. Bake the animals for 30 minutes. When cool, paint the animals gold. Start your own collection or give them away as gifts.

Kwanza

SIGN MY KWANZA TABLECLOTH

Start your own Kwanza tradition with this tablecloth filled with memories and messages.

What You'll Need: Flat twin-size bed sheet or white tablecloth, fabric markers

Decorate the center of your fabric with Kwanza symbols: corn, candles, African animals, silver goblets, the African flag, etc. At the Kwanza party, invite your guests to write their names, the date, and a special Kwanza message. The tablecloth can be brought out, reread, and added to each year.

Kwanza

KWANZA BAG

This beautiful bag is a great gift—full or empty!

What You'll Need: Burlap, ribbon or cord for drawstring, marker, embroidery thread and needle, scissors

Cut a piece of burlap 10×14 inches. Along the 14-inch side, fold the burlap down an inch to make a tube. Sew the bottom of this tube closed, leaving the sides open so you can thread a ribbon or cord through it for the bag's drawstring. Tie the ribbon or cord to a safety pin, and thread it through the tube. Then make a knot. Use a marker to write the word "Kwanza" on the bag's front. Draw some decorative shapes or lines around the word if you wish. Use embroidery thread in the traditional African colors of red, green, and black to sew along the word Kwanza and whatever else you have drawn. Then fold the bag in half so that the drawstring is at the top and the design is on the inside. Stitch the sides of the bag together; turn the bag right side out. You can give the empty bag as a gift, or fill it with small toys or Kwanza treats.

Kwanza

23 ANIMAL CRACKER MAGNETS

Paint the animals in traditional African colors and put them to work holding up all your Kwanza and holiday greeting cards.

What You'll Need: Animal crackers, permanent markers, clear nail polish, magnetic strip, scissors, glue

Celebrating the traditional African holiday of Kwanza may put you in the mood for an African safari. Create a whole herd of colorful wild animals. Select the animal crackers. Gently color them with markers in the traditional African colors of red, green, and black. Make sure you don't press too hard while you color, unless you want to end up with a headless or tailless beast! Brush a light coat of clear nail polish over the colored crackers. Let dry. Turn crackers over, and coat the back of the beasts with nail polish also; let dry. Cut a small piece of magnetic strip for each beast. Attach the magnet to the cracker with glue. Again, be careful when you press on the crackers. Stick your beautiful beasts to the refrigerator!

A HARVEST TRIBUTE

Kwanza means "the first" or "the first fruits of the harvest" in Kiswahili. Kiswahili is an East African language. Dr. Maulana Karenga began the holiday in 1966 to celebrate the rich cultural roots of people who are African American.

Kwanza

ANIMAL ANKLET

Decorate your ankle with wild beasts!

What You'll Need: Self-hardening clay, craft stick, thin wire, needle, paints, paintbrush, clear varnish or nail polish, small plastic beads, scissors, thread

Wear some of Africa's special creatures to your next Kwanza party. These bird and animal beads are so small that you can string together a whole herd! To make your tiny bead animals, roll self-hardening clay into balls the size of grapes. You can make elephants, giraffes, zebras, monkeys, or anything else you want! Use a craft stick to help you form legs, ears, horns, and trunks. Use small pieces of thin wire to make tails or tusks. Poke a needle through the back of each animal to make a hole. Turn the needle gently to make the hole big enough for thread to pass through. Let the animals dry until the clay is hard. Paint the animals with bright colors. When the paint is dry, paint the animals with a coat of clear varnish or nail polish. Measure a length of thin wire that will fit comfortably around your ankle. Leave a little extra to make a hook and loop to open and close the anklet. String small plastic beads onto the wire. Then thread a needle with colored thread and make a knot. Thread the needle through a small bead on the anklet and then through one of your clay animals. Thread through a few more beads; tie the thread onto the anklet so that the animal hangs down. Repeat this process with the rest of your animals, tying them onto the anklet every inch or so. Make two anklets—one for each leg!

Christmas (December 25)

WREATH OF CANDY

25

Here's a wreath you'll need to hang out of reach—or else it just might disappear!

What You'll Need: Vinyl-coated wire hanger, red and green wrapped hard candy, red and green twist ties, red and green ribbon, scissors

Traditional wreaths are usually made from pine boughs or pinecones, but this Christmas you might want to try something a little sweeter. Bend the bottom of the hanger into a circle. You might need an adult to help you with this. Attach a twist tie to one end of each candy. Attach the candies to the hanger by twisting the ties onto the hanger. Continue doing this until you have a wreath full of candy. You can also tie ribbon bows onto the wire to make your wreath even prettier.

26

Christmas (December 25)

CHRISTMAS SEALS

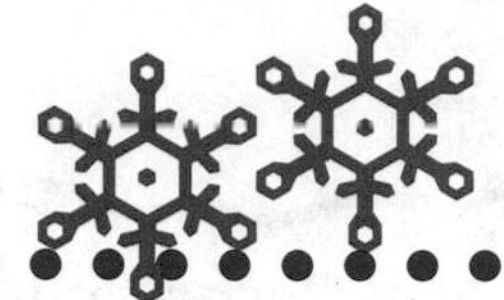

Decorate your Christmas cards with homemade Christmas stickers.

What You'll Need: Markers, white paper, scissors, mixing bowl, 2 tablespoons cold water, 1 packet plain gelatin, fork, 3 tablespoons boiling water, ½ teaspoon corn syrup, flavored extract (mint, vanilla, or lemon), small paintbrush

Draw small Christmas pictures, such as Santa, Christmas trees, elves, snowpeople, candy canes, angels, wrapped presents, and bright stars. Cut out your drawings carefully, getting as close to the edges as you can. When you have finished making your cutouts, pour the cold water into a bowl. Sprinkle the gelatin over it. With adult help, use a fork to mix in the boiling water until the gelatin dissolves. Add the corn syrup and a few drops of extract. With a small brush, paint a thin layer of the gelatin mixture onto the back of each sticker. If you have left over gelatin mixture, place it in a jar in the refrigerator. When you are ready to use it again, place the jar into a bowl of hot water. (Use mixture within two weeks.) Let the stickers dry. When you are ready to use them, lick the back and press onto the surface you are decorating—use them to decorate envelopes, cards, wrapping paper, and presents!

Christmas (December 25)

DANCING SUGAR PLUM FAIRIES

27

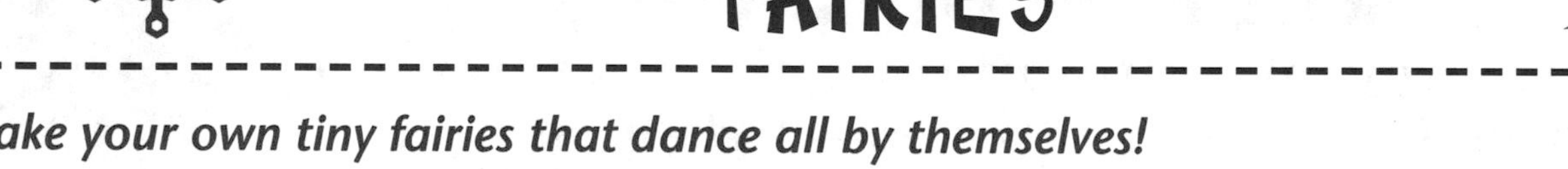

Make your own tiny fairies that dance all by themselves!

What You'll Need: Colored tissue paper, scissors, comb

Cut out tiny sugar plum fairy shapes from tissue paper—use your imagination about how you think they look! Charge a comb with static electricity by running it through your hair or rubbing it against your clothing for a few minutes. Lay the sugar plum fairies on a table. When the comb is held near the fairies, they will wiggle and move around. Do you know the tune to the "Nutcracker Suite"? Hum it for your fairies while they dance!

28

Christmas (December 25)

CANDY CANE COOKIES

Make a new kind of candy cane.

What You'll Need: 4 cups flour, 2 teaspoons baking powder, 1 teaspoon salt, ¾ cup butter, 1½ cups sugar, 2 eggs, 2 teaspoons vanilla, 1 teaspoon lemon extract, red food coloring, sifter, mixing bowls, electric mixer, cookie sheet, measuring cups and spoons

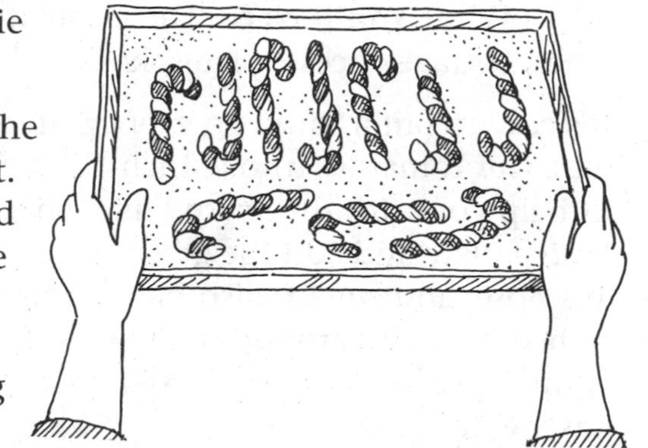

Have an adult help you with preparation and cooking! Preheat the oven to 375 degrees. Sift together the flour, baking powder, and salt. In another bowl, beat the butter and sugar until the mix is light and fluffy. Beat the eggs into the butter and sugar mixture, then add the vanilla and lemon extracts. Add the flour mixture, in small amounts, to the butter and sugar mixture, until well mixed. Divide the dough in half. Put half in a bowl; add enough red food coloring to make a nice color. Make little balls of red and plain dough. On a clean, floured surface, roll the balls into ropes. Dust your hands with flour if the dough is too sticky. Twist one red rope and one plain rope together, and shape them into a candy cane. Place dough on a baking sheet; bake for 8 to 10 minutes or until just slightly brown.

Christmas (December 25)

SANTA'S BAG GAME

29

Make up skits about the objects in Santa's bags.

What You'll Need: Assorted small objects, 3 × 5 cards, pen, box that closes, white paper bags, crayons

Gather an assortment of small objects, such as toy soldiers, small Christmas ornaments, candy canes, and other tiny toys. Make word cards with Christmas words printed on them. Put the objects and word cards in a closed box. Then have everyone decorate a white paper bag. Each person can secretly fill their bag with 3 objects and word cards from the box. Then close up the decorated bags, and put them in a pile. Divide players into small groups. Each group is given a bag. (Make sure that no one in that group made that bag.) Using the objects and word cards in the bags, the groups must create a skit. They must refer to their object or word by saying it aloud at least twice. Audience members then try to guess which 3 objects and words were in the bag.

Christmas (December 25)

SANTA SALAD

This cheery vegetable Santa will brighten up your holiday meal.

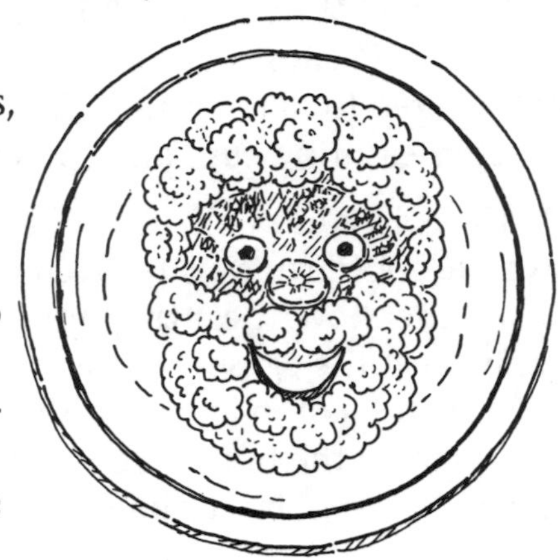

What You'll Need: Large tomato slices, green olives with pimentos, radishes, cottage cheese, plates, knife

It's easy to put a Santa on every plate at Christmas dinner! Wash all vegetables. Cut tomatoes into ½-inch-thick slices, one for each Santa. Have an adult help you with the sharp knife! Slice a few green olives. Lay the tomato slice on a plate and add the green olives for Santa's eyes. Use a radish slice for his nose, and cut a radish half moon for his mouth. Carefully spoon cottage cheese on and around the tomato for Santa's hair and beard. You can broil the tomato slices in a toaster oven before you begin. Hot or cold, these Santas are delicious!

Christmas (December 25)

SUGAR PLUM FAIRY PILLOWCASES

These enchanting fairies will bring happy Christmas dreams while everyone sleeps.

What You'll Need: White pillowcases, cardboard the size of pillowcase, pencil, fabric paints, paintbrushes

What does a sugar plum fairy look like? Is she wearing a long silver gown? A short blue tunic? Does she have wings or a wand? What color is her hair? Perhaps she is balancing a big sugar plum on the top of her head! However you want her to look, paint her in pretty colors so that any head resting on her will be full of sweet dreams. Wash and dry a spare white pillowcase. Place a piece of cardboard inside so the paint won't bleed through. With a pencil, lightly draw a picture of a sugar plum fairy on the front of the pillowcase. When you finish, color in your outline with fabric paint. After the paint dries, you may want to turn your pillowcase over and paint another sugar plum fairy on the back—for double the dreaming pleasure!

Christmas (December 25)

32 KEEPSAKE QUILTS

You can hang up this sentimental quilt for many Christmases to come.

What You'll Need: White cardboard, ruler, pencil, scissors, hole punch, yarn, large needle, markers

Traditional quilts are made by sewing together squares of fabric in a special pattern. Often, the fabric was cut from old clothes and blankets used by family and friends. That way, the person who owned the quilt could sleep surrounded by happy memories of loved ones. You can make a cardboard quilt full of memories by measuring 6 × 6-inch squares of cardboard and cutting them out. With a hole punch, punch 3 evenly spaced holes on each side inside the borders of each square. Give a square to family and friends. Have them write holiday messages, draw holiday events, or draw portraits of themselves on the squares. Collect the squares. Thread the needle with yarn, and sew the squares together through the holes you punched. You might need an adult to help you get started with the sewing. When the quilt is all sewn, hang it in the family room or on the front door of your house. Bring it out each Christmas and add more squares for new family memories.

Christmas (December 25)

33 "EXPLODING" PARTY FAVORS

Play tug-of-war with these party favors, and watch them explode with candy!

What You'll Need: Gold and silver wrapping paper, tape, scissors, ruler, small wrapped candies, colored ribbons

These party favors were popular in France before the mid-1800s! The size of the snapper you want to make will determine how big your paper should be and how much candy you will need. For starters, you might want to use a sheet of wrapping paper that is 6 × 10 inches. Overlap the paper ½ inch on the long sides to form a tube, and tape the edges together. Put 12 to 15 candies into the middle of the tube. Twist the ends of the paper, about 3 inches from the end. Tie each twist with a piece of ribbon, making a bow with streamers. Open each end of the paper so that it flares outward, and push ends together so the center puffs up. To make your snapper explode candy, hold one end while a friend holds the other. Tug and shake the snapper until the paper breaks.

34

Christmas (December 25)

EDIBLE ANGELS

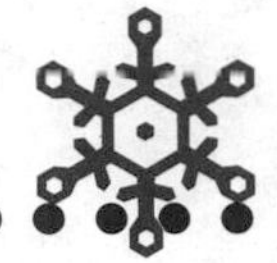

These darling angels are almost too sweet to eat.

What You'll Need: 1 cup peanut butter, 1 cup honey, 2½ cups powdered milk, bowl, snack chips, thin licorice string, raisins or currants, colored or silver jimmies or cinnamon candies

You can make your clay and eat it, too! Use the clay to make edible angels for a delicious Christmas dessert. Wash and dry your hands. To make the clay, put peanut butter, honey, and powdered milk in a big bowl. Squeeze and knead the ingredients together. If the clay is too sticky, add a little more powdered milk. If it is too dry, add a little more honey or peanut butter. When you have a nice, smooth-feeling clay, shape it into a 3-inch cone to make the angel's body. Add a little ball of clay on top for the angel's head. Carefully press 2 snack chips into the angel's back for wings. Wind a small piece of thin licorice string around the angel's head for a perfect halo. Use currants or raisins to make the face. Colored or silver jimmies or small cinnamon candies can decorate the angel's body. These angels are guaranteed to fly right off the plate and into your mouth!

Christmas (December 25)

ELF-FRIEND PINS

Do you know anyone who is nuts about Christmas elves? All of your friends will want an elf-friend when they see these pins!

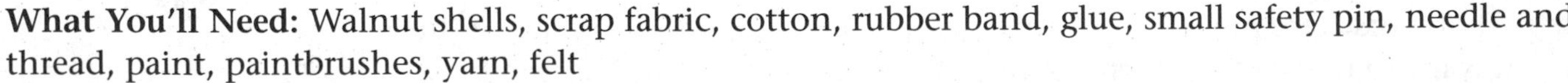

What You'll Need: Walnut shells, scrap fabric, cotton, rubber band, glue, small safety pin, needle and thread, paint, paintbrushes, yarn, felt

Offer to crack some walnuts for your mom. Pick out the walnut shells that cracked neatly in half. Dig out the nut meat. Wrap a piece of cotton in a small square of fabric. Gather the edges and wrap with a rubber band to make a ball. The fabric and cotton ball should just fill the hollow space in the nutshell. Pour a puddle of glue into the nutshell. Set the fabric ball in the glue, rubber band side down. When the glue is dry, stitch the back of a small safety pin to the fabric. You should be able to open and close the pin. Use paint and fine-tipped paintbrushes to paint an elf face on the front of the walnut. Glue on yarn or cotton for hair and beards. Cut out red or green felt elf hats, and glue them on.

Christmas (December 25)

CLOVE AND CITRUS POMANDERS

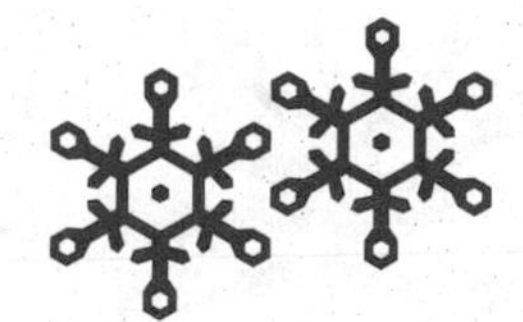

These sweet-smelling, fruity decorations also make cheery holiday gifts.

What You'll Need: Oranges or lemons, thin nail, cloves, thin string, ribbon, scissors

1. Make small holes in the orange skin with the thin nail, covering the entire orange with holes.

2. Stick a clove in each hole. If you don't want to cover the whole orange, you can make striped or heart designs on the orange.

3. When you have finished your design, temporarily tie a string around the orange, from the bottom to the top, with a loop at the top for hanging. Hang the pomander in a cool, dry place until the orange begins to shrink a bit.

4. Remove the string when the orange is dry; replace it with a colored ribbon, tied in the same way, with a loop at the top for hanging. For a variation, use a lemon instead of an orange. Make a whole grove of fragrant pomanders for your family and friends!

Christmas (December 25)

PUZZLE WREATH

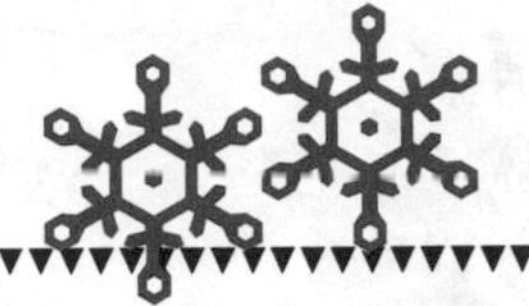

I'll bet you've never seen a wreath like this before! When someone asks you what it's made of, you can say, well . . . that's the puzzle!

What You'll Need: Sturdy 9-inch paper plate, scissors, hole punch, yarn, 1 cup white glue, large bowl, green food coloring, 4 cups old jigsaw puzzle pieces, mixing spoon, waxed paper, small Christmas balls, small candy canes, other small Christmas objects

Cut the middle out of the paper plate so that it looks like a wreath. Punch a hole through the top and tie a loop of yarn through it for a hanger. Put 1 cup of white glue in a big mixing bowl. Mix in five drops of green food coloring; mix. Pour in the puzzle pieces, and stir until they are completely covered with green glue. Lay the paper plate on some wax paper. Put spoonfuls of puzzle pieces on the plate. Arrange them so they look nice. Allow wreath to dry for several days. When the wreath has dried, glue on small Christmas ornaments, candy canes, and other Christmas objects! Hang the wreath on the door to your room, or give it to someone special—like grandma.

Christmas (December 25)

FRANKINCENSE JARS

38

This potpourri jar will make your whole room smell sweet, and it's pretty enough to give a king!

What You'll Need: Small jars (baby food jars are fine, but jars of all shapes are good), glue, uncooked rice, paintbrush, fabric brush, potpourri

Make Christmas stars or other shapes on your jar with glue. Stick rice to the glue. Let glue dry. Measure around the outside of your jar. Cut a piece of aluminum foil long enough to fit around your jar plus an overlap of ½ inch; there should also be a little extra at the top and bottom of the jar. Crush the foil into a ball, then smooth it out again on the tabletop. Using the paintbrush, spread glue evenly on one side of the foil. Carefully place the jar on the edge of the foil. Roll the jar like a rolling pin, so that it wraps itself in foil. Carefully fold the top of the foil into the mouth of the jar, making sure it sticks in place. Fold the bottom of the foil under the jar. Press gently around the jar with your fingers, making sure that the glue sticks everywhere. Tap the foil with the bristles of the fabric brush to bring out the texture of your rice pattern. Fill the jar with sweet potpourri.

Christmas (December 25)

SODA STRAW LOOM BOOKMARK

Weave this for a special reader in your life.

What You'll Need: Varigated (multicolored) yarn, scissors, 6 milkshake straws (the big kind), large needle, masking tape

Cut 6 pieces of yarn. Each piece should be about 5 inches longer than your straws. Use the needle to thread one piece of yarn through each straw. When all the straws have been threaded, tie the tops of all the yarn pieces together. Push the straws up until they touch the knot. Lay the straws on the table, side by side. Put a piece of tape across the tops of the straws, just under the knot, to hold them in place. Turn the straws over; tape the other side in the same place. Cut another piece of yarn about 6 feet long. Tie one end of the yarn onto a straw, just below the tape. Weave the yarn over one straw and under the next; when you reach the last straw, go back again. Keep weaving until the whole length of the straws is wrapped in yarn. Tie off the yarn and trim the end. Take off the masking tape. Slide the straws out of the weaving one by one. Push the weaving up to the knot. Tie an overhand knot in the yarn that was in the straws, just below the weaving.

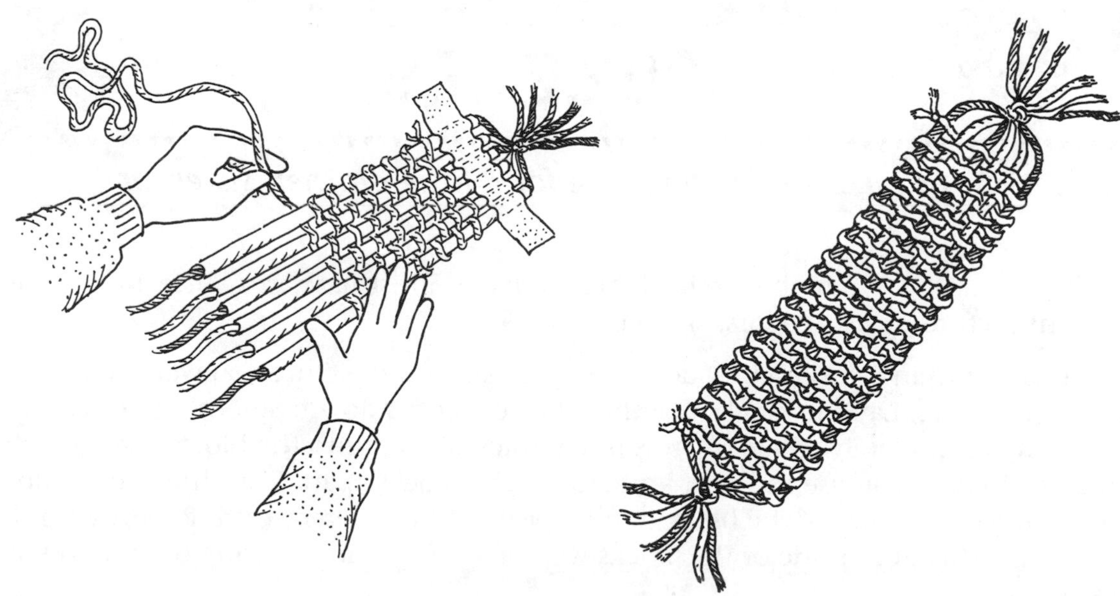

Christmas (December 25)

40 SILVER BELL ORNAMENTS

Make your own jingle bells to hang from the Christmas tree.

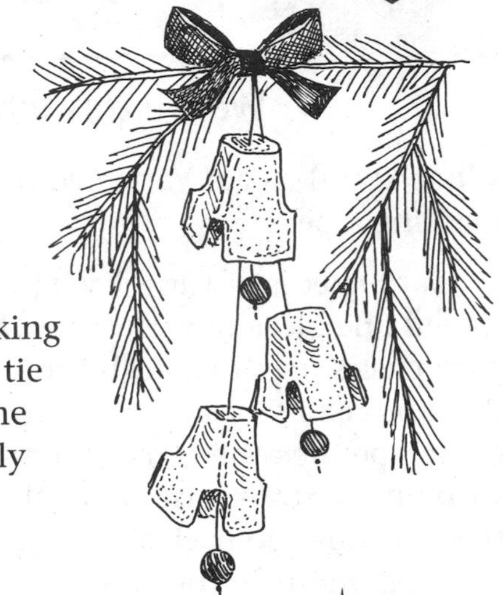

What You'll Need: Cardboard egg carton, scissors, colored string, pea-sized wooden beads, needle, silver paint, paintbrush, ribbon

Cut a single egg carton cup for each bell. String a bead on a string, and secure it with a knot. Ask an adult to help you use a needle to poke the free end of the string through the egg carton cup. Knot the end of the string, making sure the bead swings freely inside the egg cup. When you have made 3 bells, tie them to a longer string. Paint the bells silver. Tie a ribbon in a bow around the long string. Hang the ornament on your Christmas tree, and gather the family around to sing "Jingle Bells."

Christmas (December 25)

CHRISTMAS CARD PUZZLES 41

This is a great Christmas puzzle you can make for a little brother, sister, or cousin.

What You'll Need: Nine 2 × 2 × 2-inch wooden blocks, 6 large Christmas cards at least 6 × 6 inches (each must have a different picture), glue, scissors, sharp craft knife

If your cards are bigger than 6 × 6 inches, decide which part of the picture you want to be in the puzzle and trim it to a 6-inch square. Lay the blocks together, 3 across and 3 down. Smooth glue across the back of a picture. Make sure it is completely covered. Press it, glue-side down, onto the blocks. Let glue dry for a few minutes. Ask an adult to help you use the craft knife to cut the blocks apart. Trim the paper along the edges of the blocks. Turn up 6 blank sides of the blocks, and repeat with a different card. Repeat with the other cards. When you are finished, each side of the blocks will have a Christmas picture on it, and you will have a 6-picture block puzzle!

42

Christmas (December 25)

SNOWY NUTTY PIE

This dessert is so easy, and the coconut adds a snowy touch!

What You'll Need: 6 tablespoons margarine, 8- or 9-inch unbaked pie shell, 1 cup chopped pecans, 1½ cups unsweetened coconut, 1¼ cups maple syrup, ¼ teaspoon salt, 3 eggs, small saucepan, mixing bowl, mixing spoon

Ask an adult to preheat the oven to 400 degrees. Have the adult help you melt the margarine in a small saucepan over low heat. Sprinkle the pecans on the bottom of the pie shell. Cover the nuts with 1 cup of coconut. Mix the remaining ingredients (except remaining coconut) together with a spoon or electric mixer, and pour mixture evenly over the coconut and nuts. Bake for 15 minutes at 400 degrees, then lower the oven temperature to 350 degrees. Continue baking for another 25 minutes. Let cool, and sprinkle the remaining coconut on top just before serving.

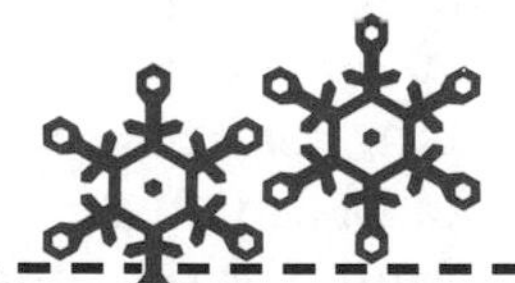

Christmas (December 25)

SOFT REINDEER TOY

43

This soft toy makes a cuddly gift for your favorite reindeer-lover.

What You'll Need: Heavy, soft brown knee sock; cotton balls, cotton batting, or foam; small jingle bells; rubber band; pencil; scraps of brown, black, pink, and white felt; scissors; thin cardboard; glue; ribbon

Stuff the sock with the cotton or foam and several jingle bells until it is full but loose enough so that the bells have room to move around. Wrap a rubber band tightly around the bottom of the sock to make a neck. Draw and cut out 4 antler shapes from brown felt and 2 antlers from thin cardboard. Glue the felt antlers to either side of the thin cardboard. Glue the antlers to the reindeer's head. Then draw and cut out eyes, nose, and a mouth from scraps of black, white, and pink felt. Glue them onto the face. Tie a pretty ribbon around the reindeer's neck.

Christmas (December 25)

WRAPPING PAPER MAKER

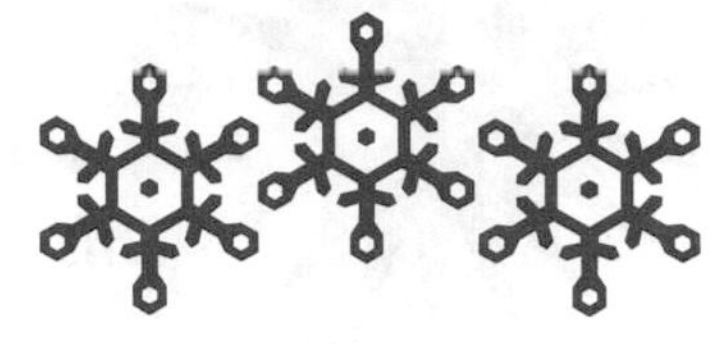

Gifts wrapped in paper you made yourself are extra special.

What You'll Need: Thin cardboard, ruler, scissors, rolling pin, masking tape, rubber weather stripping (from hardware store), craft glue, tempera paints, cookie sheet, large pieces of white paper

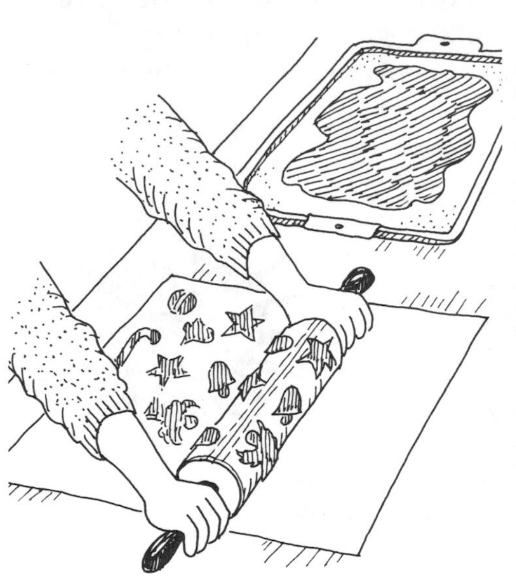

Cut a piece of cardboard so that it is the same length as the rolling pin. Tape one end of the cardboard to the rolling pin, all the way across. Roll the rolling pin so that the cardboard wraps around it, making a tight cardboard cover. When you reach the end of the cardboard, tape it in place. (It may wrap around more than once.) Cut 1-inch Christmas shapes, such as bells, stars, and angels, from the weather stripping. Coat the cardboard rolling pin cover with glue. This is easier if you set each handle on a thick cookbook, so that the rolling pin is hanging between the books. Press the shapes in place, turning the rolling pin as you go, so that your pattern goes all the way around the rolling pin. Let the glue dry. Pour a thin coat of paint on the cookie sheet, roll your wrapping paper maker through it, then roll out a pattern on plain white paper.

YOU BURN WHAT?

Kallikantzaroi are creatures from Greek legend that caused trouble at Christmastime. To get rid of these creatures, people burned an old shoe or salt. The people also believed that keeping a large fire going prevented the kallikantzaroi from going down the chimney.

Christmas (December 25)

SNOWY CHRISTMAS CAKE HOUSE

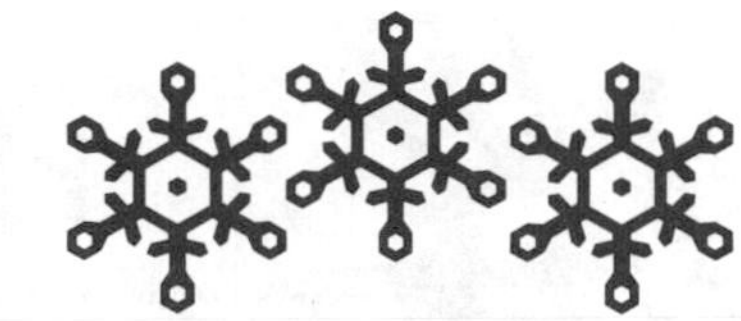

This cake house is as much fun to make as it will be to eat!

What You'll Need: Refrigerated pound cake, knife, plate, white frosting, tiny candy canes, red and green gumdrops, small thin squares of chocolate, toothpicks

Ask an adult to help you cut four 2-inch squares of pound cake. Using a plate as the base, put the squares together in a box shape to make the 4 walls of the house. Use the frosting as mortar. Cut 2 more squares to use as the sides of the roof, using more frosting as mortar. Cut another square in half, and use each half to carefully close up the front and back of the roof. Frost the house with white frosting so it looks snowy. You can make a chimney of three gumdrops on a toothpick, doors and window of chocolate squares, and then add snow (frosting) all around the house. Stick candy canes around the house.

Christmas (December 25)

WALNUT BRITTLE

Everyone will want a piece of this delicious candy.

What You'll Need: 1 tablespoon margarine, 2 cups chopped walnuts, 2 cups sugar, 1 teaspoon vanilla, cookie sheet, paper towel, saucepan, mixing spoon, hot pad

Grease a cookie sheet with a tablespoon of margarine and a paper towel (or use the margarine wrapper). Evenly spread the nuts over the cookie sheet. Ask an adult to help you melt the sugar in a saucepan over low heat. Stir the sugar until it turns into a light brown syrup. Remove melted sugar from the stove, and add the vanilla. Stir well. With an adult's help, slowly and evenly pour the mixture over the nuts on the cookie sheet. Let the candy cool until it is hard. Break candy into small pieces before serving.

Christmas (December 25)

PASTA SNOWFLAKES

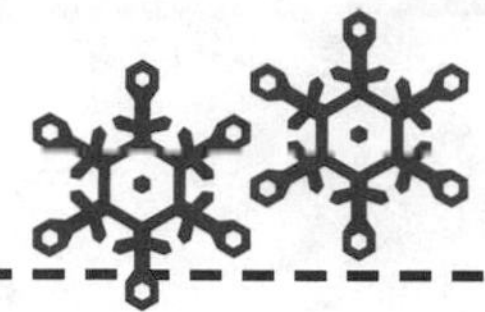

These pasta snowflakes won't melt when you hang them on your Christmas tree—but they will shine!

What You'll Need: Coffee can, pencil, paper, ruler, waxed paper, several kinds of dry pasta (wagon wheels, corkscrew, mostaccioli, spaghetti, elbow macaroni, bow ties, shell macaroni, ditali), glue, toothpick, spray paint, ribbon or dental floss

Trace around the bottom of a coffee can to make a circle on paper. Use a ruler to make lines across the circle, so that it looks like a pie cut into 8 pieces. This will be your pattern. Put a piece of waxed paper over the pattern, and lay pieces of pasta on top of the waxed paper so that they are all touching. Use the circle and lines you drew to help keep the pattern symmetrical. When you have a design you like, use a toothpick to dab glue between the pasta. After the pasta is glued together, slide the waxed paper to one side and let the glue dry while you make more snowflakes. When the glue is dry, remove the waxed paper and have an adult help you spray paint the ornaments. Your snowflakes will be fragile, but if they break, you can glue them back together. You can hang your snowflakes with ribbon or dental floss.

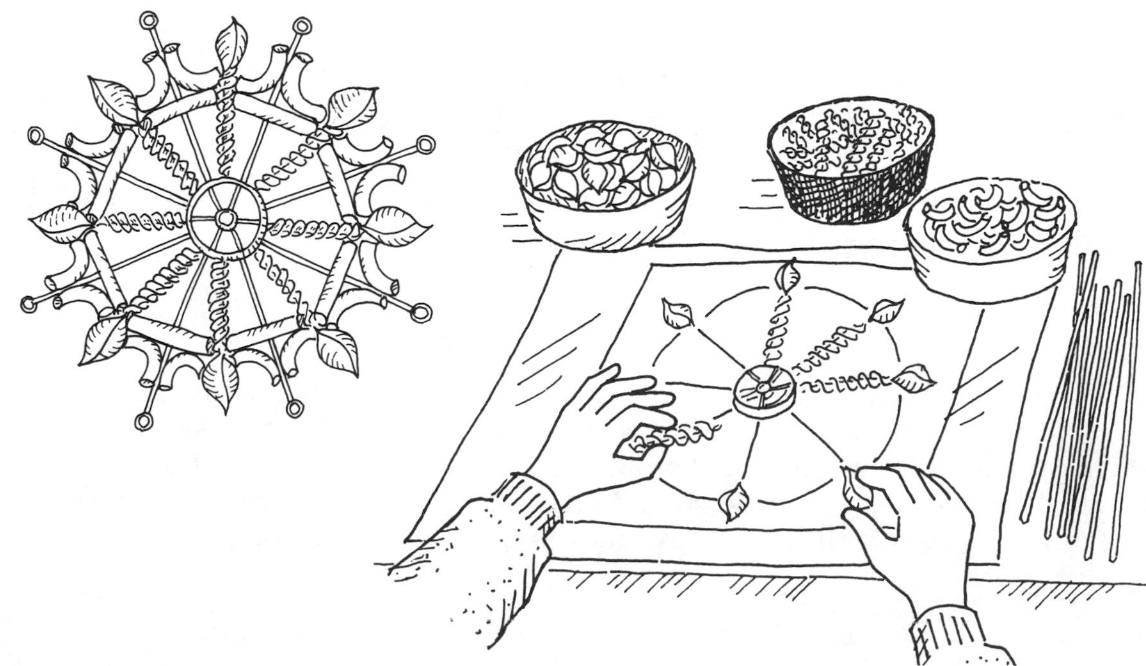

48

Christmas (December 25)

PARTY MINTS

These colorful candies are almost too pretty to eat.

What You'll Need: 3 egg whites, 7 cups confectioners' sugar, red and green food coloring, mint extract, electric mixer, 2 bowls, waxed paper, rolling pin, doll's teacup or thimble, spatula, tray

Ask an adult to help you separate the egg whites from the yolks. Put the egg whites into a bowl, and beat them at high speed with an electric mixer. Slowly add the confectioners' sugar as you beat, until the mixture is very stiff. Divide the mixture into 2 bowls. Use a few drops of food coloring to make the contents of one bowl red and the other green. Stir each well so that the color is even. Add 3 or 4 drops of mint extract to each bowl, and stir well. Lay a piece of waxed paper on a counter, and put the red mint dough on it. Cover it with another piece of waxed paper; roll it with the rolling pin until it is about ¼ inch thick. Take off the top layer of waxed paper, and use a doll's teacup or a thimble to cut out small circles. Use a spatula to lift the circles off the waxed paper. Put them on a tray to dry. Repeat the process with the green mixture. Let all your mint candies dry overnight. Serve them at your holiday party, and watch them disappear! (Caution: Use only clean, uncracked eggs. If any egg yolk gets into the egg whites, discard and start with new eggs.)

Christmas (December 25)

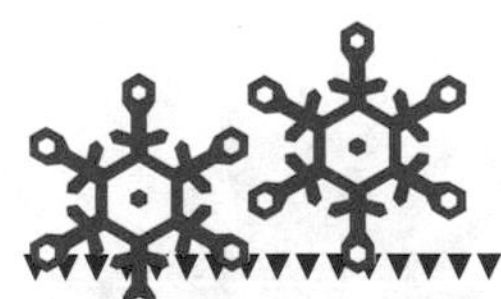

GIFT-WRAPPED DOOR

49

Turn your house into a big present!

What You'll Need: Measuring tape, wide colored ribbon, scissors, tape, one or several large bows, Christmas greenery, cardboard, marker, hole punch, yarn

Measure the height and width of your front door. Double the measurements and add 2 inches so you can wind the ribbon around to the inside of the door. Tie the ribbon around the door to look like a gift package, and tape the ends of the ribbon together. Glue one or more large bows onto the ribbon in the center of the door. Add Christmas greenery around the bow(s) with tape. Cut a large gift tag shape out of cardboard, and a write a holiday message on it. Punch a hole at the top of the gift tag, and attach it to the ribbon with a colorful piece of yarn.

50

Christmas (December 25)

TAKE-ONE PLATE DECORATION

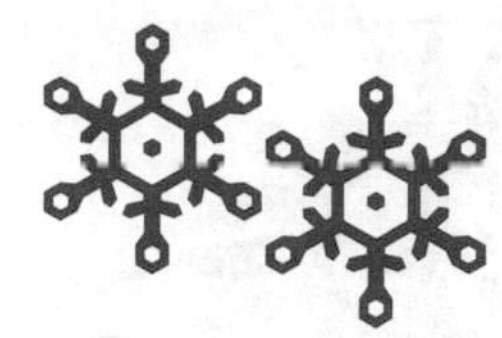

This pretty decoration makes a tasty welcome when hung on the front door of your house.

What You'll Need: 2 aluminum-foil pie plates, heavy scissors, colored tape, glue or stapler, hole punch, ribbon, Christmas greenery, candy canes, licorice sticks, pretzel rods, ribbon, construction paper, markers

Ask an adult to help you cut one pie plate in half. Cover the cut edge with colored tape to make it smooth. Glue it onto the whole pie plate to make a pocket. Punch a hole at the top of the whole plate and thread it with ribbon to make a hanging loop. Fill the pocket with Christmas greenery, candy canes, licorice sticks, pretzel rods, and other candies. Make a pretty label that says, "Take One." Glue it onto the front of the pocket. Hang the decoration on your front door so that guests will have a welcome treat before they even get inside the house! (Remember to refill the pocket as the treats start to run out.)

Christmas (December 25)

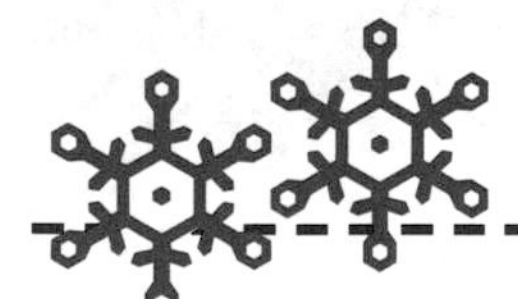

WATER GLASS CAROLS

Serenade your party guests with some tinkly tunes!

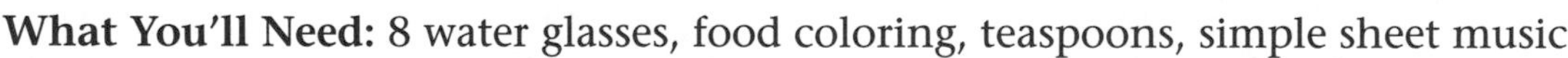

What You'll Need: 8 water glasses, food coloring, teaspoons, simple sheet music

The best sounds are made with the thinnest glass, but check with an adult to see which glasses you can use for this project. Do this inside a large plastic tub in case of breakage. Fill the first glass ⅛ full of water, the second glass ¼ full, the third glass ⅜ full, and so on until the eighth glass is full. (You are adding ⅛ of a cup of water to each glass). Use a teaspoon to tap on each glass. Add or pour out water to make the musical scale as you sing do, re, mi, fa, sol, la, ti, do. You can add a few drops of food coloring to each glass after your glasses are tuned. Practice tapping out songs such as "Silent Night," "Jingle Bells," and other Christmas favorites. Give a holiday concert for family and friends.

Christmas (December 25)

STRINGY SNOWPERSON SCULPTURE

You can actually see through this snowperson!

What You'll Need: 3 balloons, white string, scissors, yardstick, petroleum jelly, white glue, paper plate, waxed paper, pin, construction paper, paper party hat

Blow up 3 balloons. For each balloon, cut 30 pieces of white string between 12 and 15 inches long. Rub a thin layer of petroleum jelly on each balloon. Pour a little glue onto a paper plate. Dip a string into the glue, and paste it on a balloon. Continue dipping and pasting the strings in overlapping designs on a balloon. Place on waxed paper to dry. Let glue dry completely, at least overnight. Do the same for the other balloons. When the glue has dried, ask an adult to use a pin to pop the balloons. Cover your ears! Carefully pull out the balloons through a space between the hardened strings. (Promptly discard balloon pieces—they are choking hazards for small children!) Tie the 3 balloons together with more string to make a snowperson shape. Glue on construction paper eyes, nose, mouth, and buttons. Poke a hole through the top of a party hat, and thread string through it. Tie one end to the top of the snowperson's head before you put the hat on it, and use the other end to hang your snowperson.

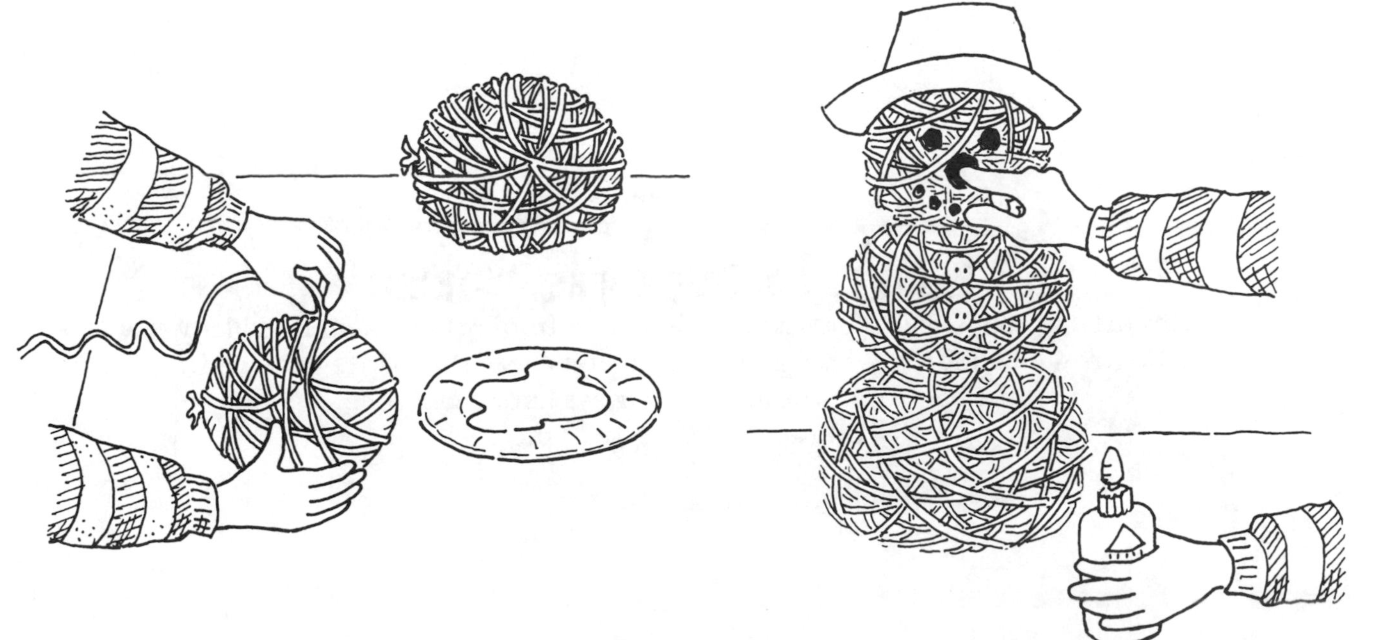

Christmas (December 25)

CHRISTMAS POCKET PIXIE

Who's that peeking out of your pocket?

What You'll Need: Self-hardening clay, large paper clip, markers

Make a Pocket Pixie for everyone to wear at your next Christmas party. Roll a ½-inch ball of self-hardening clay to make the pixie's head. Press it onto one end of the paper clip. Roll a small cone shape out of clay and press it on top of the head to make the pixie's hat. Put a tiny clay ball on top of the cone to make the hat's pom-pom. Color the hat and pom-pom with markers when the clay dries. Draw on a cheerful pixie face. Try to draw a different face on each pixie. Give one pixie big blue eyes, another a long pointy nose, another a missing tooth in his smile. You could write the name of each party guest along the front of each pixie's hat. Invite your guests to clip them onto their pockets or collars.

CHRISTMAS OVER THE WORLD

Children in Italy receive presents on January 6 from Befana, a kind old lady who loves all children. Many people in Japan believe that Santa has eyes in the back of his head, so he always knows whether children are naughty or nice!

Christmas (December 25)

SANTA LIGHT

Light up the holiday table or a window with this electric Santa.

What You'll Need: Paper bag, pencil, scissors, markers, cotton balls, glue, flashlight, clay, saucer, Santa hat, tape

Flatten the bag along its creases and turn it so the opening faces you as you draw the face. Draw the outlines of Santa's eyes, nose, and mouth. Cut them out. Use markers to draw on his eyebrows, eyelashes, lips, and cheeks. Glue cotton balls on for hair, mustache, and beard. Stand the flashlight (beam facing up) in clay on a saucer. Put the bag over the flashlight, and add a Santa hat to the bag. When the light is turned on, Santa glows.

55

Christmas (December 25)

GLITTERING GIFT JEWELRY

Help someone sparkle this Christmas with beautiful homemade jewelry.

What You'll Need: Corrugated cardboard, pencil, scissors, string, glue, gold and silver foil, flat-backed colored glass gems, jewelry pin backings, tape, thin wire, gold cord

Draw and cut circles, hearts, Christmas trees, and star shapes out of cardboard. Drizzle glue on the shapes, and lay string in tight spirals or circles on the glue. Let the glue dry for several hours. Cover each shape with silver or gold foil, and glue it down in the back. Rub the foil so the string pattern shows through. Glue on jewels in attractive designs. If you are making pins, glue a pin backing onto the back of each shape. If you want to make a medallion, tape a loop of thin wire onto the back of the shape. Thread gold cord through the loop to make a necklace.

Christmas (December 25)

PACKING PEANUTS SNOWPERSON

Make a snowperson you can keep indoors!

What You'll Need: White and colored construction paper, pencil, scissors, poster board (large enough to paste the snowperson on), glue, foam packing peanuts, salt

Draw 3 circles (one dinner-plate size, one salad-plate size, and one saucer size) on white construction paper. Cut them out. Draw and cut out a hat from black construction paper. Glue the circles and hat onto the posterboard to make a snowperson shape. Glue packing peanuts on the circles. You may need to cut some of the peanuts to make them fit in the circles. Draw and cut out eyes, nose, pipe, buttons, and a scarf from construction paper. Glue them onto the snowperson. Drizzle glue onto the poster board, and sprinkle glue with salt to make the background sparkle.

Christmas (December 25)

SANTA'S STORY

Invite a group of friends over to write a silly story about Santa.

What You'll Need: Paper, pencil

On the top of a piece of paper, write "On the night before Christmas, Santa . . . ." The first person adds a few sentences to the story about Santa. That person folds the paper over so that the words are hidden. The story is passed to the next person, who continues the story without reading what the first person wrote. Continue folding, writing, and passing until everyone has had a chance. Then read the story aloud to hear about Santa's silly adventures.

Christmas (December 25)

PEEK INSIDE CHRISTMAS TREE

This Christmas tree has gifts inside instead of under!

What You'll Need: Half-gallon milk carton, colored felt, glue, ribbons, thin cardboard, scissors, masking tape, gold foil, treats or small gifts for inside the tree base

Make the base of your tree from the bottom half of a milk carton. Glue squares of felt onto it, and trim the edges with ribbons. Cut 4 triangles from thin cardboard that fit over the base. Cover them with green felt. Attach the sides of the triangles, underneath, with masking tape. Fold edges into a Christmas tree shape. This will be the lid for the base. Glue small colored felt circles on the tree to look like Christmas ornaments. Cut a star from cardboard, and cover it with gold foil. Glue the star to the top of your tree. Fill the base with treats or small gifts.

Christmas (December 25)

SANTA SWITCHPLATE

59

What You'll Need: Sturdy cardboard, pencil, scissors, felt, glue, cotton balls, screwdriver, heavy-duty tape

Draw a jolly Santa on a piece of sturdy cardboard. Make your Santa at least 6 inches tall and about 4 inches wide. Have an adult remove the wall switchplate. Ask the adult to use it for a guide to mark off the hole for the light switch in the middle of Santa's belly. Have the adult replace the switchplate. Cut out pieces of felt to glue onto your drawing. Make sure to leave the hole open for the light switch. Glue on cotton balls for Santa's beard and moustache. When your Santa is dry, have an adult tape him in place on your light switch. Every time you give Santa's tummy a tickle, the lights will turn on and off!

Trivia Day (January 4)

FAMILY FACTS

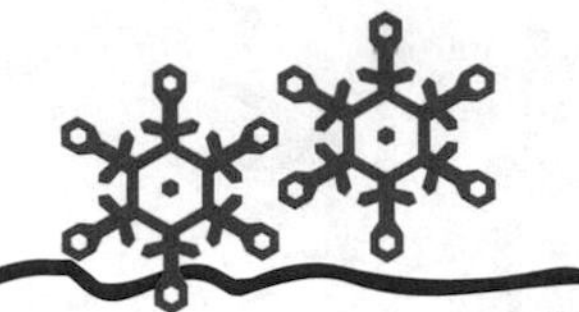

Who's got the best memory in the family?

What You'll Need: Prewritten short descriptions of family experiences and facts on index cards, white paper, markers, timer

Gather up Mom, Dad, and all the kids to play this fun family trivia game. Divide family members into two teams. Each team then writes down 20 short descriptions of experiences or facts related to the family, such as "Ben's high school graduation" or "Nick hates carrots" on index cards. Teams trade their stacks of index cards but can't look at them. Players on each team take turns choosing an index card from their stack and trying to draw it so the rest of the team members can guess what the card says before the timer goes off. Decide as a group how long you want to set the timer for. Remember, you want to give people enough time to draw and make guesses, but you also want to keep the game exciting!

Trivia Day (January 4)

T-SHIRTS OF TRIVIA

Keep them guessing when you wear this puzzling shirt!

What You'll Need: White T-shirt, fabric markers, research books

Trivia Day is a celebration of little-known facts. For every subject in the world there is tons of trivia! What is your favorite subject? Animals? Music? Sports? Dig up some interesting facts by reading encyclopedias and other informative books on the topic. Then form questions about the facts you learned. Write the questions on a T-shirt using fabric markers. Write them in interesting patterns on the shirt. Some should be in very tiny letters and others in large letters. For one question, use a combination of words with large letters and words with small letters. Try different types of handwriting. Then challenge your friends to answer the questions on your shirt!

Christmas (December 25)

62 WHEEL OF MEASURE

Discover some little-known facts about your home.

What You'll Need: Cloth measuring tape, marker, stiff paper plate, ruler with hole at one end, paper fastener (also called a brad)

Use a cloth measuring tape to mark off the inches around the paper plate. Attach the middle of the paper plate to the ruler with a paper fastener. Run your measuring wheel along any surface to see how long the surface is in inches. Count how many times the wheel goes around from one end of a surface to the other, and multiply by the number of inches you marked on the wheel. For example, did you mark off 12 inches on your wheel? If a 12-inch wheel goes around 4 times from one end of a table to the other, then the table is 48 inches long. Find out how long or wide things are, and quiz your family and friends.

Epiphany (January 6)

WELCOME MAGI SIGN

Celebrate this German custom of welcoming the Magi to your home.

What You'll Need: Cardboard, scissors, glue, glitter, markers, crayons or paints, foil, ribbon, tape

It is a custom in Germany to make a welcome sign with the names of the Magi: Caspar, Melchior, and Balthazar. (These are the names that have come down through tradition; we don't really know the names of the Magi, or even if there were three). Cut out a square of cardboard for the sign. Decorate the sign with markers, crayons, or paint, and by drizzling glue and sprinkling the glue with glitter. You can also write the names of the Magi using this glue-and-glitter method. Cut out shiny stars from foil, and glue them on the sign. Glue the ends of ribbons to the back of the sign so that the ribbons stream out from the bottom of the sign. Tape a loop of ribbon on the back of the sign for hanging. Place the sign on your front door. Some people believe that this sign also protects the house from floods and fire.

Epiphany (January 6)

STAR TRIVET

Make this beautiful star to protect your table from hot pots.

What You'll Need: Corrugated cardboard, pencil, scissors, paintbrush, glue, silver foil, many metal soda bottle caps, silver paint

The three Magi were guided by a star. Keep a guiding star in your kitchen all year 'round. Cut a large star from cardboard. Paint the star with a thin layer of glue, and wrap it with foil until it is entirely covered. Glue bottle caps in rows, with the flat side up, to the front of the star. When the glue has dried, paint the bottle caps silver. The star trivet also makes a nice decoration when you are not using it.

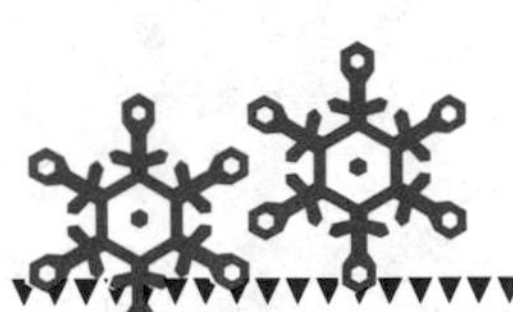

Epiphany (January 6)

THREE TINY KINGS

65

These kings are no bigger than a thumb!

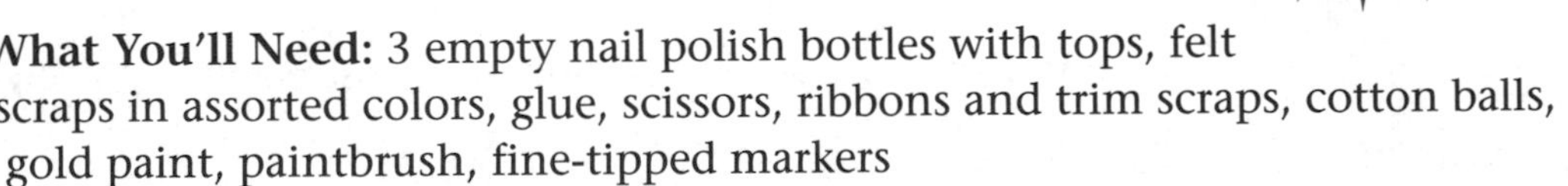

What You'll Need: 3 empty nail polish bottles with tops, felt scraps in assorted colors, glue, scissors, ribbons and trim scraps, cotton balls, gold paint, paintbrush, fine-tipped markers

See if you can find three different nail polish bottles to make your kings. Make sure they are either empty or that no one will mind if they are turned into little kings! Glue layers of felt onto the body of each bottle to make the kings' robes. Use different colors for each king. Glue ribbons and other trim to the robes to make each one fancy. Pull a thin strip of cotton from a cotton ball, and glue it to the top of the robe to make a fur collar for each king. Paint each bottle top with gold paint. Let paint dry. Cut a small circle of felt to make a face for each king. Draw eyes, nose, mouth, and hair with markers. Glue each face to the bottle, above the fur collar. Try to make each king look wise!

66

Thank You Day (January 11)

POP-ME THANK YOU

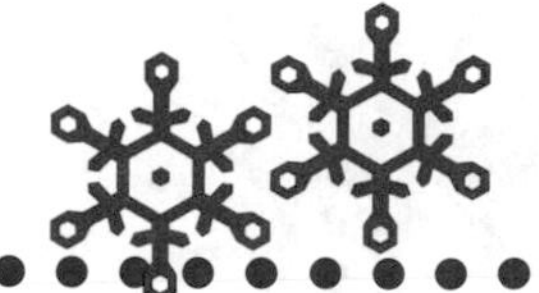

Burst out with big thanks to someone you love.

What You'll Need: Paper, pen, fabric ribbon, balloon, curling ribbon, permanent marker

On a small piece of paper, write a thank-you message to the person you want to thank. Roll the paper into a scroll, and tie it with a bit of ribbon. Carefully insert the scroll into the balloon. Blow up the balloon, tie it off, and tie curling ribbon to the end of the balloon. Write "Pop Me" in big letters on the balloon with a marker, deliver the balloon to the person you want to thank, and wait for the bang! (Discard balloon pieces promptly—they are choking hazards for small children.)

Dr. Martin Luther King, Jr., Day

MARTIN'S MATCH GAME

67

Use the facts you learn about Dr. King to play a matching game.

What You'll Need: 32 index cards, markers, research books

Find out more facts about Dr. King to use in this concentration-type game. Divide 32 index cards into 4 groups. Mark the backs of one group "Open Doors." Mark the backs of the second group "Closed Doors." Mark the backs of the third group with positive situations, including "Peaceful march on Selma." Mark the backs of the fourth group with obstacles, including "Must pay poll tax to vote." Turn all the cards face down and try to match "Open Door" cards with positive situations and "Closed Door" cards with obstacles. If no match is made, the cards are turned face down again. The player with the most matches wins. By the time you are through playing this game, you will be an expert on the extraordinary life of Dr. Martin Luther King, Jr!

68

Dr. Martin Luther King, Jr., Day

PEACE MEDALS

Award a medal of peace to a peace-loving friend.

What You'll Need: 1 cup salt, 1½ cups hot water, 3½ to 4 cups flour, measuring cups, mixing bowl, mixing spoon, rolling pin, drinking glass, cookie sheet, gold or silver paint, paintbrush, markers, glue, glitter, ribbons, scissors, pin backs

Honor Dr. King's love of peace by awarding medals to family and friends who have shown great patience or thoughtfulness or who have been helpful in resolving a conflict. To make the clay: Stir 1 cup salt into 1½ cups hot water. Ask an adult to help with the hot water; be careful that you don't burn yourself. When the mixture cools, add 1 cup flour. Mix until smooth. Add another cup of flour, and continue to mix with a spoon. Add the last 1½ to 2 cups of flour by kneading the clay with your hands. If the clay is sticky, add more flour. If it is dry, add a little more water. Have an adult preheat the oven to 300 degrees. When your clay is just right for shaping, form a 3-inch ball and roll it out on a floured counter with the rolling pin. Press the rim of a drinking glass onto the flattened clay to cut out a circle. Continue doing this until you have cut out all the medals you want to bake. Bake the medals on a cookie sheet for 30 minutes. When they cool, paint them gold or silver. When the paint is dry, write messages on them with markers, such as "World Peace." Drizzle glue around the edges, and sprinkle the glue with glitter. Cut two 5-inch pieces of ribbon and glue to the back of each medal when they are dry. Glue the pin backs to the medals or a piece of ribbon long enough to fit over your head. Have you done your part for peace? Give yourself a medal!

THE LIFE OF MARTIN LUTHER KING, JR.

In 1964, Martin Luther King, Jr., was awarded the Nobel Peace Prize. Only 35 at the time, he was the youngest recipient ever. Dr. King modeled his work after the nonviolent methods of India's Mahatma Ghandi.

69

Dr. Martin Luther King, Jr., Day

PEACEFUL PUPPETS

These cute puppets will bring peace into everyone's heart.

What You'll Need: Felt, scissors, fabric marker, glue, old colorful socks, yarn

It's easy to put on a puppet show about friendship and equality. To make the puppets, cut out 3 circles from felt. Make 2 the same size and 1 slightly smaller. Draw a peace sign on each circle. Glue larger circles on the toe of a sock to make the eyes and the smaller one below to make the nose of your puppet. Glue on yarn for hair, and cut out a smile from more felt to make the mouth. You can also cut out neckties and buttons or bows from the felt and glue these on, too. Cut 2 small holes on either side of the sock so your fingers can fit through to become the puppet's arms. Then put on a play about peace!

Dr. Martin Luther King, Jr., Day

FREEDOM MARCH GAME

70

Learn the facts of Dr. King's life while playing a game.

What You'll Need: Research books, long pieces of poster board, tape, markers, die, buttons

Use research books, including encyclopedias and biographies, to learn facts about Dr. King's life. You can use the facts you learn to make a board game to play with your friends. Tape long pieces of poster board together, and draw a winding road of 15 to 20 squares on it. The first square can be marked with the word "Start" and information about Dr. King's birthplace and birth date. The rest of the squares have either "Open Door" or "Closed Door" written in them. The last square is marked "Freedom."

The Open Doors should also be marked with different successes that Dr. King enjoyed in his fight for freedom, including "Supreme Court declared segregation on buses unconstitutional." The Closed Doors should be marked with setbacks, such as "Dr. King's home bombed." When all the squares are marked, you are ready to play. Take turns tossing a die and moving your buttons the number of squares shown on the die. If you land on an "Open Door," you stay there. If you land on a Closed Door, you must go back to Start. The first person to reach "Freedom" wins the game.

Dr. Martin Luther King, Jr., Day

PEACE PLANE

Fly a flock of peaceful doves.

What You'll Need: White paper, scissors, black marker

Bring peace into your house and the sky above it with these easy-to-make paper doves.

1. Fold an 8 × 11-inch piece of white paper in half.

2. Draw the side-view of a dove as shown.

3. Cut off the extra paper around the outline of the dove and its wing.

4. Fold each wing down to make an airplane shape.

5. You can write a peaceful message or quote from Martin Luther King, Jr., such as "I Have a Dream" inside the dove.

6. Then, let peace fly!

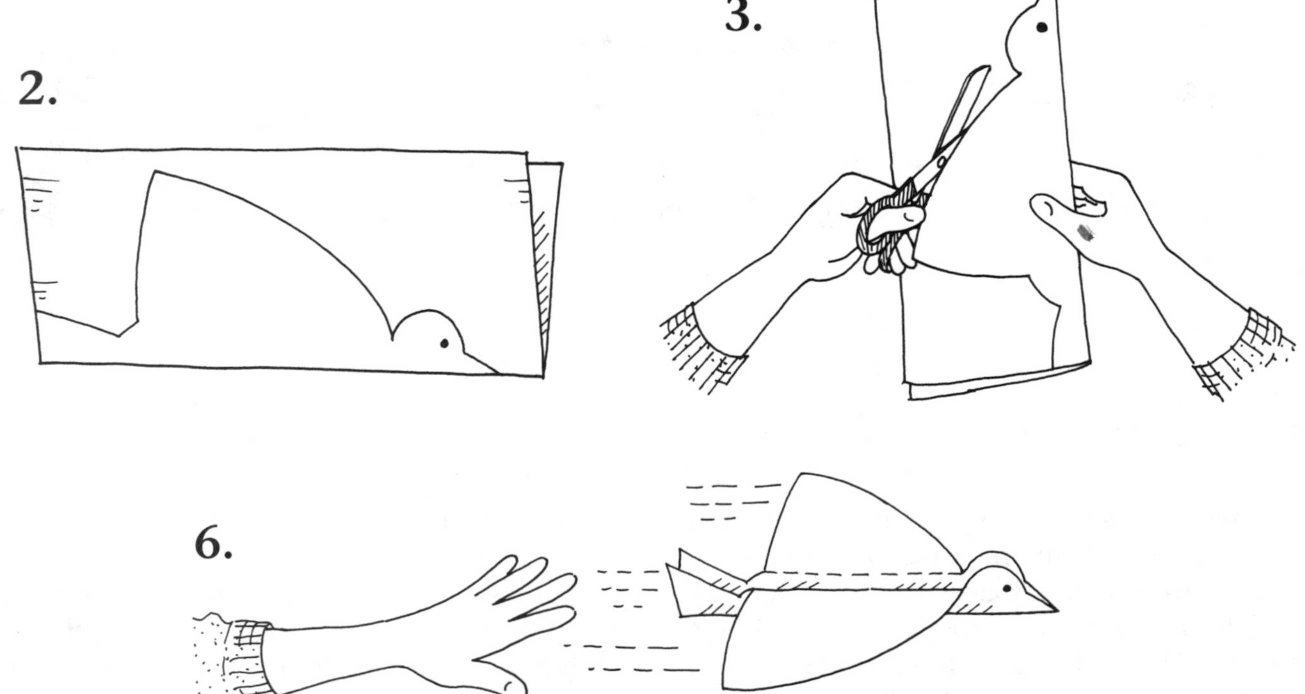

72

Chinese New Year

LUCK LANTERN

Put this lantern on your table on the night of the first new moon of the new year to bring your family good luck.

What You'll Need: Empty soup can, permanent marker, water, hammer, nail, sand, small red candle

Remove the label and wash and dry the can. Draw the Chinese character for luck on the can with permanent marker, either four times evenly spaced or many times in smaller characters. Leave the lower ¼ of the can blank. Fill the can with water and freeze. When the water is frozen, take the can from the freezer, and (with adult help) use the hammer and a nail to punch holes to outline the characters. If the ice starts to melt, put the can back in the freezer until it is solid again. When the holes are all punched, let the ice melt. Fill the bottom of the can ¼ full of sand. Put the candle in the sand.

GOOD LUCK SYMBOL

Chinese New Year

NEW YEAR'S DRUM

73

Gong xi fa cai! (It's pronounced Kung hsi fa tsai!) Best wishes and congratulations! That's the way you say "Happy New Year" in the Mandarin Chinese dialect.

What You'll Need: Margarine tub, craft knife, large red balloon, scissors, large rubber band, wooden spoons

The Chinese people have many holidays and celebrations. But the new year is the most important. The celebration goes on for days and days. In fact, the whole celebration lasts about a month and a half!

Red is considered a very lucky color on Chinese New Year. Make yourself a red New Year's drum so that you will have it handy during the Lion Dance or the Dragon Dance! Have an adult use the craft knife to cut the bottom off the plastic tub. Blow up the balloon to stretch the rubber. Let all the air out of the balloon. Slit the side of the balloon with scissors, and stretch the rubber tightly over the top of the margarine tub. (Keep balloons away from small children; balloons are choking hazards!) Wrap the rubber band around the rim of the tub to hold the balloon in place. Use wooden spoons to beat the drum.

74

Chinese New Year

LION MASK

On the third day of the Chinese New Year the Lion Dance begins. Some people believe putting money in the lion's mouth will bring them luck!

What You'll Need: Paper plate, scissors, stapler, 2 paper egg carton sections, tape, newspaper, white glue, measuring cup, mixing bowl, spoon, tempera paint, paintbrushes, beads, sequins, feathers, ribbon scraps

1. Cut a slit in each side of the paper plate. Pull the edges of each slit together, and overlap them. Staple the edges together. This will bend the plate into a face shape.

2. Tape on the egg carton sections for bulgy eyes. Make a fist-sized ball of newspaper and tape it in place for the lion's snout. Crumple up some newspaper and put it under the mask so it will keep its form while you work.

3. Tear newspaper into strips. Mix ½ cup white glue with ½ cup water. Soak the newspaper strips in the glue/water mixture. When you take the strips out of the mixture, slip them between your fingers to remove extra liquid. Cover the mask front and back with one layer of newspaper strips. Let it dry overnight.

4. Add a second layer of strips; smooth the strips over the mask with your fingers. Let dry overnight.

5. Paint with 2 coats of red tempera paint. Let dry.

6. Paint on the lion's mouth; decorate the mask with beads, sequins, and feathers. Tape a loop of ribbon to the back of the mask so you can hang it on your wall.

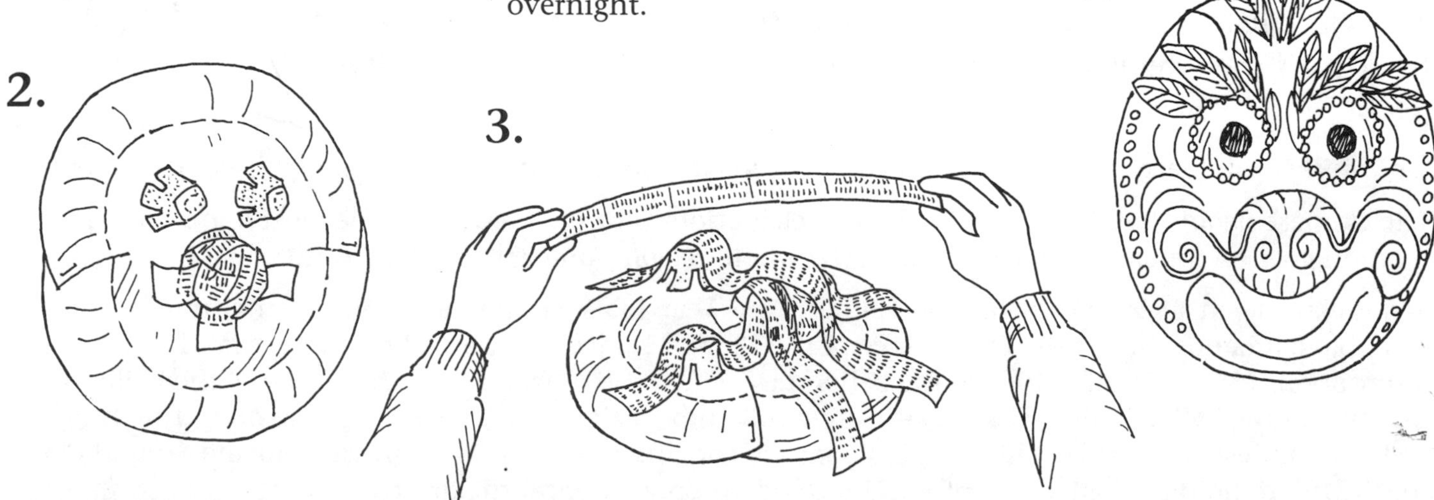

75

Chinese New Year

FROZEN FIREWORKS

There are always fireworks on Chinese New Year—the Chinese invented fireworks! You can make tissue paper "frozen fireworks" to celebrate the new year.

What You'll Need: 2 pieces of graph paper, ruler, 4 to 6 pieces of colored tissue paper, glue stick, tag board, scissors, paper clip

1. Stack 2 pieces of graph paper. Accordion fold them along the lines into ¾-inch folds.

2. Unfold and place 4 to 6 pieces of tissue paper between the graph paper; refold to make fold marks in the tissue.

3. Take a piece of folded tissue, and put a line of glue on the inside edge of the first fold. Take the next piece of tissue paper and place the inside edge of the first fold over the glued edge. Continue in the same way with all the sheets of paper, making one long continuous pleated sheet.

4. Cut 2 pieces of tagboard that are the same length as the tissue sheets but half as wide as folded edge. Completely cover one side of each tag board with glue. Glue one on top of your stack of tissue, and the other on the bottom. At the very top edge, staple the pieces of tagboard together (with tissue between). Let glue dry.

5. Draw fireworks patterns on the edge of the tissue paper. Cut out.

6. Spread fireworks until the tag board sides are back-to-back. Fasten with a paper clip.

76

Chinese New Year

GOLDEN DRAGON PUPPET

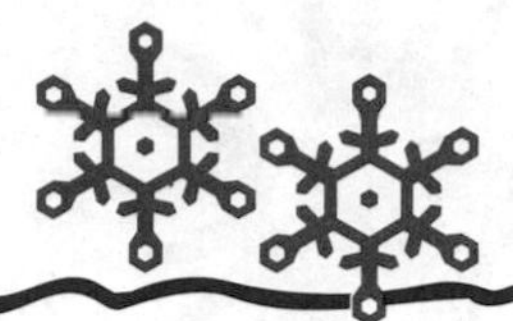

This Golden Dragon has a special trick—when you curl your fingers to make him look at somebody, his ears stand up!

What You'll Need: 2 old solid-color neckties, scissors, ruler, gold fabric paint, sponge, glue, red yarn, 2 safety pins, felt scraps

Cut across one of the ties about 15 inches above the point. This will be the dragon's body. Cut the narrow end off both ties 4 inches from the narrow point. These will be the dragon's ears. Use a sponge to press golden fabric paint onto the tie. Let dry. For the dragon's whiskers, glue 2 pieces of red yarn to the point at the wide end of the tie. Cut 2 black felt triangles for the dragon's nose, and glue them on. Cut the dragon's eyes out of white and blue felt, and glue them on. Cut the dragon's fangs out of white felt, and glue them to the sides of the dragon's face. Make 2 small slits in the tie about 2 inches above the eyes. These slits should be just big enough for the gathered end of the ears to fit in. Pin the ears to the body, hiding the pins in the folds of the ears.

Groundhog Day (February 2)

HIDDEN SHADOW COLLAGE GAME

77

Race to find the groundhog's shadow in these tricky collages.

What You'll Need: Construction paper, old magazines, scissors, glue

Have everyone make a board. Cut lots of pictures out of magazines. Paste them onto a piece of construction paper so they completely cover it. Cut out a small groundhog from brown construction paper and another out of black for the shadow. Paste them onto your collage. Now make flaps. To make a flap, cut a small square from a magazine page that will completely cover one of the objects in your collage. Paste down one edge of the flap onto your collage. Continue doing this all over your collage. Let the glue dry. When the flap is lifted, the object is revealed. To play the game, the players exchange boards. When start is called, the players race to find the groundhog and its shadow. If they tear a flap, they lose the game.

78

National Inventor's Day (February 11)

ROBOT COSTUME

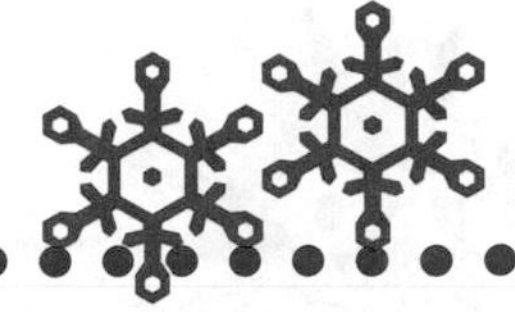

Here's an invention that you can wear!

What You'll Need: Large round ice cream or movie popcorn carton, markers, scissors, paint, paintbrush, colored tape, colored chenille stems, colored foam balls, glue, brightly colored T-shirt, small plastic lids, fabric glue, gold cord, silver stars, fabric markers, colored poster board, stapler

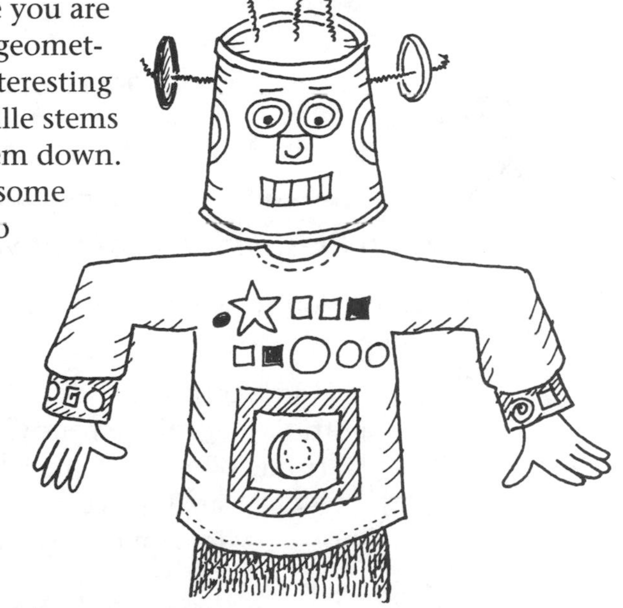

Put the carton on your head, and have a friend mark where the eyes, nose, and mouth of your robot will be. Cut them out in whatever shape you wish—remember, they do not have to look human because you are making a machine! Paint the carton in a bright, fun color. Cut geometric shapes from colored tape, and tape them to the carton in interesting patterns. Poke small holes in the carton and stick colored chenille stems in the holes. Bend the stem ends inside the carton and tape them down. Bend the free ends into squiggle shapes or stick a foam ball on some of them. Paint small plastic lids, and glue them onto a T-shirt to look like knobs and electronic buttons. Decorate the rest of the T-shirt with squiggles of gold cord, silver stars, lines of colored tape, or draw your designs on with fabric markers. Let the costume dry. Draw designs on 6- to 8-inch lengths of colored poster board to make arm and leg cuffs. Once you are wearing your costume, you can have a friend staple the cuffs around your arms and legs. Now it is time to see if your invention really works. Can it walk? Can it talk? What else can it do?

SPRING INTO FUN!

Richard James, a mechanical engineer, watched a torsion spring fall from a shelf to the table to the floor. After some hard work finding the right material to make it out of, the Slinky was born in 1965. To date, over 250 million Slinkys have been sold!

79

Abraham Lincoln's Birthday (February 12)

FOUR SCORE GAME

You don't have to be a president to enjoy this game.

What You'll Need: Sports and/or stock market page of a newspaper for each player, colored markers, timer

Give each player one sports or stock market page from the newspaper. Set the timer for 5 minutes, and yell "Start." Each player must put a colored dot on every number 4 that they find on their page. Players call out "4 Score" each time they find a 4. The player who has found the most 4s when the timer rings is the winner.

Abraham Lincoln's Birthday (February 12)

LINCOLN RING

80

Keep President Lincoln at your fingertips all day long.

What You'll Need: Thin cardboard, scissors, paint, glue, shiny penny, colored tape

Cut a thin strip of cardboard long enough to go around your finger. The strip should be a little wider than a penny. Paint the strip with a pretty design. Glue a shiny penny to the front. When the glue is dry, have a friend tape the ring closed on your finger with a small piece of colored tape. Wear the ring on Lincoln's birthday—make sure you do a lot of waving so everyone can enjoy your presidential jewel!

LAND OF LINCOLN

While President Lincoln did begin his political career in Illinois, he wasn't a native of Illinois. Lincoln was born in Hodgenville, Kentucky, near Knob Creek, in 1809. His family then moved to the backwoods of Indiana when he was 5 or 6, in 1816. It wasn't until 1830 that Lincoln's family moved to Illinois, near Decatur.

81

Valentine's Day (February 14)

DRINKING STRAW NECKLACE

Shower your valentine with jewels!

What You'll Need: Thin red and white poster board, pencil, scissors, plastic red and white drinking straws, red embroidery thread, embroidery needle, white box or bag, markers

Draw and cut out ½-inch hearts from red and white poster board (cut out between 15 to 25). Have an adult help you cut the drinking straws into ½-inch pieces. (To keep pieces from flying, cut the straws inside a large grocery bag.) Cut a length of embroidery thread the length you want the necklace—be sure the loop is long enough to pass over a person's head. Tie the thread to a straw piece at one end to keep the pieces from falling off as you string them. Thread the other end of the thread with an embroidery needle. To make your necklace, take turns threading hearts and straw pieces until the thread is full. You may need an adult to help you carefully push the needle through the center of each cardboard heart. To finish, remove the needle and the end straw piece, and tie the two ends of the string together. Put your necklace in a small white box or bag that you decorated with the words "Be Mine." Whoever gets these beautiful jewels will surely want to be yours forever!

LOVE IS FOR THE BIRDS

Doves, common Valentine's Day symbols, signify loyalty and love. They mate for life and always return home to roost. Lovebirds, also symbols of Valentine's Day, were named for their tendency to bond with each other and perch in pairs.

82

Valentine's Day (February 14)

BLOWN-EGG SACHET

Treat your loved one's nose with this sweetly scented gift.

What You'll Need: Egg, hat pin, bowl, cotton, scented oil, miniature dried craft flowers, paints and paintbrush or markers, cardboard egg carton cup, glue

Ask an adult to help you make the blown egg for your sachet. Stick a hat pin into the top of a raw egg. Carefully dig away tiny pieces of shell to make an opening ⅛ inch wide. Use the pin to stir the egg inside to break the yolk so it can be blown out. Make a tiny hole in the other end of the egg. Blow through the smallest hole so that the egg's insides come out. Make sure you are holding the egg over a bowl while you blow. When the egg is empty, run water through it to clean out the rest of the egg. Let the egg dry. Dip a small piece of cotton in scented oil, and carefully insert the cotton into the egg. Poke more tiny holes in the egg, and insert miniature flowers. Use paint or markers to draw hearts around the flowers. For the base, decorate the egg carton cup red or pink, turn it upside-down, and glue the sachet egg onto it. Happy sniffing!

Valentine's Day (February 14)

CARAMEL NUT SWEETS

83

Everyone will go nuts for these delicious sweets!

What You'll Need: Margarine for greasing, 2 cups pecan halves, 14-ounce bag of caramels, cookie sheet, metal spatula, waxed paper, colored foil

Ask an adult to preheat the oven to 325 degrees. Grease a cookie sheet, and arrange pecan halves to make the petals of a flower. Put 1 unwrapped caramel candy in the center of each flower. Bake for 5 minutes or until caramels have melted. Grease a metal spatula, and use it to carefully spread the softened caramel over the pecans to coat them. Place the candies on waxed paper. When the candies are cool, wrap them in foil, and give them as Valentine's treats.

Valentine's Day (February 14)

QUEEN OF STOLEN HEARTS GAME

Be quick and outsmart the Queen—steal her hearts!

What You'll Need: Construction paper, scissors, clear tape, fake jewels, glitter, cardboard tube, foil, crepe paper or ribbons

Make a queen's crown out of a band of construction paper that has been taped together at the ends. Cut out and tape triangular shapes around the band to make the crown's points. Glue on fake jewels and glitter. Cover a cardboard tube with foil. Form a ball out of foil, and tape it onto the top of the tube to make the queen's scepter. Tape on crepe paper streamers or ribbons to the other end. Decorate a chair with ribbons and more foil to make a throne. Cut out large hearts from red construction paper.

Now you are ready to play the Stolen Hearts Game. The large hearts are the bases. One person is chosen to be the Queen and sit on the throne. The other players are the Knaves, and they stand on the heart bases. Whoever is left without a heart is the Court Fool. She or he must try to steal a heart whenever the Queen raises her scepter and says "All change hearts." Whoever is left without a heart to stand on must be the new Fool. Players can take turns being the Queen. For variety, the Queen can turn on a tape, CD, or the radio when she wants the Knaves to change places; she turns it off when she wants them to grab a heart.

FLOWERS OF LOVE

The colors of flowers have been used as codes on valentines since they were first sent in the 1400s. Red flowers mean "Our love will last forever." Pink flowers mean "Our love is dying." White flowers mean "Our love is gone."

Valentine's Day (February 14)

THUMBELINA VALENTINES

Make guaranteed one-of-a-kind valentines with your thumb.

What You'll Need: White construction paper, washable colored stamp pads, sponges, markers, waterproof pen

What could show your love more on Valentine's Day than a valentine only you could make? Use the most unique part of your body, your thumb, and give your valentine a heart-shaped thumbprint message. Fold a piece of white construction paper in quarters to make a greeting card. Think of how many thumbprint hearts you want to include on the front of your card, or experiment as you go. To make a thumbprint heart, press your clean thumb firmly on a stamp pad. Then press your thumb on the paper at a 45-degree angle. Let the print dry, then reink your thumb, and press it right next to the first thumbprint so the bottoms overlap. The second thumbprint should be tilted in a 45-degree angle in the opposite direction. If you want, draw an arrow through your heart, and write a valentine's message on the card. Or you could make several thumbprint hearts, draw faces on them, and add speech balloons to write your messages in.

I Love You!

Here's how to say that wonderful phrase in a few languages. Italian: *"Ti amo"*; French: *"Je t'aime"*; Sioux: *"Techihhila"*; Zulu: *"Mena Tanda Wena"*; Icelandic: *"Eg Elska thig."*

Valentine's Day (February 14)

LOVE POTION NUMBER NINE

Be careful who you get to taste this drink—they may fall in love with you!

What You'll Need: Maraschino cherries, red food coloring, ice cube tray, pink lemonade

Put a maraschino cherry and a drop of red food coloring in each section of an ice cube tray. Fill the tray with water, and freeze. Add an ice cube to a glass of pink lemonade, and serve up some Love Potion Number Nine at a Valentine's party. (Remind everyone to take care not to bite into or swallow the frozen cherries). Everyone will fall in love with this tasty drink!

Valentine's Day (February 14)

CANDY CLIPS

These decorative clips tell your valentines exactly how you feel about them.

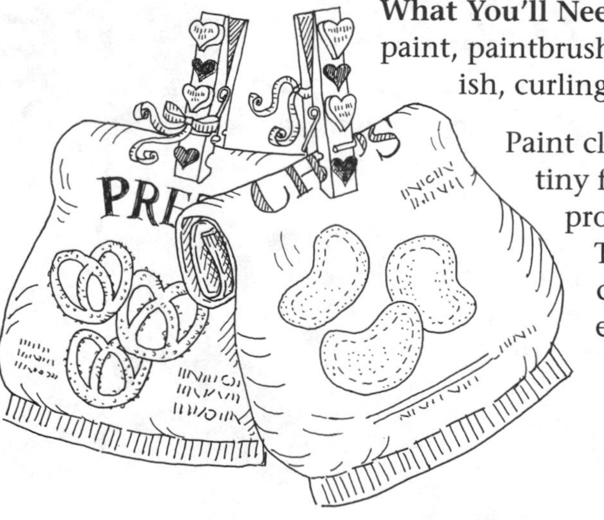

What You'll Need: Metal hair clips or wooden spring clothespins, paint, paintbrush, felt scraps, candy message hearts, scissors, glue, clear nail polish, curling ribbons

Paint clips and clothespins red or pink. When the paint dries, glue on tiny felt hearts and candy message hearts. Use the clear nail polish to protect the candy from breaking and to give the clips a shiny finish. Tie on some thin red, pink, and white curling ribbons. Give these clips as Valentine's Day presents to friends and family. They make excellent snack bag closers or bookmarks.

Valentine's Day (February 14)

CHENILLE STEM PUP

This adorable puppy will make your valentine want to bark with delight!

What You'll Need: Red construction paper, scissors, ruler, 3 red chenille stems, glue, marker, 2 small wiggle eyes

Cut a strip of red construction paper 2 × 3 inches. Hold the 3 chenille stems together so that the ends are even. Roll the paper strip around the middle of the chenille stems. Glue the paper closed. Bend one stem at each end to make the puppy's neck and tail. Curl the tail up so it looks like a little hook. Bend the remaining stems down to make the puppy's feet. Cut a small heart shape out of construction paper to make the puppy's head. Cut out 2 smaller heart shapes to make the puppy's ears; glue them to the larger heart. Glue on the wiggle eyes, and draw a nose and mouth. Glue the head to the puppy's neck. Give your puppy a name, and deliver it to a lucky valentine!

Valentine's Day (February 14)

BROKENHEARTED PUZZLE

Tell your valentine to put this broken heart together to get a sweet message.

What You'll Need: Red construction paper, scissors, thin cardboard, glue, markers, envelope

Draw and cut out a large construction paper heart. Glue it onto a piece of thin cardboard, and cut around the heart when the glue is dry. Write a message in large letters on the heart. Some ideas for messages are: "I Went to Pieces," "Together Forever," or "How Do You Mend a Broken Heart?" You may want to decorate your message and the rest of the heart with pretty designs and colors, maybe with tiny hearts, bluebirds, flowers, and small cupids. When you are finished, cut the heart into several pieces, and put the pieces into a pretty, decorated envelope. Give your broken-heart message puzzle to someone you love for a really special Valentine's Day card.

90

Valentine's Day (February 14)

FLYING CUPID MOBILE

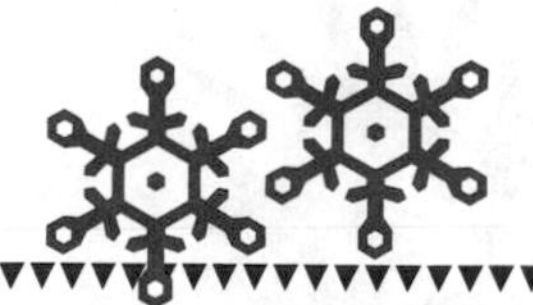

Flying high over a Valentine's party, or just in your room, watch out for this cupid! He might help someone steal your heart!

What You'll Need: Pencil, paper, scissors, light cardboard, large needle, colored markers, black fine-tipped marker, clear nylon thread, dowel

Use cupid's body and wings from this book as a pattern to draw your own. Cut out the paper patterns and use them to trace the parts onto the cardboard. Mark where the holes for the thread will be with a dot. Cut out the cardboard wings and body. Push the needle through the dots to make holes. Color cupid's body and draw feathers on the wings; use a fine marker to make his eyes and mouth. Sew the wings to the body. Attach a long piece of nylon thread to each of the outside holes on the wings. Tie these threads to the dowel, as shown. Hang up your mobile. Poke cupid's tummy, and watch him fly!

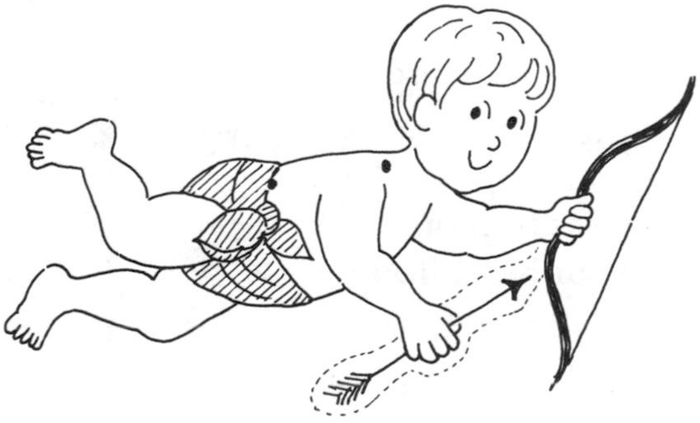

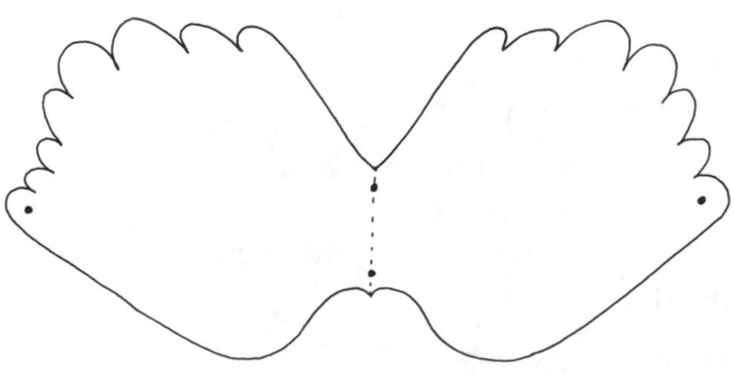

Valentine's Day (February 14)

HEART FLOWERS

Give your valentine colorful flowers, even in the middle of winter.

What You'll Need: Green chenille stems, construction paper, scissors, markers, glue, candy message hearts, stapler, ribbons, tissue paper

Take a bouquet of heart-shaped flowers to a loved one this Valentine's Day. To make the stems of your flowers, twist 2 chenille stems together. You can make some chenille stems longer by laying them end to end and twisting the ends together. You may want some flowers to be longer than others to give your bouquet more variety. Cut 2 same-size hearts out of construction paper. You will need 2 hearts for each flower you want to make. Cut each set of hearts different sizes. Staple the hearts front to back around the stem so that the chenille stem is held tightly in place. Then decorate the hearts with markers and by gluing on 1 or 2 tiny candy message hearts. Tie ribbons in bows around the stems, and gather the bunch of heart flowers and wrap them in a tissue paper cone. Tie the cone with more ribbons to keep the flowers together. Present your heart flowers to your beloved!

WAS THERE A ST. VALENTINE?

The original St. Valentine lived during the time of Roman Emperor Claudius II, who wanted the men in the army to stay unmarried so they wouldn't desert the army to stay with their families. But St. Valentine would secretly marry the men and their sweethearts.

92

Valentine's Day (February 14)

SWINGING VALENTINE PUPPET

This heart-shaped puppet will show you a swinging good time!

What You'll Need: Red construction paper, scissors, 4 large colored rubber bands, glue, stapler, markers

Cut 2 same-sized hearts out of red construction paper. Make sure they are big enough for your hand to fit inside. Cut four 1-inch hearts to use as the puppet's hands and feet. Cut each rubber band to form a long elastic string. Glue the rubber bands to one of the large hearts to make arms and legs (glue 2 at the top sides and 2 at the bottom sides). Staple the 2 large hearts together (with the glued rubber bands on the inside). Remember to leave enough room for your hand to fit inside. Glue a small heart to each of the loose ends of the rubber bands. Draw a face on your puppet with markers. If you have made several, draw different expressions to make characters for a Valentine's Day play.

Valentine's Day (February 14)

SPECIAL VALENTINES

93

Have you ever sent a secret valentine? It can be even more fun when your secret valentine has a secret meaning!

What You'll Need: Colored paper, markers, ribbon, lace, hard candies, glue

When paper valentines were first sent in the 1400s, each valentine carried a code. If you sent your sweetheart a valentine with a ribbon on it, that meant "My heart is tied to you." If the valentine had a fan on it, that meant "Open your heart to me." Lace and net are the same word in Latin, so a valentine with a ruffle of lace meant "You have caught my heart in a net." Make your own cards with your own codes. Use colored paper, markers, ribbons, lace, hard candies, and anything else you can think up. Do you think your valentine is sweet? Glue on hard candy as part of your design. You don't have to tell your valentine what your code means!

94

Valentine's Day (February 14)

LOVE KNOT

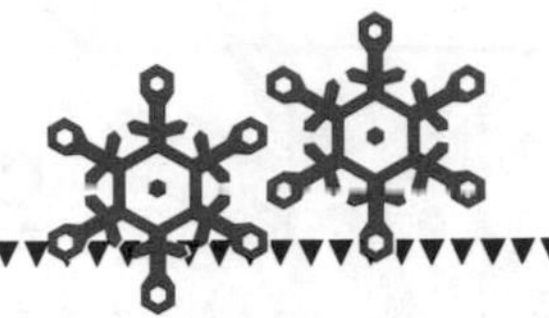

Wearing a love knot on your sleeve means that you have a love that will never end.

What You'll Need: Red felt, 3 × 2-inch piece of stiff cardboard, gold braid, white glue, pins, scissors, cool-temp glue gun, pin back

Love knots are one of the oldest traditions of Valentine's Day. Wearing a love knot on your sleeve means that you have a love that will never end. Here are instructions to make your own love knot. Glue red felt to the front and back of the cardboard. Glue gold braid to the front of the felt in a sideways figure 8, as shown in the illustration below. Hold the braid in place with pins until the glue is dry. Carefully cut around the knot with sharp scissors to make your pin. Glue the pin back to the back of your love knot.

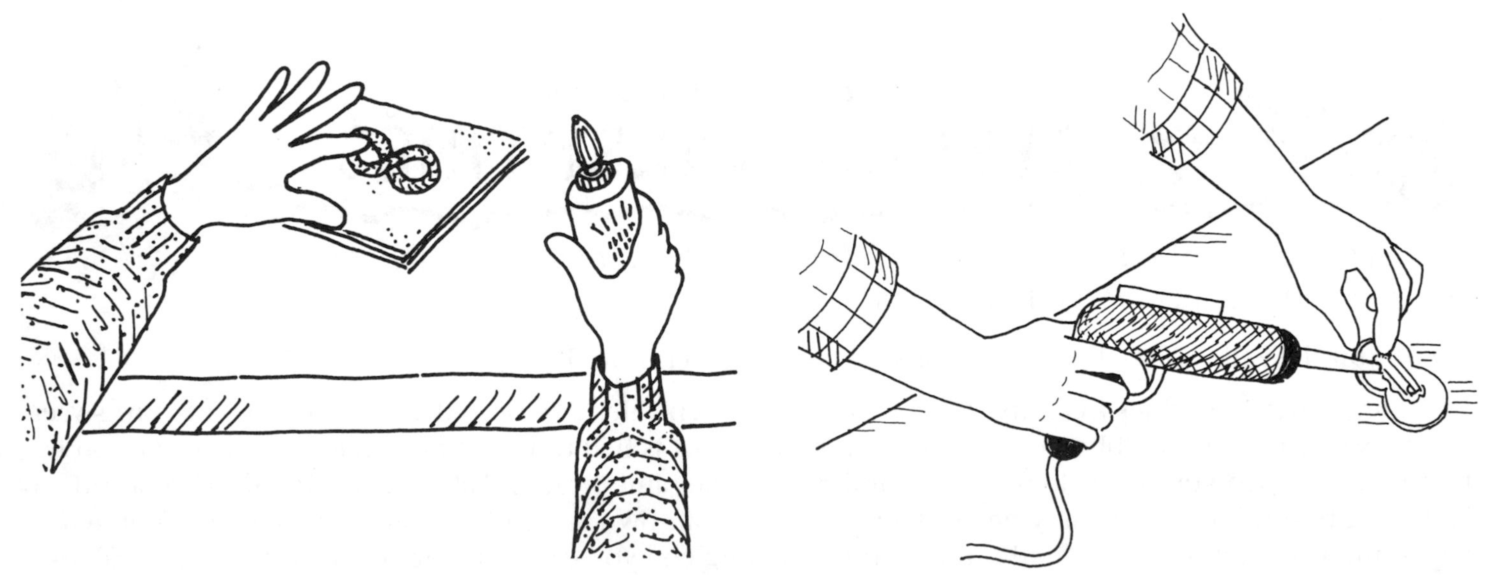

Valentine's Day (February 14)

"HEART OF GOLD" PICTURE FRAME

Put yourself in someone's heart forever!

What You'll Need: Cardboard, pencil, scissors, glue, gold raffia, photo

Draw and cut out a heart-shaped piece of cardboard to make the frame. You can make your frame big or small, depending on the size of the photo you want to put in it. In the inside of your heart, draw and cut out a smaller heart that is big enough for your photo. Be sure the important part of the photo is visible inside the heart shape. Wind the gold raffia around the frame, going from the outside of the frame in through the middle and then around to the outside again. Cover the frame completely. Secure ends of raffia on back of frame with glue. Place the frame on another piece of cardboard, and trace its outline. Cut the outline out just inside the line, to make the back a little smaller than the front. Using the raffia heart as a guide for placement, glue your photo to the backing heart. Glue the backing heart to the back of the raffia frame. Using the pattern shown below right as a guide, draw and cut out a cardboard stand to fit your frame. Glue it to the back of your frame. It's a golden gift!

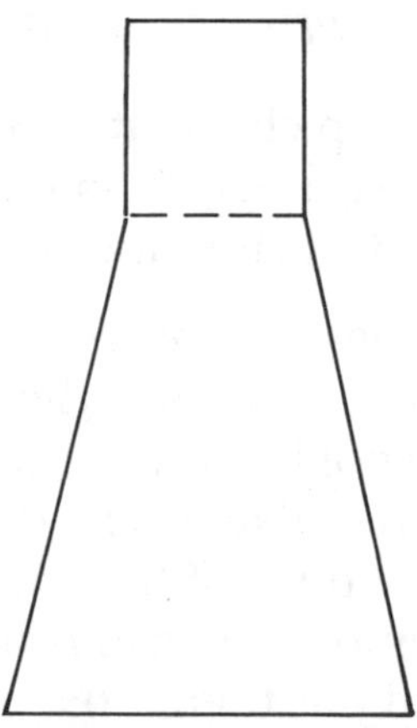

George Washington's Birthday (February 22)

TRICKY GEORGE

Even George Washington himself couldn't do this trick!

What You'll Need: Dollar bill, wall

Tell your friends you'll give them each a dollar if they can pick it up from the floor. But there is a catch; they have to pick it up using your instructions! Have your friends stand with their feet together and heels up against a wall. Put dollar bills on the floor 12 inches in front of their feet. Tell them to pick up the dollars without bending their knees or moving their feet. It is impossible to do! Why? When you are standing against a wall, your center of gravity is over your feet. If you bend forward, you have to move your center of gravity forward in order to keep your balance. Since you can't move your feet during this trick, you're flat out of luck! But that's better than being flat on your face!

George Washington's Birthday (February 22)

"I CANNOT TELL A LIE" TARTS

This dessert will be very popular—and not just with presidents!

What You'll Need: ¾ cup chocolate cookie crumbs, 8 ounces cream cheese, ⅓ cup sugar, 1 teaspoon lemon juice, 1 teaspoon vanilla, 1 egg, 20-ounce can cherry pie filling, measuring cups and spoons, 2 clean dishtowels, rolling pin, muffin cups and pan, mixing bowl, electric mixer, pot holders, can opener

Ask an adult to preheat the oven to 375 degrees. To make the cookie crumbs, put plain chocolate cookies between two dishtowels, and crush them with a rolling pin. Place the muffin cups into the muffin pan, and drop 1 tablespoon of cookie crumbs into each. Mix the cream cheese, sugar, lemon juice, and vanilla for 3 minutes with an electric mixer on medium speed. Crack the egg into the mixture, and continue beating for 2 minutes. Put 2 tablespoons of this mixture over the cookie crumbs in each muffin cup. Bake for 15 minutes. Have an adult remove the pan from the oven. Let them cool for about 1 hour. Take the muffin cups out of the muffin pan, and put them on a plate. Spoon about 2 tablespoons of cherry pie filling onto each of the muffins. Refrigerate for 2 hours before serving. These tarts are delicious—and that's no lie!

98

Mardi Gras

PARTY PLATE MASKS

Hide your true identity behind these glittery half-masks.

What You'll Need: Paper, pencil, shiny or colored plastic-coated paper party plates, scissors, glitter glue, shiny stickers, hole punch, curling ribbon, beads, elastic thread, needle, wooden dowel, paint, paintbrushes

Use our pattern as a starting point for making your own mask. Draw your pattern, and lay it on the paper plate. Trace around the pattern, and cut it out. Carefully cut out the eye holes. Use glitter glue to draw lines around the eye holes. Let glue dry. Paste shiny stickers onto your mask. Punch holes at the bottom corners of your mask, and thread strands of curling ribbon through the holes. String beads on the ends of the ribbons. If you want to wear your mask, poke small holes on either side of the mask and thread a loop of elastic string long enough to stretch around your head. If you'd like to hold the mask in front of your face, paint a wooden dowel. Glue it to the bottom corner of the mask. Make lots of different masks, and switch identities all through Mardi Gras. Keep everyone guessing who you are!

99

Mardi Gras

CLINK-CLANK NOISEMAKER

Sound off at Mardi Gras with a clink and a clank!

What You'll Need: Empty tissue box (the long, flat kind), pencil, scissors, heavy paper, tape, 2 jar lids, glue, paint, paintbrushes, gold, purple, and green glitter

Mark a line across the top and sides of the tissue box; the line should be across the shorter length of the box. Cut down the line on all 3 sides. Bend the box so the back sides touch. Cut straps from heavy paper, and tape them down inside each half of the box so that they are slightly curved. The straps will hold your hand inside the noisemaker. Glue the jar lids to the outside of each half. Paint your clink-clank in the Mardi Gras colors of gold, purple, and green. When the paint is dry, draw designs with glue, and sprinkle glitter on top. Shake off the extra glitter, and let the glue dry. Insert your fingers under the top strap and your thumb under the bottom strap to make some music!

Mardi Gras

KING CAKE

100

This delicious Mardi Gras cake has a baked-in surprise!

What You'll Need: 2 cups flour; ¼ cup sugar; 1 package active dry yeast; ½ cup milk; ¼ cup butter; 3 eggs (at room temperature); ½ cup each mixed candied fruits and raisins; foil-wrapped toy figure (a baby) that is heat-proof; gold, purple, and green sugar sprinkles; measuring cup and spoons; mixing bowls; saucepan; mixing spoon; spoon; electric mixer; dish towel; 10-inch tube pan

Have an adult help you make this traditional Mardi Gras treat. Mix ¾ cup flour with the sugar and yeast. Pour the milk into a small saucepan, add the butter, and stir over low heat. Slowly add the milk mixture to the flour mixture and beat with an electric mixer until well blended. Add the eggs one by one; beat well after each egg. Add ½ cup flour, and beat until a thick batter is formed. Add the rest of the flour, and beat for 2 minutes. Cover the mixture with a dish towel, and set it in a warm place for about 1 hour. Have an adult preheat the oven to 350 degrees. Using a large spoon, fold candied fruits and raisins into the batter. Pour the batter into a greased tube pan, and poke the foil-wrapped toy into the batter. Traditionally, this toy is a baby that represents the Christ child. Whoever finds him will have good luck for the coming year. This person must host the next Mardi Gras party! Bake your King Cake for 40 minutes or until golden brown. Let it cool, and sprinkle it with gold, purple, and green sprinkles. The cake will serve 8 to 10.

101

Mardi Gras

THROW-ME BEADS

Colorful beads are a tradition at Mardi Gras.

What You'll Need: Cardboard, pencil, ruler, old color magazines or comics, scissors, stiff cord, glue, small paintbrush, clear varnish or nail polish, embroidery thread, large embroidery needle

Make a cardboard template of a triangle that has 2 long sides that are 5 inches long and a shorter side that is 1 inch long. Use the template to trace and cut triangles from old magazines or comics. Each triangle will be a bead. To make a bead, take a triangle, wrong side up, and roll the wider end around a piece of cord. Work carefully and continue to roll, making sure the bead builds up evenly. Keep rolling the paper tightly until the last 2 inches. Brush the wrong side of the 2 inches with glue, and roll it up. Let the bead dry on the cord. When the glue is dry, give your beads a coat of clear varnish or nail polish to protect them and make them hard. Be sure the beads don't touch each other until they are dry. When dry, thread the beads on embroidery thread to make necklaces, bracelets, and anklets. The traditional Mardi Gras cry is, "Throw me something, Mistuh!" Now you can throw your beads into the air during a parade or party.

SPRING

The flowers are blooming, the birds are chirping, the sun is shining—the signs of spring are everywhere! And there are many wonderful holidays to celebrate at this time of the year. We celebrate mothers and children and our earth, and so many other wonderful holidays. Get ready to decorate some eggs, make some fun flowers, clean up your neighborhood, and so much more this spring!

Hinamatsuri (March 3)

JAPANESE EGG DOLL

Observe Hinamatsuri, a Japanese holiday that celebrates girls, by making your own Hina-dolls!

What You'll Need: 2 raw eggs, needle, bowl, 2 large soda bottle caps, glue, colored tissue paper, black yarn, paints, fine paintbrushes

You can make your own Hina-dolls to help you celebrate. Use a needle to make a small hole in one end of a raw egg. Stick the needle inside the egg to break the yolk. Make a slightly larger hole in the other end of the egg. Hold the egg over a bowl, and blow on the small hole until the raw egg comes out the larger hole. You have to blow hard! When the egg shell is empty, gently rinse out the inside and wash the outside. Let it dry. Glue the large end of the egg into a soda bottle cap so that it will stand up. Use tissue paper to make kimonos for your dolls. Glue on black yarn for hair. Paint the dolls' faces. Use the raw eggs to bake a cake, and have a Hinamatsuri tea party!

103

Hinamatsuri (March 3)

TINY STRAW KITE

Lots of things are decorated with Hina-dolls or peach blossoms on Hinamatsuri. You can paint them on the sides of this kite!

What You'll Need: Dental floss, 6 straws, thread, tissue paper, glue, paint, fine paintbrushes, string

1. Thread 1 long piece of dental floss through 3 straws. Tie the ends of the floss together, which will form the straws into a triangle.

2. Cut 3 pieces of dental floss 2 inches longer than the straws. Thread a piece of floss through each of the last 3 straws, leaving an inch sticking out of each end.

3. Tie together 1 end of the floss from all 3 straws. You will have a 3-armed star. Tie the floss hanging from the other end of each straw to a corner of the triangle. You will have a 4-sided shape called a tetrahedron.

4. Cover 2 sides of the tetrahedron by gluing tissue paper to the straws.

5. On the triangles with tissue paper, poke small holes in the paper ⅓ of the way from the top of the kite. Thread a piece of floss through each hole, and tie them around the straw.

6. Tie a slightly longer piece of floss around the straw near the bottom ⅓ of the kite. Tie the floss together, then tie a long string to this to fly the kite. Paint a Hina-doll or a peach blossom on your kite, and see how high it can fly!

3.

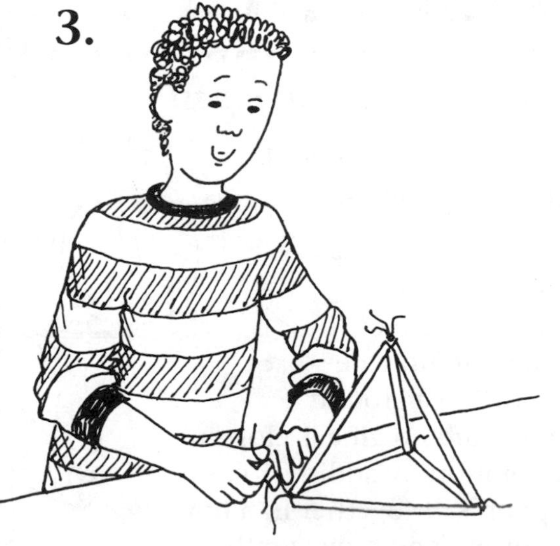

6.

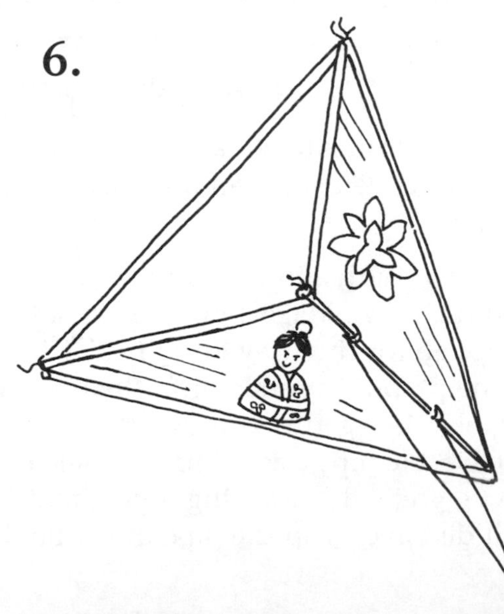

Purim

PURIM MOVIE

Tell the story of Purim with this homemade movie!

What You'll Need: Scrap paper, pencil, roll of white butcher paper or shelf paper (or tape paper together to make 60 inches); two ½-inch dowels, 12 inches long; crayons or markers; tape

Reread the story of Queen Esther, Mordecai, and Haman to get ideas for a movie that explains the story of Purim. Make a storyboard before you begin by sketching ideas for each scene in your movie. You might start by writing down the events of the story and then drawing a picture that shows each scene. Or start by drawing all the characters so you can introduce them one by one at the beginning of your movie. When you have decided the order of the scenes, draw each picture on a length of butcher paper, starting at one end and continuing until the story is finished. You can write titles, captions, and speech balloons, like a comic strip, too. Leave a few inches of blank paper at either end. Tape each end around a dowel. Then roll up the paper onto the dowel that is nearest the end of the story, which will make a scroll. When you are ready to show your movie, hold one end and have a friend hold the other end. Then slowly unroll the paper as you narrate the story that goes with each picture. Pop some popcorn, and invite the whole family.

St. Patrick's Day (March 17)

LEPRECHAUN BUBBLE PIPE

Legend says that fairies catch rides on bubbles from leprechaun pipes!

What You'll Need: Acorn, kitchen knife, nail, straw, cool-temp glue gun and glue, 1 cup warm water, ½ cup green dishwashing liquid, 1 teaspoon salt, bowl, plastic spoon

Find a large acorn. With adult help, cut the top off and dig out the meat to make a little bowl. Make a hole in the side near the bottom of the bowl, just big enough for the straw to fit into. Using the cool-temp glue gun (with adult help), put the straw into the hole and fill the area around the straw with glue. Blow gently through the straw to make sure no glue is clogging the hole. Set the bubble pipe aside. Mix up some bubble solution by adding 1 cup warm water, ½ cup green dishwashing liquid, and 1 teaspoon salt together in a bowl. Stir until the salt dissolves. Dip the pipe in the bubble solution, and blow gently.

St. Patrick's Day (March 17)

106 LIMBER LIAM LEPRECHAUN

This little leprechaun might be dancing a jig behind your back—but he'll not so much as hop while you watch him!

What You'll Need: Pink and green crepe paper, ruler, scissors, 5 chenille stems, cotton ball, thread, clear tape, markers, green and black felt or cloth scraps, glue, spring clothespin

Cut the pink and green crepe paper into 6 × 1½-inch pieces. Twist the chenille stems together as shown to make the leprechaun's "bones." Stick a cotton ball on the top of the neck, and wrap it with thread to keep it in place. Wrap the pink crepe paper around the head and the green crepe paper around the figure. Wrap each body part separately so that you can bend the chenille stems at the joints in order to pose your leprechaun. Use more paper on the upper legs or arms to make them thicker; use less on the knees so you can pose them. Secure the ends of crepe paper with clear tape. Use markers to draw a leprechaun face. Make your leprechaun a green suit and black belt out of felt or cloth scraps and glue them on him. To make him stand up, clip a clothespin to his heel.

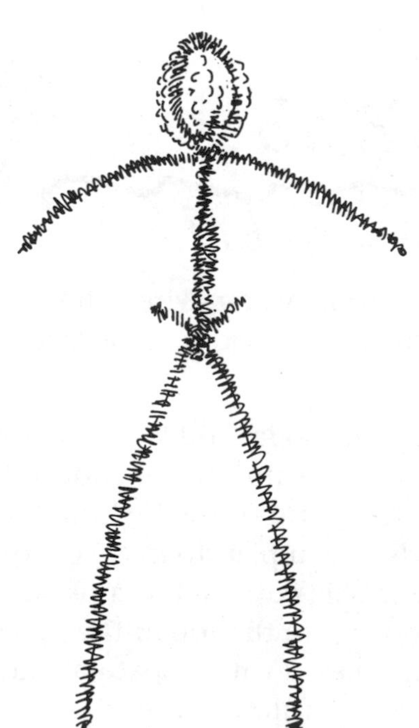

107

St. Patrick's Day (March 17)

GREEN-MAGIC RINGS

You don't have to kiss the Blarney stone to make some magic.

What You'll Need: Plastic screw-on cap, 3½ inches of narrow elastic, glue, spring clothespins, 5-inch circle green fabric, dried rose petals or mint leaves, jingle bell with small holes, rubber band

Glue both ends of the elastic inside the cap, on opposite sides. Turn the cap over, and glue the elastic to the outer sides of the cap. Clamp the elastic to the lid with clothespins until the glue is dry. Put rose petals or mint leaves and the jingle bell (the holes in the bell should be small so the dried petals or leaves don't get inside) in the middle of the fabric. Gather the edges, and wrap them with a rubber band to make a ball. Pour glue into the cap. Set the fabric ball in the glue, opening side down. When the glue is dry, slip your finger though the elastic loop under the cap. Shake your ring to make magic.

St. Patrick's Day (March 17)

LUCKY CHARMS

108

Faith and begorra! A lucky charm may help you catch a wee folk!

What You'll Need: 1 cup cornstarch, 2 cups baking soda, water, wire, wire cutters, rolling pin, St. Patrick's day cookie cutters, plastic knife, spatula, wire rack, glue, acrylic paint, clear nail polish, yarn

Have an adult help you cook the cornstarch, baking soda, and water over medium heat, stirring constantly. It will boil, then thicken. Cook until smooth. Let cool. While the dough is cooling, bend the wire into a small U shape. Each arm of the U should be about ½ inch long. Clip off the excess wire. Make as many Us as you plan to make charms. Roll the dough out to ¼ inch thick. Cut out shapes with the cookie cutters. Use a plastic knife to smooth the edges. Press the open ends of the wire loops into the top of the figures; a little bit of the loop should be left sticking out. Lift the charms with a spatula, and put them on a wire rack to dry for at least one day. Fill the holes around the wire with glue. When dry, paint the charms. Let dry completely. Paint with clear nail polish to seal. Let dry. String the figures on a yarn necklace, tying each one in place.

109

St. Patrick's Day (March 17)

POT O' GOLD GAME

What brings good luck on St. Patrick's Day? Finding a four leaf clover, wearing green socks, kissing the blarney stone, and playing the Pot o' Gold game!

What You'll Need: Yellow, black, and green construction paper; scissors; glue; pennies

This is a game for 2 to 5 people. Use yellow construction paper to make a large circle. Cut 10 quarter-sized shamrocks out of green paper. Glue them on the circle in a random pattern. Cut out 10 black banshee spots—these circles should be twice as large as the shamrocks. Glue them on the circle in a random fashion. Stand 5 or 6 feet from the Pot o' Gold. Each player gets to toss a penny a turn. If your penny lands on a lucky shamrock, then you get to keep it. (The penny does not have to be completely on the shamrock, it can be touching the pot. Also, if your penny touches both a shamrock and a banshee spot, it is counted as landing on a banshee spot.) But if it lands on a banshee spot, you have to leave it on the board. (If your penny doesn't land on either a shamrock or banshee spot, you get another chance to throw it. After that, you must leave your penny on the pot.) The next player whose penny lands on a lucky shamrock gets to pick up all the "gold" on the board! The player with the most pennies at the end of the game wins.

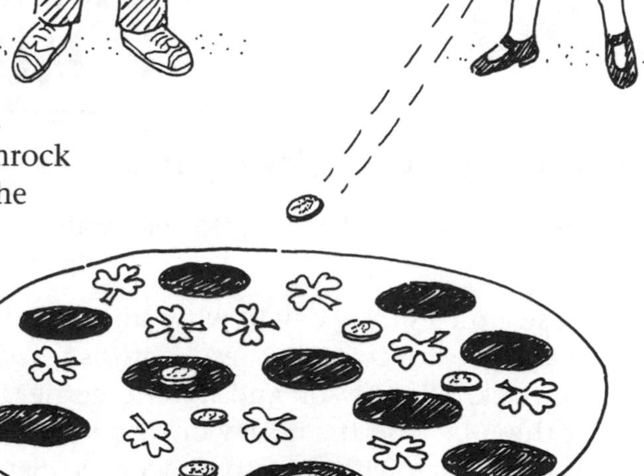

St. Patrick's Day (March 17)

LEPRECHAUN'S CORSAGE

You don't have to be Irish to enjoy making and wearing this special green pin!

What You'll Need: Embroidery needle, thin green yarn, scissors, pencil, acorn cap, glue, small safety pin

Thread the needle with a 5-inch length of green yarn. Wrap more yarn around a pencil 30 times. (Not too tight!) Slip the threaded needle under the loops. Pull the pencil out. Tie the ends of the thread around the loops, and pull the knot tight. Cut loops to make a pom-pom. Glue the bottom of the pom-pom into the acorn cap. Glue a safety pin to the back of the acorn cap.

Vernal Equinox

BUTTERFLY'S DELIGHT MUFFINS

Butterflies love these flowery treats.

What You'll Need: Soil, water, flower petals, ½ cup honey or corn syrup, individual muffin cups, spoon, flowers

Choose a nice sunny day to whip up a batch of these sweet "mud muffins," and watch to see who flies by! You won't want to place these muffins too close to the house, since there might be bugs also dropping by for a snack. Mix the soil and water together to make a nice, firm mud. Collect some wildflower petals, and stir these in. Add the honey or corn syrup, and stir well. Then spoon the mix into individual muffin cups, and top each with a pretty flower top. Set them in a place where you have seen butterflies before. These muffins look good enough to eat, but unless you're a butterfly, don't try them!

112

Vernal Equinox

MR. AND MRS. SPRING

These green pepper people are bursting with springtime color!

What You'll Need: 2 green peppers, knife, broccoli, celery, peeled potatoes, green food coloring, small plate, green olives, toothpicks, bunch of fresh parsley

Make lunch or dinner full of springtime fun with these green pepper characters sitting on a plate. Wash and dry the green peppers. Have an adult help you with the cutting! Cut off the very top of the peppers, and scoop out the insides. Cut the broccoli, celery, and potatoes into small pieces (keep potatoes in water until ready). Slice the green olives. Color the potatoes by soaking them in a small plate of green food coloring. For each pepper, stick a triangle-shaped piece of cut and dyed potato on the end of a toothpick and poke it into the pepper body to make a hand and an arm; repeat for other side. Attach 2-inch pieces of celery to the ends of toothpicks and stick them into the bottom of the pepper to make feet. Attach other vegetable pieces in this way to make the face: green olive slices for eyes, a broccoli-flower nose, a half-circle of green potato for the mouth, and 2 pieces of potatoes for ears. Fill the peppers with fresh parsley to make hair.

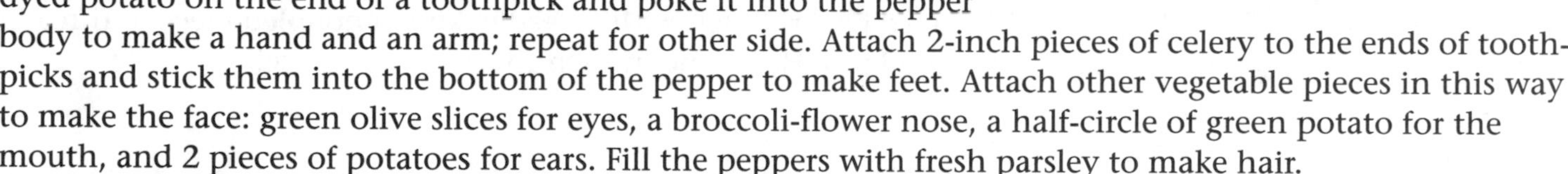

THE GREAT SPHINX

The Great Sphinx, in Egypt, was built so that it directly faces the rising sun on the day of the Vernal Equinox.

113

Vernal Equinox

PRESSED SPRING ORNAMENTS

It will be spring forever with these pressed ornaments decorating the house.

What You'll Need: Brown paper, scissors, waxed paper, paper clips, leaves, flowers, crayons, butter knife, iron, needle and thread

After a long winter, everyone gets excited to see the new little buds and leaves appear when spring begins. Gather up some of these fresh and pretty new growths, and make them into ornaments to bring spring right inside your house. Cut several shapes, such as a circle, star, leaf, and tulip, out of brown paper. Paper clip 2 pieces of waxed paper onto the brown paper shapes, and cut them to match. Put 1 piece aside and keep one on top of the brown paper. Then arrange a few fresh leaves or flowers on it. With a butter knife, scrape crayon shavings over the leaves and flowers. Make sure you hold the knife facing away from your body. Use different colored crayons for the shavings. Place the other sheet of waxed paper on top of the crayon shavings. Cover this with another sheet of brown paper. Have an adult help you slide a warm iron over the paper to melt the waxed paper and crayon shavings. Lift the top piece of brown paper, and see your spring design sealed inside. Poke a hole at the top of the waxed paper design with a needle, knot a doubled piece of thread, and pull it through the hole to make a hanging loop. Hang one in each room of the house!

Vernal Equinox

MINIATURE GARDEN

114

Share a magic miniature garden with a grown-up friend.

What You'll Need: Pieces of sponge, rock, and brick; water; old fishbowl or large glass jar; food coloring; 4 tablespoons ammonia; 4 tablespoons liquid bluing; 4 tablespoons water; glass jar; rubber gloves; salt

Ask an adult to help you grow this special garden. It will take around 5 to 6 hours. Wet the pieces of sponge, rock, and brick, and arrange them in an old fishbowl or a large glass jar. You might want to stack some of them so that your garden has a variety of heights. Then sprinkle a few drops of food coloring over each piece. Try to use lots of different colors. Ask an adult to help you mix the ammonia, bluing, and water in another glass jar. Carefully pour the mixture over the colored pieces. Do this where there is good ventilation. Whoever is pouring should wear rubber gloves. When the mix has been poured, sprinkle lots of salt over all the pieces. That's all there is to it. Just sit back, relax, and watch your garden bloom!

115

Vernal Equinox

DAY AND NIGHT FLIP STONES

At the time of the Vernal Equinox, the hours of the day equal the hours of the night. Longer days mean it is a great time to go rock hunting!

What You'll Need: Smooth round stones, old newspapers, acrylic paint, paintbrushes, water cup, clear varnish or nail polish

Find a smooth, round stone. Wash it, and let it dry for several hours. Lay out some old newspaper on your work surface. On one side of a stone, paint a bright sky-blue background. Make sure you don't get any paint on the other side of the rock. When the blue paint dries, paint a large, smiling sun in the middle of it. When that side dries, paint the other side black. Add a crescent moon when the black background is dry. To protect your painted stones, paint them with clear varnish or nail polish. You might want to do 2 or 3 coats, waiting for each coat to dry before you add another. Now you are ready to play a toss game, much like heads or tails. Take turns calling "day" or "night" and tossing the stone on the grass to see if the side you called lands face up. Keep score, and see how many "days" and "nights" you can guess. Paint other rocks with pretty spring scenes, and give them out as prizes.

ANCESTRAL VISITS

In Japan, the day of the Vernal Equinox is a national holiday. The Vernal Equinox is the middle day of the equinoctial week. People visit the graves of their ancestors in this week.

Vernal Equinox

116 PEBBLE AND SPROUT GARDEN

Have springtime right on your table!

What You'll Need: Beet and carrot tops, knife, pie plate, pebbles, water, small plastic figurines

Ask an adult to cut the tops from the largest, fattest beets and carrots you can find. The tops should be at least 1 inch long. If there are any greens sprouting from them, cut these off, too. Next, fill a pie plate with pebbles, leaving 1 inch of space at the top. If possible, use all white pebbles or alternate circles of white and dark pebbles for a pretty look. Place the carrot and beet tops on the pebbles with the cut sides down. Add water until it covers the bottom of the vegetables. Stand small plastic figurines in between the pebbles to make a funny springtime scene. Put the arrangement in a place that gets good light but not direct sun. Check the water level each day to make sure the vegetables are always touching the water. In a week, you should see little green sprouts growing from the top of each carrot and beet. You may want to change the water and wash the pebbles after a few weeks. Your arrangement will last a little over a month.

Easter

CARROT CASSEROLE

Make this treat for your favorite Easter Bunny!

What You'll Need: 1 pound carrots, knife, baking pan, ½ teaspoon salt, 2 tablespoons maple syrup, 2 tablespoons margarine, aluminum foil, fresh parsley

Everyone will hop right on over to the table at Easter dinner when they smell this dish! Have an adult preheat the oven to 325 degrees. Wash the carrots. You may need an adult to help cut the carrots into quarter-sized rounds. Place the carrots in a baking pan. Sprinkle them with the salt and maple syrup, and dot them with margarine. Cover the pan with foil and bake for 1 hour and 15 minutes. Before serving, make a circle of fresh parsley to put on top for decoration.

Easter

EGG-STREAMLY SILLY BASKETBALL

This is a fun game to play with one or more friends on an Easter afternoon.

What You'll Need: Rope, large Easter basket, tree, plastic Easter grass, 3 plastic Easter eggs for each player

Tie one end of the rope to the basket's handle. Tie the other end to a tree limb. Mark a line 3 to 6 feet from the basket. One player starts the basket swinging. The players then try to toss their eggs into the moving basket. Who can get the most eggs in? When you have mastered the art of Egg-streamly Silly Basketball, challenge your friends to a game of "Egghead." Make a mark on the ground. Toss the plastic egg from your mark. If you make it in the swinging basket, your friends must make it from the same mark. If they miss, they have an E. Keep playing until someone spells "Egghead." For tie-breakers, try special shots, like over the shoulder or between the legs.

Easter

CRACKED PICTURES

Make beautiful mosaics from Easter eggshells!

What You'll Need: Leftover Easter eggshells, colored markers, construction paper, glue

Wash and dry the shell bits. It is good if you have an assortment of shapes and sizes. A lot of the shells will still have their color, but if you use plain eggshells, paint them with colored markers. Draw the simple outline of an animal, person, or some favorite object on a piece of construction paper. You might want to use a darkish piece of paper to contrast with your shells. Glue the shells into the outline. Glue them close together so no paper shows through. When you have filled in the outline completely, let the glue dry. Color in the details, such as faces, with markers.

120

Easter

EASTER BUNNY RACES

They're off! The bunnies race across the floor... it's the pink bunny... no, it's the blue bunny. It's... it's... lots of fun no matter who wins!

What You'll Need: 2 pieces of cardboard about 12 inches long, pencil, scissors, markers, two 10-inch pieces of string

Cut 2 Easter bunnies from the heavy cardboard, using the pattern below as a guide. Color the front and back of the bunnies with markers. With the pencil, punch a hole through the middle of each bunny just below the head—punch from the front to the back so the edges of the hole are smooth. Thread a piece of string through the hole in each rabbit. Tie one end of each string to the leg of a table, just high enough so that the rabbit's legs touch the floor. Back up, taking the rabbits with you, to the end of the string. Stand the rabbits up, making them lean toward the table a little. When you jerk the string, the rabbits will walk toward the table. (Bunnies walk best on smooth floor or low carpet.) The first Easter bunny to reach the table wins!

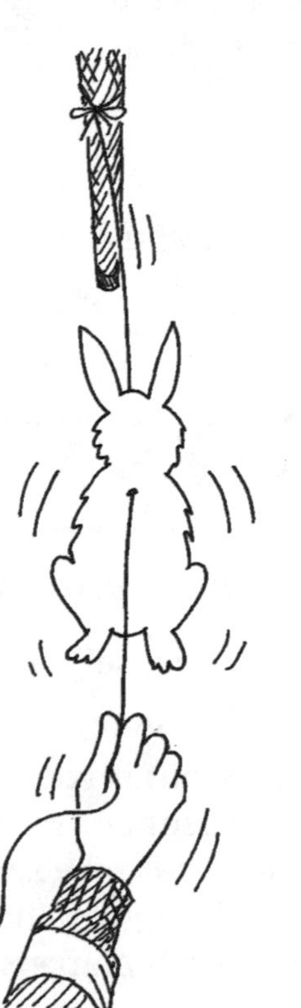

Easter

"BONNY" BONNETS

When you wear this bonny Easter bonnet, everyone will want one of their own!

What You'll Need: Empty berry basket, ribbon, Easter grass, jelly beans, silk flowers, tissue and construction paper, chenille stems, scissors, glue, markers, pom-poms, wiggle eyes, feathers

It wouldn't be Easter without beautiful Easter hats. Make a special hat of your own—it can be silly, pretty, or both. An empty berry basket is the base of the hat. Turn it upside down, and tie ribbons at the bottom of 2 opposite sides. Glue Easter grass all over the basket. Let it dry. To decorate your hat, glue on jelly beans and silk flowers. You can also glue rabbit and egg cutouts to chenille stems and twist them around the basket in various places. The chenille stems will make your cutouts stand up out of the Easter grass. Be creative and make your Easter bonnet full of surprises. Is that a yellow pom-pom chick hiding in the grass?

Easter

SMART EGG TRICK

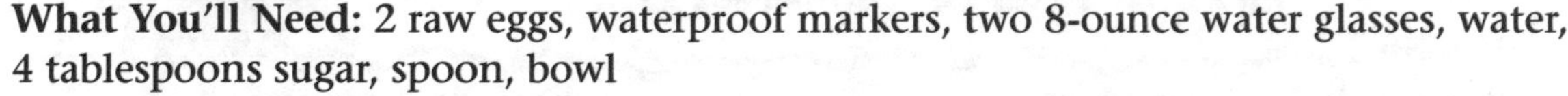

These eggs have a mind of their own!

What You'll Need: 2 raw eggs, waterproof markers, two 8-ounce water glasses, water, 4 tablespoons sugar, spoon, bowl

You can tell your friends that these eggs have been specially trained by the Easter Bunny to know whether to sink or float in a glass of water. Before performing the trick, decorate 2 raw eggs with waterproof markers. Leave a blank rectangular space on each of your designs so a friend can label the eggs during the trick. Then fill the glasses with water to about ¾ inch from the top. Put the sugar in 1 of the glasses, and mix well. Remember which glass has the sugar in it, but don't tell anyone about this part! When you are ready to perform the trick, tell your friends about your smart eggs. Explain that these eggs can obey written commands. Have a friend use a waterproof marker to label the eggs with the word "sink" on one and the word "float" on the other. After your friend gives you back the eggs, put the "sink" egg in the plain water, and the "float" egg in the sugar water. Watch the eggs obey the commands. If friends wonder how you did it, have them break the eggs into a bowl so they can see that there were no tricks inside the eggs!

123

Easter

EGGS GROW ON TREES?

This lovely tree is with ribboned with egg and flower blossoms.

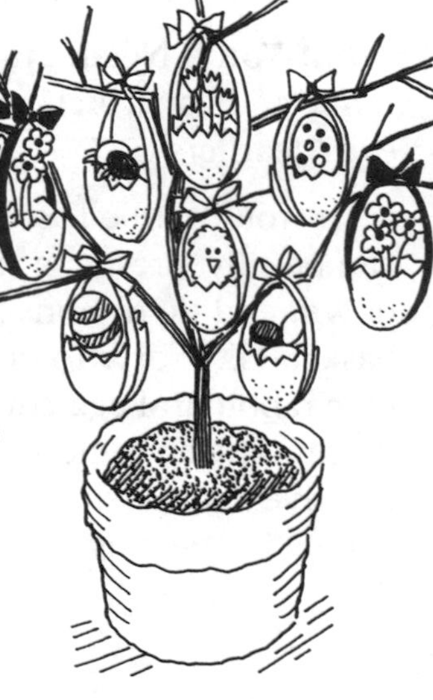

What You'll Need: Plastic flowerpot, crepe or tissue paper, glue, potting soil, branch with 5 or 6 shoots, dried moss, 4 eggs, butter knife, small container, ribbons, small fresh flowers, water, Easter grass, miniature chocolate eggs

Cover a plastic flowerpot with tissue or crepe paper. Glue the paper inside and out, and try to tuck in all the edges so they fit smoothly on the plastic. Fill the pot with soil, and stick a branch with 5 or 6 twiggy shoots into the center. This is the tree. Cover the soil around the tree with moss. Use a butter knife to gently crack the eggs so that you get 2 equal halves. Have an adult help you with this. Save the insides of the eggs for baking or cooking. Carefully wash and dry the shells. Glue an 8-inch piece of ribbon around the bottom and up the sides of each egg half so that enough ribbon is left to tie to a branch in a neat bow. Tie the eggshells to the branches. Place a small amount of water into some of the eggshells, and place a few small flowers in each. In others, place a bit of Easter grass and a single tiny chocolate egg.

Easter

CHECKERED AND PLAID EASTER EGGS

124

Have you ever seen a plaid Easter egg? Well, you can make your own plaid or checkered eggs!

What You'll Need: Easter egg dye, hard-boiled eggs, duct tape, ruler, scissors

Mix the egg dye according to directions. Dye each egg a solid color. Use the lightest color first. Take the eggs out of the dye bath, and let them dry. Cut ⅛-inch-thick strips of duct tape. Put the tape strips on the colored eggs, running some strips top to bottom and others around the egg. Be sure you leave some eggshell showing. Place the egg into the medium color of dye; let it sit for 20 minutes. Take the egg out, and take off every other strip of tape. Place the egg into the darkest color; let it sit for 20 minutes. Take the egg out. Remove the last strips of tape. Experiment with different patterns.

125

Easter

PRICKLE CHICK

This little chick is cute on your Easter table, or give him as a fun gift!

What You'll Need: Large pinecone, yellow spray paint, fiberfill, craft stick, pencil, white glue, felt scraps, feathers (available from a craft store), 2 wiggle eyes

Choose a fat pinecone that will stand up by itself. In a well-ventilated room or outside, have an adult help you spray paint the pinecone yellow. Let the paint dry. Wrap the pinecone in a thin layer of fiberfill. Use a craft stick to poke the fiberfill between the scales of the pinecone. This will give your Prickle Chick a fluffy look. Draw and cut out wings, a beak, 2 feet, and a tail from yellow felt. Glue them in place. Glue a few small feathers on the ends of the wings and tail. Cut 2 circles of white felt for the outer eyes, and glue the wiggle eyes on them. Glue eyes to the chick. Set the Prickle Chick in the center of the table for an Easter decoration!

Easter

JELLY BEAN GAME

126

Tired of hunting Easter eggs? Bitten the head off each and every chocolate bunny? Then it's time for... the Jelly Bean Game!

What You'll Need: 3 foam egg cartons; bottle cap; tape; red, yellow, and green jelly beans; 2 plastic spoons

Wash and dry the egg cartons and the bottle cap. Cut the tops and flaps off the egg cartons. Tape the egg cartons together, side by side the long way. When finished, you should have egg cups that are 6 rows across and 6 rows deep. Put a jelly bean in each egg cup—mix the colors randomly. Mark a starting line on the table with tape—about 2 feet away. Holding the bottom of the spoon with your right hand on the table (left, if you are left-handed), put the bottle cap into the bowl of the spoon and press down. Try to flip the bottle cap into an egg cup. If it lands in an egg cup, you get to keep the jelly bean from that cup. Red jelly beans are worth 10 points, yellow jelly beans are worth 5 points, and green jelly beans are worth 1 point. When all the jelly beans have been won, count them up, and see who has the most points. If you eat the jelly beans before the game is over, you lose the points!

127

Easter

BUNNY BOX

This shadow box has a cotton-ball bunny standing on a hill of jelly eggs.

What You'll Need: Shallow box (such as a shoe box lid), paint, paintbrush, colored cellophane Easter grass, glue, jelly beans, cotton balls, white tissues, 2 wiggle eyes, construction paper, scissors, jar lid, self-stick picture hanger

Start with a shallow box such as a handkerchief or tie box, or the lid of a shoe box. Paint the outside of the box a pastel Easter shade. Let paint dry. Paint the inside a pretty sky-blue color. Glue a layer of cellophane grass along the bottom and sides of the box. Glue jelly beans inside the box to make a hill shape. To make your Easter bunny stand on top of the hill, stack two cotton balls, add a tiny puff for the rabbit's cottontail, and glue them down. Twist tissues into 2 floppy ears, and glue them down as well. You can glue on tiny wiggle eyes, construction paper whiskers, nose, and mouth. You might want to give your Easter bunny a big smile or cut its mouth in an O shape, as if it were surprised. Fold construction paper into a basket shape, glue on a strip for a handle, and place it at the bottom of the jelly bean hill, as if it had rolled down. Paint a jar lid to look like a bright, smiling sun, and glue it on. Press a self-stick hanger onto the back of your box, and hang it for all to see.

Easter

SLEEPING CHICKS

128

Tuck these sleepy little chicks in their egg cradles.

What You'll Need: Plastic eggs, glue, yellow poms, wiggle eyes, construction paper, scissors, scraps of cloth

You can use the plastic egg halves that held your Easter candy for lots of crafts. You can even turn a plastic egg into a tiny cradle! Put a little dab of glue on the bottom of one half of a plastic egg, and set it inside the other half so that one is horizontal and one is vertical. This is your cradle and canopy. Glue 2 wiggle eyes onto a yellow pom. Cut out a tiny orange construction paper beak, and glue this on the pom to make a baby chick. Glue on a little circle of fabric to make a baby cap, and set your little chick in its egg cradle. Use a small square of scrap fabric as a baby blanket.

129

Easter

ONE-OF-A-KIND BASKETS

Make a unique Easter basket for every member of the family.

What You'll Need: Empty oatmeal or milk cartons, scissors, paint, paintbrushes, glue, old magazines, Easter stickers, old Easter cards, crepe paper, colored cord or ribbon, Easter grass, treats

Get busy the week before Easter and make homemade Easter baskets for your family. Sneak the baskets onto their chairs before breakfast on Easter morning, and get everyone's holiday off to a great start! Cut off and throw away the top half of a clean milk or oatmeal carton. On the bottom half of the carton, poke 2 holes near the top, one on each side, for the handle. You might need some adult help to do this part. Paint the carton inside and out in a pretty, Easter color. (To paint milk cartons, mix a little white glue into the paint to make the paint adhere better to the waxed surface.) Use a different color for each member of the family. Then look through old magazines to find pictures of things that each family member likes or things that remind you of them. Cut the pictures out, and glue them all around the basket. You may want to add Easter stickers, pictures from old Easter cards, and thin streamers of crepe paper to complete your design. When you finish, loop a colored cord or ribbon through the 2 holes you poked earlier, and tie a bow to make a handle. Fill your baskets with Easter grass and delicious Easter treats.

Easter

ALPHABET EGG HUNT

130

Here's an egg hunt with a wordy twist!

What You'll Need: Construction paper, pencil, scissors, markers

Here's an egg hunt that will give your brain a real workout. Draw lots of eggs on colorful construction paper. You can make them different sizes, anywhere from 2 to 6 inches long. Decorate one side with interesting patterns. Write a letter on the other side. Make enough eggs to use all the letters of the alphabet, and then make at least 3 more eggs for each vowel. Make some extra blank eggs. These will be used as "wild" eggs, which means they can be any letter. When you are done creating, hide the eggs inside the house or in the yard. Let the hunt begin! Players try to find as many eggs as they can, but the game isn't over simply by finding the eggs. Everyone has to use their alphabet eggs to make words. The person who can make the most words wins.

131

Easter

EARTH-TONED EGGS

The shades made from natural dyes will give your eggs a soft, earthy look.

What You'll Need: Spinach, grass, broccoli, blueberries, coffee, tea, cranberries, beets, tomatoes, enamel pots, water, kitchen knife, colander, cheesecloth, hard-boiled eggs, vegetable oil, soft cloth

Try something different this Easter—make your own Easter egg dye. People living in the country have done this for years. Wash and chop up the fruits and vegetables. Have an adult help you with the cutting and with boiling the water. When you have your ingredients ready, put one kind of fruit or vegetable in an enamel pot and fill it with water until your ingredient is completely covered. Boil for 10 minutes or longer, depending on how dark you want your color to be. The longer you boil, the darker the color. Just make sure that you don't boil all the water out! Strain the ingredients through a colander lined with cheesecloth or a clean rag. (You won't need to do this if you have used tea bags or made your coffee in a machine.) Once your dye has cooled, dip hard-boiled eggs into the liquid for several minutes. Repeat the process with all the ingredients to have cartons of earthy Easter eggs. You can also make your eggs shine by wiping them with a soft cloth that has a few drops of vegetable oil on it.

Easter

MR. FUNNY BUNNY

132

This funny-bunny friend will stand up on your table or on the dresser by your bed.

What You'll Need: Old knit glove, 2 small safety pins, fiberfill, felt, scissors, sand, sealable plastic bag, needle, thread, glue, cotton ball, yarn scraps, fabric paint

Fold the middle finger of the glove over the back of the glove. Reach up inside the glove with a safety pin. Push the pin through the fabric from the inside and pin the finger to the back of the glove. Stuff the rest of the glove with fiberfill all the way to the cuff, so that the fiberfill holds the cuff open. Cut a circle of felt just bigger than the hole in the cuff. Put ⅛ cup sand in the sealable bag, and push it into the glove under the fiberfill. Use the needle and thread to stitch the circle of felt onto the cuff. Pull the thumb and the little finger forward until the tips touch to make the bunny's arms. Pin the bunny's hands together (from behind) with a safety pin. Glue a cotton ball to the tip of the folded-down finger behind the bunny. Glue on yarn whiskers. Use fabric paint to draw the rest of the face.

Easter

TWIG EASTER BASKET

This Easter basket is strong enough to hold all the eggs you can find!

What You'll Need: Small green (not dry) branches, small saw, twine, cool-temp glue gun

Gather some branches that are ¼ to ½ inch thick. Cut eighteen 9-inch branch pieces, and 1 thin, bendable 18-inch piece. Stack your sticks as if you were making a log cabin. Lay 2 branches parallel to each other, and then 2 branches across the ends of those. Using a piece of twine for each corner, wrap and tie the sticks at each corner as you go. Make a stack of 3 sticks on each side. Slide the six remaining 9-inch sticks through the lowest space and across to form the bottom of the basket. Tie the sticks in place with twine, then glue them to keep them more firmly in place. Bend the 18-inch branch into a U shape, and tie it to the basket for a handle. Use the glue gun to glue the handle in place. Use the basket for an Easter egg hunt, or fill it with flowers and put it on your table for a centerpiece.

BUNNY-NOSE EGG RACE 134

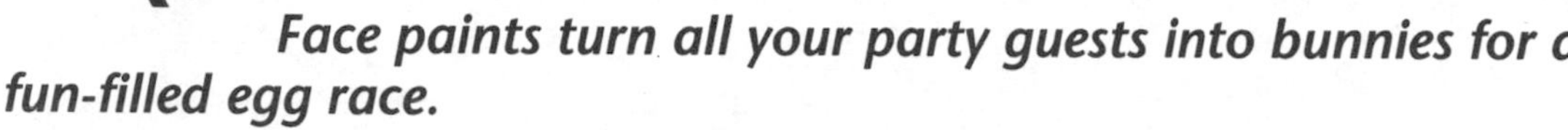

What You'll Need: Water-based face paints, hard-boiled Easter eggs, recorded music, white string, carrots

This race will be the hit of any Easter party. With the face paints, color all the players' faces like Easter bunnies. When the paint has dried, you are ready to start the race. Set the course by laying down a long white string that has been weighted at various points with carrots. You can do this outside on the lawn or indoors if you have enough space. You can make the string as long or as short as you'd like, but about 20 feet is a good length. It's also best if you lay your string down in a straight line, but you may want to experiment by adding a turn for a slightly harder game. When you are ready to play, give 2 players a hard-boiled egg each. Tell them they have to push the egg along either side of the string with their noses until they get to the end. Whoever gets there first is the winner. As a variation, you can play a short, recorded song, and the players must get to the end before the music stops. However you play, this game will give those bunny noses a good hard wriggle!

Easter

BEAUTIFUL BONNET

Have you ever wished you could make your own Easter bonnet just the color and shape you wanted? You can!

What You'll Need: White paste, 2 pieces wallpaper or wrapping paper with a design, 4 sheets of newspaper, heavy scissors, a bowl the size of your head, ribbons, artificial flowers, buttons

Find wallpaper or wrapping paper that is the color you want your bonnet to be. You will need 2 pieces about the size of half a sheet of newspaper. Spread paste on the back of one piece of wallpaper. Press a piece of newspaper down on it, and smooth it with your hands. Repeat with each piece of newspaper. Paste the final piece of wallpaper down with the print side up. While the paste is still wet, cut a big circle out of the paper. Press the center of the circle over the bowl, and shape it into a hat. Turn the brim up, and brace it while it dries. When your bonnet is dry, decorate it with ribbons, flowers, buttons, and bows.

EASTER ISLAND GIANTS

On Easter Island, in the Pacific Ocean off South America, there are 887 moai (huge, carved statues). The largest weighs up to 145 to 165 tons! Scientists and archaeologists have been trying to figure out how the ancient people of the island raised the statues without modern equipment. The statues date from A.D. 1400 to 1600!

136

Easter

GREEN-HAIRED EGGHEADS

Keep the whole family giggling over these funny eggshell people!

What You'll Need: Empty eggshell halves, waterproof markers, cotton balls, sprout seeds, egg carton

Ask your family to save all their empty eggshell halves for you. Let them know that soon the family is going to have some green-haired visitors! Carefully wash and dry the eggshells. Using the markers, draw funny or scary faces on each one. If you wish, write a name on the back of each egghead. Sprinkle a little water on the cotton balls to dampen them. Press cotton balls into each eggshell until the shells are almost full. Poke holes in the cotton, and plant a few sprout seeds in each one. Place your eggshell people in an egg carton, and find a sunny window ledge for them to live on. Make sure the cotton is always damp. In a few days, the seeds will sprout and your eggshell friends will start to grow green hair. When the sprouts have grown a few inches, you can use them to make green-hair sandwiches for a fun-filled Easter lunch!

Passover

MAKING MATZO

137

When the Jews fled slavery in Egypt, they only had time to bake unleavened bread—matzo. It's a crunchy treat!

What You'll Need: 3 cups flour, 1 cup water, rolling pin, knife, fork, large bowl, measuring cup, greased cookie sheet, sesame and/or poppy seeds

Ask an adult to preheat the oven to 475 degrees. Mix and knead together the flour and water. When it's smooth and rubbery, roll out the dough on a floured surface. Cut out your dough. Prick designs in the dough with a fork. Traditional matzo is square, but you can cut your dough in other shapes, such as a camel or a Star of David. You can also sprinkle your dough with poppy seeds or sesame seeds for extra flavor. Place the dough on a greased cookie sheet. Bake it for 10 to 15 minutes or until light brown. Let the matzo cool. Serve it with cream cheese, butter, or jam. Regular yeast bread can take hours to make. Now you know how to make something just as tasty—only much faster!

Passover

PASSOVER PEEK BOX

See a miniature scene of the Jews fleeing Egypt in this charming, old-fashioned peek box.

What You'll Need: Shoe box with lid, thin cardboard, glue, markers, construction paper, scissors, clear cellophane or tissue paper, modeling clay, chenille stems

To re-create the scene in which the Jews fled slavery in Egypt, draw and cut out thin cardboard figures of robed people carrying bags and leading camels. You may want to look at some Bible story illustrations to get ideas. Before you cut out the figures, make sure to add a ½-inch tab at the bottom of each one to glue onto the bottom of the box so your figures will stand. You can also draw and cut out palm trees, a round sun, and several boulders. Before gluing your figures down, line the bottom of the box with sand-colored construction paper. You can line the sides and top of the box with sky blue construction paper. Then cut a small round hole about 1 × 1 inch at one end of your box. This is the peek hole. Cut a larger square 3 × 2 inches at the other end of your box. Glue a square of colored tissue paper or cellophane over this hole on the outside of the box. If you want figures that move in your peek box, cut a slot at the back of the box, and glue a 6- to 8-inch strip of cardboard onto the bottom of the tab on the figure you want to move. Slip the loose end of the cardboard strip through the slot in the peek box and slide your figure backward and forward. You can make desert birds fly up and down by poking 2 holes ½ inch apart in the lid of your box. Slip a horseshoe-shaped chenille stem into the holes, and glue the free ends onto the back of a bird cutout. Pull the chenille stem up and down to make the bird fly. For variety, add figures made of modeling clay. A peek box is a great way to give a three-dimensional view of a scene. Even something that happened long, long ago can seem real.

Passover

ELIJAH'S CUP

The prophet Elijah will visit your house with joy when he can drink from this lovely goblet.

What You'll Need: Large drinking glass or wine glass (plastic may be used for younger children), felt, markers, scissors, old newspaper, acrylic paint, paintbrush, glue, glitter, fake jewels

The prophet Elijah is busy at Passover. Think of all the homes he will visit and how many different wine glasses he will sip from! Show him how pleased you are to welcome him into your house with this specially decorated glass. Wash and dry a drinking glass or wine glass. Trace a circle of felt around the glass, cut it out, and glue it on the bottom. Spread old newspaper on your work surface, and paint a design on your glass with acrylic paint. Once the paint is dry, you can write the name "Elijah" in glue as part of your design and sprinkle glitter on it. If you like, glue sequins and fake jewels around the top and bottom of the glass. Make Elijah's cup as fancy as you like. These glasses also make nice presents if you are invited to seder at a friend's or relative's home.

Passover

PASSOVER PLACES

140

Set a special place for each guest at seder.

What You'll Need: Poster board, ruler, scissors, pencil, colored tissue paper, glue, colored markers, clear adhesive vinyl paper, pinking shears (optional)

Everyone will want to keep lifting their plates to look at these beautiful, multicolored place mats. For each place mat, cut a piece of poster board 10 × 18 inches. You can use colored poster board or plain. Lightly draw your design in pencil on the poster board. You can draw a seder plate, a camel, the map of Israel, or anything else that is meaningful to you about the seder. Draw large, simple shapes. Tear colored tissue paper into small pieces to glue inside the outlines of your shapes. Layer the paper to look like a mosaic. The tinier the tissue paper pieces, the more your place mat will have a mosaic look. You can decorate the place mats with the markers also, if you wish. When you have finished decorating, cut 2 sheets of adhesive vinyl paper 11 × 19 inches. Place the poster board onto the sticky side of one sheet and press the second sheet sticky side down on top. Smooth out any air bubbles, and trim the edges. Use pinking shears or cut a scalloped edge for a fancier look. These place mats can be cleaned with a damp sponge and reused.

141

Passover

AFIKOMON HIDERS

Hunt for the Afikomon hidden in this decorative slipcover.

What You'll Need: 2 light-colored cloth napkins, embroidery needle, embroidery thread, glue, glitter or sequins, tracing paper, tracing wheel, waterproof pens or puffy fabric paint, cardboard

The word *afikomon* comes from the Greek word meaning "after-meal" or "dessert." After seder dinner is over, the children try to find the Afikomon, which has been broken in half, wrapped in a napkin, and hidden. Whoever finds it gets a reward, and everyone at the seder tastes a piece of Afikomon for dessert.

To make a pretty slipcover for the Afikomon, use colored embroidery thread to sew the 2 napkins together. Sew 3 edges and leave the fourth open. You can use either an overhand stitch or a running stitch, whichever is easier for you. Turn the slipcover right side out, and slip a piece of cardboard inside before you begin to paint. Draw your design on tracing paper cut to the same size as the slipcover. You can write the word "Afikomon" in large letters to be colored in with a fancy pattern. You might want to draw a large Star of David or a picture of a reward someone might get for finding the Afikomon. Then lay the tracing paper over the slipcover, and trace your design by pressing down hard along the outline with a tracing wheel. Lift off the tracing paper, and use waterproof pens or puffy fabric paint to color your picture. When the Afikomon is found in this beautiful slipcover, the finder will get double the treasure!

A Clean House

Before Passover, many Jews clean their homes of *chametz,* which is leavening (it makes breads and cakes rise). A complete cleaning of the house is done, sometimes starting weeks before Passover begins. All leavened foods must be taken out of the house, and all crumbs must be cleaned out completely.

April Fool's Day (April 1)

WIGGLE-WOGGLE BALLOON

Invite friends to play a game of catch with this April Fool's balloon!

What You'll Need: Two 10-inch balloons, water

(Balloons are choking hazards—keep them and any broken pieces away from little children!) To make your tricky balloon, roll one balloon lengthwise and slide it inside the other, leaving only the stem (mouthpiece) sticking out. Place the mouthpiece of the inside balloon over the faucet, and fill the balloon with water until it is about 4 inches across. Tie the stem, and push the balloon the rest of the way inside the outer balloon. Blow up the outer balloon, leaving it a little soft, and tie it. Watch out! This balloon will wiggle-woggle when you toss it. If you start the water balloon rolling around inside before you toss it, the balloon will wiggle-woggle even more! Play wiggle-woggle balloon outside on the grass, away from stickers and thorns.

April Fool's Day (April 1)

SILLY PARTY

143

Fool around at the silliest party of the year!

What You'll Need: Crackers, cheese, apple juice, green food coloring, old magazines, scissors, construction paper, glue

Invite all your friends to act the fool at this silly party. You can make invitations by looking in a mirror and writing everything backward. (You might want to write a hint in regular writing that lets your guests know that they need a mirror to read their invitations!) Ask everyone to wear funny outfits, like a striped shirt with polka-dotted or plaid pants, mismatched socks, and a funny hat. When they ring the front doorbell, walk backward and greet them by saying "Goodbye" instead of "Hello." Ask everyone to do the same! Serve your guests inside-out sandwiches (a cracker between two pieces of cheese) and bug juice (apple juice with green food coloring). Have a box full of pictures of people and animals that you have cut out of magazines and have cut in half. Invite your guests to make wacky creatures from the pictures. They should glue the creatures onto construction paper. Later, you can use these wacky creatures as prizes for a silly stunt contest. To hold the contest, ask guests to do silly things, such as walk backward on their knees while holding their ankles behind them or balance a penny on their noses while walking across the room. Make up lots of silly stunts; it's a great day to be foolish!

144

April Fool's Day (April 1)

FOOT JUGGLING BALL

Use only your feet to play with this April Fool's ball!

What You'll Need: 12-inch balloon, funnel, sand, pencil, three 8-inch balloons, scissors, hole punch

Balloons are choking hazards—keep them and any broken pieces away from little children! Slide the end of the funnel into the stem (mouthpiece) of the 12-inch balloon. Pour sand into the balloon, tapping with the end of a pencil if the funnel jams, until the balloon is about 4 inches across. Tie the stem. Cut the stems off the 8-inch balloons. One at a time, stretch them over the sand-filled balloon, making sure the hole from the stem is on the opposite side each time. Before you put on the final balloon, use the hole punch to make 4 or 5 holes in it. When you pull it over the ball, the color of the last balloon will show through the holes. See how long you can keep the ball in the air. (Be sure to play outside—Mom won't be happy if the ball breaks in the house!)

April Fool's Day (April 1)

APRIL FOOL'S CAN

145

This tricky April Fool's can will amaze your parents and friends.

What You'll Need: Can opener, 1-pound coffee can (empty), 2 plastic coffee can lids, scissors, large medium-weight rubber band, 2-ounce fishing sinker

Use the can opener to remove both ends of the can. Lay the plastic lids on top of each other. Punch 2 holes about 1 inch apart through both of the lids. Put one lid on the can. Cut the rubber band. Thread the ends through the holes in the lid. Slip the fishing weight on one of the pieces of rubber band inside the can. Thread the rubber band ends through the holes on the other plastic lid, and tie the ends of the rubber band together. Put the lid on the can. When you push the can, it will roll across the floor—then it will stop and roll back! You may have to experiment with the tension of the rubber band. It should not be so loose that the weight touches the side of the can or so tight that the weight cannot flip around and "wind up" the toy.

Children's Book Day (April 2)

FAIRY CASTLE BOOK

This book is shaped like a fairy castle, complete with a drawbridge and doors that open!

What You'll Need: Construction paper, paper clips, straight pin, needle, colored embroidery thread, scissors, pencil, brads (paper fasteners), glue, markers

Make this castle-shaped book and write a fairy tale inside to celebrate the birthday of the famous fairy tale author Hans Christian Andersen. To make a 12-page book, fold 6 sheets of construction paper in half. Make a crease on the center fold and open the pages. Use paper clips to hold the pages together at the corners. Mark 7 evenly spaced dots along the center fold. Punch holes in the dots with a straight pin. Begin sewing by knotting the thread on the inside of the middle hole. Sew in and out of the holes until you have gone through each hole at least twice. Cut another piece of paper the size of one page, with a border cut at the top to look like a castle. Glue this page onto the front of your book. Use another page-sized paper to draw a smaller castle front, complete with towers and turrets and a large, arch-shaped door. Cut the door so it opens in the middle (see illustration). Stick a brad in each door for a door handle.

For the drawbridge, cut out a rectangle that covers the doors for the drawbridge, plus 1 inch longer. Glue the second castle shape on top of the first castle shape. Attach the drawbridge by folding under the extra inch, fit it so the flap folds over the bottom back and the front of the drawbridge covers the doors. Tape the flap to the back of the cover. Thread a needle with thread, and tie a knot in the end of the thread (do not double thread). Coming from the back of the cover, where the top corner of the drawbridge hits above the door, push thread through the cover and the drawbridge. Pull the drawbridge until it is completely open, and mark the thread. Make a knot at the mark. Repeat for other side of drawbridge. Use different colored paper for the towers, doors, and drawbridge. Draw on windows, and don't forget to leave room for the title of the story you will write inside.

Children's Book Day (April 2)

CARDS OF WONDER

Send a homemade thank-you card to your favorite author.

What You'll Need: Construction paper, markers, pen

A good book is like a good friend. Reading about people in other countries can make you feel like you're actually in that place. Make a homemade thank-you card to send to a favorite author of a story set in another place or about people of a nationality different from yours. Fold a piece of construction paper into quarters to make a greeting card shape. With markers, draw characters and scenes from the story on the outside of the card. Inside the card, write down all the things you liked about the story and how glad you are that the author wrote it. You can send your card to the author in care of the company that published the book. Did the book surprise you? Teach you something new? Let the author know!

Flower Festival (April 8)

PAPER LOTUS CHAIN

Celebrate Buddha's birthday with this beautiful lotus chain.

What You'll Need: White paper, pencil, scissors, pink and green tissue paper, white glue

Use the patterns below as guides to make your own patterns. Make the leaves green and the petals pink. Make stacks of 5 to 10 pieces of tissue paper. You will need 1 green leaf piece for every 2 pink petal pieces. Pin the patterns to the tissue paper and cut out. The more pieces you cut, the longer your garland will be. When all of the petals and leaves are cut, lay a green leaf on the table. Put a dot of glue in the middle of the leaf, and press a petal on top of it. Put a dot of glue on each point of the petal, and press another pink petal on top. Put a dot of glue in the middle of the top pink petal, and add a green leaf. Repeat this pattern until you have used all the tissue paper. Remember, green leaves are glued to petals in the center; petals are glued to petals at the points. Let the glue dry. When you stretch out your creation, you will have a beautiful lotus garland!

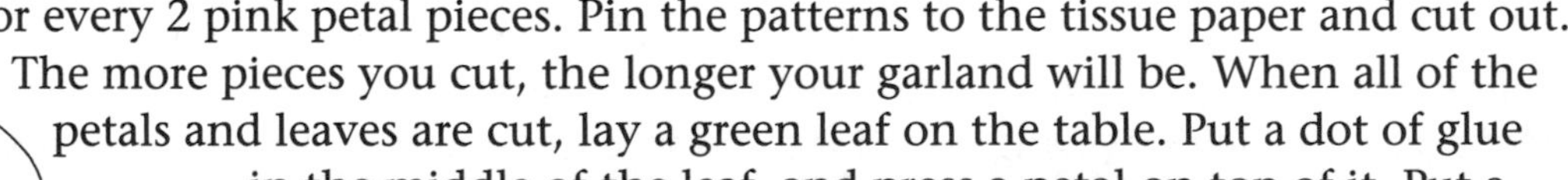

Earth Day (April 22)

SPROUTING SUNFLOWERS

Grow these plants—then eat the seeds!

What You'll Need: Raw sunflower seeds, empty plastic containers, soil, newspaper, scissors

Everyone loves to look at a great big yellow sunflower. But the little sunflower sprouts are also very popular—as food. They are sweet, crunchy, and good for you, too. To make sunflower sprouts, fill your containers with soil, and place the raw seeds on top. Make sure that your seeds are raw—if they have been salted or roasted they will not sprout. Cover the seeds with a double layer of newspaper, and water the seeds through the paper. Put the containers in a sunny window, and check them every day to make sure the newspaper stays wet. In a few days you will see tiny sprouts coming out of your seeds under the paper. After they have grown an inch, take away the newspaper, and let the sun shine on them. The sprouts will turn green and grow bigger. Before the second set of leaves opens on each sprout, snip them with scissors. Rinse the sprouts off, and pat them dry. Now you can put your fresh sprouts into a salad or sandwich. If you want to grow sunflowers, soak the unshelled seeds overnight. Plant them in a large container, and keep the soil moist. Your seeds will sprout in about 2 weeks. The plants grow very large and need to be transplanted to bigger and bigger containers or to an outside garden.

Earth Day (April 22)

GOOD NEWS HEADBANDS

150

Wear your Earth Day messages around the neighborhood on these recycled headbands.

What You'll Need: Old newspaper, stapler, crayons, markers, scissors

Cut a strip of old newspaper long enough to wrap around your head with a couple inches left over. When you have the length you want, cut 6 to 8 more strips the same length. Staple them together to make a thick strip. Then staple the ends together to make a headband that fits your head. Think of a good Earth Day message to write in big letters around the band. "Save the Earth!" and "Clean up Your Earth Today!" are some sample messages you might write. Use your imagination to come up with your own slogan. Decorate the headband with drawings of fruits, flowers, birds, fish, animals, trees, and butterflies. As you walk around the neighborhood wearing your Good News Headband, people will surely get the message!

Earth Day (April 22)

151 GARBAGE GOBBLER

Make the planet beautiful and trash-free with the help of this energetic Earth Day Garbage Gobbler!

What You'll Need: Large cardboard box, scissors, paint, paintbrushes, extra cardboard, glue, 24 inches of thin rope, work gloves

On Earth Day, people all over the world are celebrating the earth's wonderful natural resources. Think of what the planet would be like without green grass, clean oceans, or the lovely smell of fresh flowers. When people neglect to throw their trash in garbage cans, they are destroying this natural beauty. That's where you and your Garbage Gobbler come in to save the day. Have an adult help you cut or fold the flaps of a cardboard box so that the top is open. This is the Garbage Gobbler's big, empty belly. Paint the box to look like a fantastic creature. Nobody has ever seen a Garbage Gobbler before, so you can make your creature look however you want. An adult can help you cut a nose, tail, and ears from the extra cardboard. Attach these parts to the Gobbler with glue. When the paint is dry, ask an adult to cut a small hole in the front of the box to attach the rope for the Gobbler's leash. Once you have your Garbage Gobbler ready, walk it around your neighborhood and start filling up it's empty belly with trash. Wear work gloves when you pick up trash, and be very careful of broken glass. Also, don't forget to wash your hands after you a done feeding the Garbage Gobbler!

152

Earth Day (April 22)

ANIMAL ALPHABET GAME

Earth Day is a day to celebrate all the living things on our planet. How many kinds of animals can you name?

This is a game for 2 or more people. It will help you remember different kinds of animals—and maybe help you learn a few more! Count off to decide what order you will play in. Player 1 thinks of an animal, such as elephant. Elephant ends with the letter T, so player 2 must think of an animal that begins with the letter T. Any animal will do, including insects, sea creatures, mammals, reptiles, birds, even dinosaurs and other creatures that once walked the earth. But you can use an animal only once! When the last player thinks of an animal name, the first player must think of an animal that begins with the last letter. If you want to make the game harder, play only sea creatures, land dwellers, or birds.

Earth Day (April 22)

INSECT DETECTIVES

Do you know all your neighbors? Are you sure?

What You'll Need: Sketch pad, colored pencils, magnifying glass

Whether you have a well-kept yard or a forest out back, you can be sure of one thing: There are creepy-crawly creatures living all around you. In fact, unless you live in the arctic, there is a spider not more than 3 feet away from you right now! But don't worry. It's not watching you with its 8 spider eyes. It's looking for insects to eat. Take your sketch pad and pencils and go find out who they are! Do you know their names? Each bug you find has an important job to do. It's part of the ecosystem in which they, and you, live. Can you figure out what it eats? What do you think would eat this insect? How do you think this insect is important to the ecosystem? After drawing them, take your pictures to the library and do a little research for fun!

154

Earth Day (April 22)

FELT WEATHER CHANNEL

Use colorful felt weather symbols to predict tomorrow's weather.

What You'll Need: Cardboard, scissors, colored felt, pencil, ruler, clear cellophane, glue, colored tape, puffy fabric paint

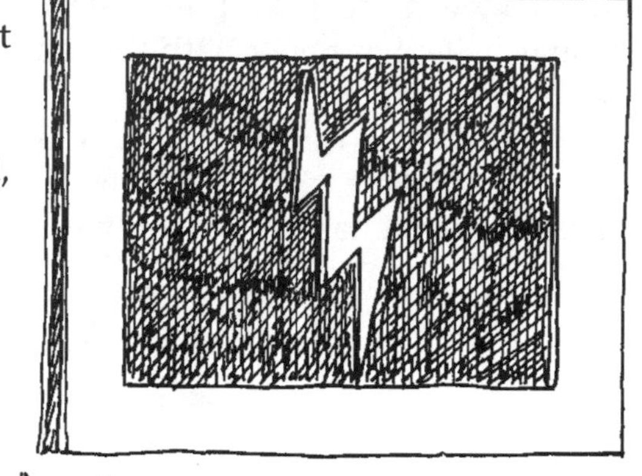

If you've ever dreamed of becoming a weather person, here's your chance. Make your own weather channel, and treat the family to a morning and evening forecast. Find or cut 2 same-sized pieces of cardboard. Glue a piece of dark felt onto one so it covers it completely. On the other piece of cardboard, draw a large square opening with a 1-inch border all around. Cut out the opening so you have a frame. Cut a piece of clear cellophane to match the frame's size. Glue the cellophane to the wrong side of the frame. This is the TV screen. Attach the screen to the background by taping a piece of colored tape along the length of the top borders to make a hinge. Be sure to tape it loosely so that the screen can be lifted easily enough for you to place your weather symbols inside. Cut different weather symbols out of colored felt. Cut a sun, puffy white clouds, dark storm clouds, umbrellas, snowpeople, snowflakes, rain drops, and lightning bolts. Decorate them with puffy fabric paint. You are ready to forecast. Use your best weather person announcer voice to let folks know that a storm is coming their way.

WE CELEBRATED IT WHERE?

In 1998, Earth Day was celebrated for the first time in outer space! On space station Mir, cosmonauts and astronauts aboard had a ceremony, with radio contact with Earth. The Peace Bell at the United Nations was rung.

155

Earth Day (April 22)

ANIMAL TRACKS

Make animal tracks across your letters and notes.

What You'll Need: Paper, pencil, block of wood, double-sided tape, foam tray (from fruit or vegetables), scissors, markers or ink pad, paper towels

Draw some animal tracks—either do some research about your favorite animal or make up your own tracks. Cover a side of the wooden block completely with double-sided tape. You may need to use more than one piece of tape. Don't peel the paper off the front side of the tape yet. Lay a piece of paper over the tracks you have drawn. Trace them with a black marker. This is your pattern. Lay your pattern on top of the foam tray. Trace over the tracks with a dull pencil, pressing hard enough to leave marks in the foam. Cut out the tracks with sharp scissors. When all the tracks are cut out, peel the backing off the double sided tape on the block. Press the tracks onto the tape. Apply color to the stamp with a marker or an ink pad—apply as evenly as possible. Press the stamp firmly onto a piece of paper. Before you use a different color, clean your stamp by pressing it a few times on a damp paper towel, then on a dry paper towel.

WHICH DAY IS IT?

There is some dispute about what day is truly Earth Day. John McConnell is the founder of the first Earth Day, which was begun on March 21, 1970. Gaylord Nelson also claims to be the founder of Earth Day; his first Earth Day celebration was April 22, 1970.

156

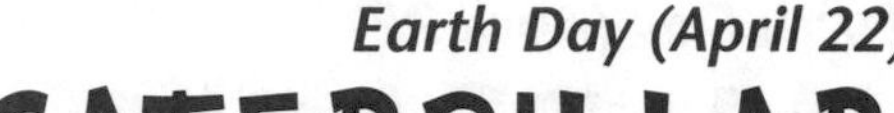

Earth Day (April 22)

CATERPILLAR PALS

Create a cuddly caterpillar!

What You'll Need: Light-colored panty hose or knee-high hose, cotton or polyester fiberfill, 3 small rubber bands, fabric paints

Tie a knot in the end of the panty hose. Pull it tight. Measure back about 6 inches from the knot. Cut the panty hose. Turn the tube inside out, and stuff it with fiberfill. Tie a knot in the other end for the caterpillar's tail. Trim the excess material that hangs from the knot. Wiggle the filler material around until the tube looks like a worm. Wrap a rubber band around the middle of the caterpillar's body. The tighter the rubber bands, the fatter the caterpillar. Wrap the second rubber band halfway between the first one and the tail and the third one halfway between the first one and the nose. Decorate with fabric paint. Let paint dry.

Arbor Day (April 22)

BONSAI

157

Small is beautiful—even when it comes to trees!

What You'll Need: Potting soil, sand, copper wire, shallow clay pot, gravel, juniper seedling, manicure scissors

Bonsai trees are trained and clipped so that they don't grow very big. It doesn't hurt the tree. In fact, bonsai trees can live for over 100 years! Find a juniper seedling growing in your yard or buy one at a nursery. Select a shallow clay pot with a hole in the bottom for drainage. Put a 12-inch piece of copper wire in the pot with 1 inch sticking out the bottom hole. Spread a layer of gravel in the bottom of the pot. Set the baby tree in the pot. Wrap the copper wire around the root ball—be sure to keep 1 inch sticking out of the bottom hole. Bend the end flat to hold the tree in place. Fill the rest of the pot with a mixture of ¾ potting soil and ¼ sand, and water it well. After a few weeks, wrap pieces of copper wire around the tree's branches, and carefully twist them. Clip the tips of the branches so they do not grow too long. Water your bonsai well once the soil has dried out completely.

158

Arbor Day (April 22)

MAGAZINE PAGE ENVELOPES

How can you help save trees? Reuse and recycle the paper we already have!

What You'll Need: Magazine pages, tape, address labels

A good way to recycle is to make your own envelopes out of magazine pages. Pick a page with a pretty picture on it. Fold ⅓ of the page over, and tape up the sides. Fold the last part of the page down to make the flap. When you put your letter inside, seal the flap with a piece of tape. Use an address label on the front so the postal carrier can read the address!

Arbor Day (April 22)

BUTTON PARK

159

Don't have room in your yard for a tree? Even tiny plants become towering trees in a button park!

What You'll Need: Large button, cool-temp glue gun, baby food jar with lid, tiny air plants, dry moss, tiny pebbles, small ceramic animal, eyedropper or mister

Get the biggest button you can find. Have an adult help you glue the button to the top of the lid of a baby food jar with the cool-temp glue gun. Collect tiny pebbles for boulders. Ask your florist to help you select tiny air plants. Some possibilities are silver beads, toy cypress, *Sedum Moranenci, Sedum dasyphyllum,* cobweb houseleak, and *Echeveria microcalyx*. These tiny plants need no soil or sand. You can attach them to your button with a drop of cool-temp glue. Fill the spaces between your plants with little bits of moss, pebbles, and a tiny ceramic animal. Keep your park somewhere safe. The plants will stay healthy if you give them a few drops of water from an eye dropper or mister every few days. Fill the jar up with fun buttons or interesting pebbles. Then put the jar lid on top for an extra-special look!

160

May Day (May 1)

GLORIOUS GARLANDS

Guests at May Day festivities were "wreathed": Each wore a crown of green leaves with flowers in their hair. Here's how to make a May Day wreath.

What You'll Need: Leaves, stems, flowers

Go on a leaf hunt. Look for a bunch of the same kind of leaves with strong stems. Break off the stems, but hold on to them. Overlap the leaves and push the broken-off stems through the leaves as if they were pins to hold them together. Make a chain of leaves. When your leaf chain is long enough to fit around your head, fasten the final leaf to the first one. Add flowers by slipping their stems under the stem-pins on the top side of the leaves. (Warning! If you live in an area where poison ivy or poison oak grow, make sure you know what they look like before you go leaf hunting. They could give you a terrible rash!)

May Day (May 1)

MAY DAY BASKETS

161

Make May Day baskets for your neighbors.

What You'll Need: Poster board, pencil, ruler, wallpaper with spring pattern, white paste, stapler, fresh flowers

Draw a circle 5 inches across and a strip 10 × 1 inches on the poster board. Cut them out. Use the poster board circle and strip as a pattern. Lay them on the back of the wallpaper. Trace around them. You will need 2 wallpaper circles and 2 wallpaper strips for each basket. Cover one side of your poster board circle with glue, and glue a wallpaper circle to it with the pretty side up. Cover one side of your poster board strip with glue, and glue a wallpaper strip to it, pretty side up. Turn the strip over, and glue the other wallpaper strip to the other side. Lay your circle on the table wallpaper-side-down. Center the strip, and glue it across the middle of the circle. Glue the last wallpaper circle pretty-side-up on top of the strip. Turn it over. Pull the ends of the strip together to make a handle. (The sides of your basket will curl up.) Staple the handle together at the top.

May Day (May 1)

ROBIN HOOD HATS

Celebrate the coming of spring on May Day just as they did in merry olde England.

What You'll Need: Measuring tape, pencil, paper, green felt, scissors, needle, green thread, feather, small safety pin

Using the measuring tape, measure around your head and add 1 inch. On a piece of paper, draw a line half as long as your measurement. From the middle of your line, measure up 9 inches, and make a dot. Draw a semicircle (half circle) from the end of the line, through the top dot, to the end of the other side of the line. This half circle is your hat pattern. Stack 2 pieces of green felt, and pin your pattern to them. Cut along the pattern. Stitch or staple ½ inch in from the edge—only along the half circle. Turn up a 1-inch brim. Pin a feather to the side of your Robin Hood hat. Gather all your merry friends, and head for Sherwood Forest!

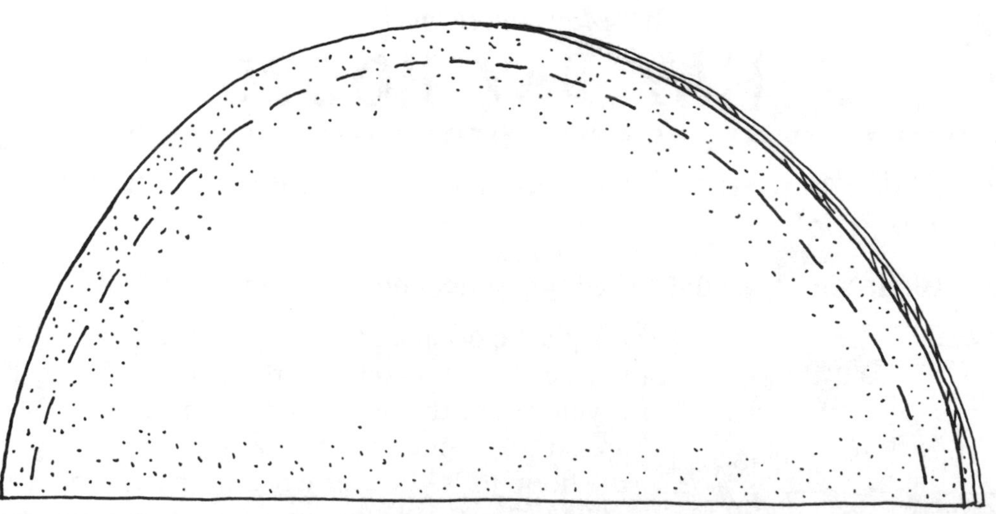

May Day (May 1)

NINE MEN'S MORRIS

Nine Men's Morris was one of the most popular May Day games in England.

What You'll Need: Large cardboard square, marker, 9 black stones, 9 white stones, coin

Copy the Morris board (as seen in the illustration) onto a piece of cardboard. Each player starts with 9 stones of one color. Flip a coin to see who moves first. Take turns putting the stones on the dots on the Morris board one at a time. You can put a stone on any vacant dot. The goal is to make a "mill"—3 of your stones together on any line. Each time you make a mill you get to take one of your opponent's pieces. If your opponent forms a mill, they get to take one of yours. Pieces in a mill are safe—they can't be taken. When all the stones have been placed on the board, the goal is to create new mills by taking turns moving the stones. A stone can be moved one space along any line, but there can't be a stone already sitting on the dot you move to. The game ends when 1 player has just 2 pieces left or when 1 player is unable to move.

May Day (May 1)

MAY DAY HOOPS

164

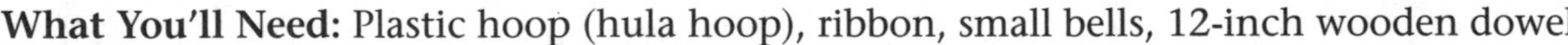

Children used to have hoop races on May Day; now you can, too!

What You'll Need: Plastic hoop (hula hoop), ribbon, small bells, 12-inch wooden dowel

Use a plastic hoop and decorate it the way children did hundreds of years ago. Cut 6-inch lengths of thin ribbon. Tie as many ribbons as you can to the hoop, all the way around. Make sure the knots are on the inside of the hoop so they won't get in the way when the hoop rolls. Tie a tiny bell to the end of every third or fourth ribbon. Practice rolling your May Day hoop, touching it with the dowel. How fast can you go? Invite your friends to a race!

Cinco de Mayo (May 5)

TASTY TORTILLA ROLL-UP TREATS

These easy-to-make snacks will help you celebrate the wonderful flavors of Mexico!

What You'll Need: Flour tortillas, cream cheese, mild salsa, lettuce, tomato, olives, table knife, spoon

Spread a thin layer of cream cheese on a flour tortilla. Spoon a little salsa over the cream cheese (if you don't like spicy foods, you can skip this step). Then put some lettuce, sliced tomatoes (ask an adult to help you slice them), olives, and any other veggies you like on top. Roll the tortilla up, and eat it. Mucho gusto!

Cinco de Mayo (May 5)

MAGNETS DE MAYO

166

These colorful flowers are actually made of corn and beans!

What You'll Need: Assorted dried corn and beans; white, green, or red felt; white, green, and red paint; paintbrush; scissors; glue; waxed paper; sticky-backed magnetic strip

Green, white, and red are the colors of the Mexican flag, and you can combine them in lots of interesting ways when painting the corn and beans that make up these flower magnets. Use an assortment of dried beans to vary the shape of your flowers. Tiny lentils and corn kernels will make delicate poseys, while larger fava beans can become the leaves of a gorgeous bloom. Paint lots of dried beans and corn in the colors of Mexico and let dry. Then arrange 6 to 10 beans and kernels in a flower shape. Place the points of the corn kernels toward the center of the flower. Cut a circle of felt a bit larger than your flower. Cover the circle with glue, and arrange your flower on it. Put the felt-flower on the waxed paper, and cover it completely with glue. If some of the glue runs over the edges of your flower, don't worry. You can break off the extra glue when it is dry. When your flower is completely dry, peel it off the waxed-paper and press a piece of sticky magnetic strip on the back.

Cinco de Mayo (May 5)

167 MARACA MUSIC

Keep the beat colorful and lively with these multicolored maracas.

What You'll Need: Small screwdriver, 2 clear stiff plastic cups, colored tape, colored pencil, medium-sized colored beads, ribbon

Have an adult help you use the screwdriver to poke a pencil-sized hole in the bottom of one of the plastic cups. Wind colored tape around the colored pencil to make a candy-cane striped pattern. Then slide the pencil into the hole you just made. Wind more colored tape thickly around the pencil to hold it in place. Fill the cup with an assortment of colored beads. Then place the other cup rim-to-rim with the first cup to make a closed container. Stick the cups together with colored tape. If you'd like, tie a ribbon around the pencil where it meets the cup's bottom to make a pretty streamer.

Cinco de Mayo (May 5)

CHOCOLATE MEXICANO 168

Make delicious Mexican hot chocolate for a breakfast treat.

What You'll Need: Two 3-ounce squares of Mexican chocolate (or 6 ounces of sweet baker's chocolate), 6 cups milk, 1½ teaspoons cinnamon (if using baker's chocolate), saucepan, eggbeater, mixing bowl, wooden spoon, cups, measuring spoons, cinnamon sticks for garnish, cayenne pepper (optional)

Wake up early on Cinco de Mayo, and surprise the whole family with this special breakfast beverage. You can get Mexican chocolate in stores that sell foods from different countries. If you can't find it, use sweet baker's chocolate instead. Combine all the ingredients in a saucepan and cook over low heat. Let an adult in on your secret breakfast treat so they can help you adjust the stove temperature. Stir the mixture constantly so it doesn't burn. When all the chocolate has melted and the mixture is blended, carefully pour the liquid into a large mixing bowl. Using an eggbeater or electric mixer, whip until frothy. (You could also pour the liquid into a blender and whip it that way.) In Mexico, hot chocolate is poured into a large pottery jug and whipped with a wooden beater called a *molinillo* (moh-lee-NEE-yoh). When the hot chocolate is ready, pour it into mugs and garnish with a cinnamon stick. A pinch of cayenne pepper can be added for some real south of the border heat! This recipe serves 4 people.

169

Cinco de Mayo (May 5)

MOCK SILVER JEWELRY

Dress up for your Cinco de Mayo party with this festive pasta jewelry.

What You'll Need: Dried pasta (tubes, wheels, macaroni, etc.), string, scissors, needle, turquoise and silver paint, paintbrushes, pencil

Traditional Mexican jewelry is often made of silver, set with turquoise stones. Make your own out of pasta, string, some paint, and lots of imagination. Use an assortment of pasta. If the pasta you choose doesn't have holes to thread, have an adult make a hole in the pasta with a needle. If you want to make a necklace, cut a length of string and shape it into a loop big enough to fit over your head. Make it a little longer than that so you have enough thread to make the knot. Then lay out your pasta shapes along the loop in different arrangements until you get one you like. You might want to write numbers lightly in pencil on the pasta so you know the order in which to string them. Now you can paint the pasta in silver and turquoise. You might paint alternating colors, or paint the whole necklace silver except for the middle 2 pasta pieces. Follow your own design sense! Lay the pasta out to dry in the same arrangement in which you will thread them. When the paint is dry, thread the pasta on the string, and knot the string ends.

170

Mother's Day

BEAUTIFUL BATHS

Mom will love to relax in a sweet-smelling bath.

What You'll Need: 4 tablespoons baking soda, bowl, food flavorings (almond, mint, orange, or vanilla), food coloring, spoon, markers, envelopes

Your Mom will thank you again and again for these wonderful homemade bath salts. Put the baking soda in a bowl, and mix in a few drops of flavoring and a few drops of food coloring. Mix them together with a spoon until all the ingredients are well-blended. Choose colors that go well with the flavors, such as green food coloring with mint flavoring, and orange food coloring with orange flavoring. Name the different bath salts you create (Sweet Vanilla Dream or Minty Refresher), and write the names on the envelopes. Decorate the envelopes with pictures of Mom's favorite things and other pretty pictures. Fill the envelopes with the bath salts.

Mother's Day

CLEAN HANDS DISH

This pretty soap dish will help everyone remember to wash their hands!

What You'll Need: Air drying clay, rolling pin, pencil, knife, toothpick, acrylic paint, paintbrushes, sealer

Roll the clay to about ¼ inch thick. Lay your hand on top of the clay with your fingers together. Use a pencil to trace the outline of your hand onto the clay. Use a knife to cut the clay hand out. Smooth the edges with your fingers. Draw a design, maybe a heart or star, in the palm of the hand. Poke 6 small drainage holes through the center of the palm with a toothpick. Make sure the holes go all the way through. Bend the edges of the hand and fingers up into the shape of a dish. Prop up the edges so that they won't sag as it dries. Paint the dish with 2 coats of acrylic paint. Let dry between coats. Waterproof the dish with a sealer.

Mother's Day

MAGIC MOM PAPERWEIGHT

172

Mom will treasure this glittery scene forever!

What You'll Need: Small wide-mouth clear jar with lid, small china or plastic figure of a woman, other waterproof figures or trinkets (including fake gems, shells, rocks, etc.), waterproof glue, glycerin or mineral oil, water, glitter, tablespoon, super glue

Snow globes are popular any time of the year. Make one for Mom that is full of glittering magic dust instead of snow. Glue a small figure of a woman onto the inside of your jar. Glue on other tiny, waterproof figures to personalize the scene: How about Mom's favorite cat or dog? Or a small shell or rock from a family vacation? Fake jewels are nice, too. So are miniature plastic trees or flowers that can be found at most hobby or craft shops. Use your imagination to put "Mom" in an interesting and colorful scene. When the glue has dried, fill the jar with mineral oil or glycerin with a small bit of water added. Finish by adding a tablespoon of colored or silver glitter. Screw the top on tightly (have an adult use the super glue to keep the lid on). Shake up the magic dust—this gift will really show your mother how much you appreciate the magic she makes for you all year long.

173

Mother's Day

ROLL-UP ROSES

Would you like to give your mom a beautiful vase of roses that will never wilt? Spray them with perfume to make them smell sweet!

What You'll Need: 10 × 20-inch pieces of tissue paper, yardstick, florist tape, floral stem wires, stapler, vase, perfume (optional)

1. Lay the yardstick on the long edge of a sheet of crepe paper. Fold the paper over the ruler, turning the ruler as you keep folding. The folds should be a bit loose. Leave 1 inch unwrapped at the bottom (we will call this the fringe).

2. When you are done folding, grab an end of the paper in each hand and push it all to the center of the ruler. This will give the petals a nice texture. Pull the ruler out.

3. Make a little loop at the end of a stem wire. Staple the loop onto the folded portion at one end of your crepe paper strip; the fringe of unfolded crepe paper should be just below the staple.

4. Starting with the end where your stem is stapled, roll the paper up. Roll it tightly at first, and then a little more loosely at the end. Gather the fringe and twist it so that it wraps around the stem.

5. Wrap florist tape around the twisted crepe paper fringe and 2 inches down the stem of the rose.

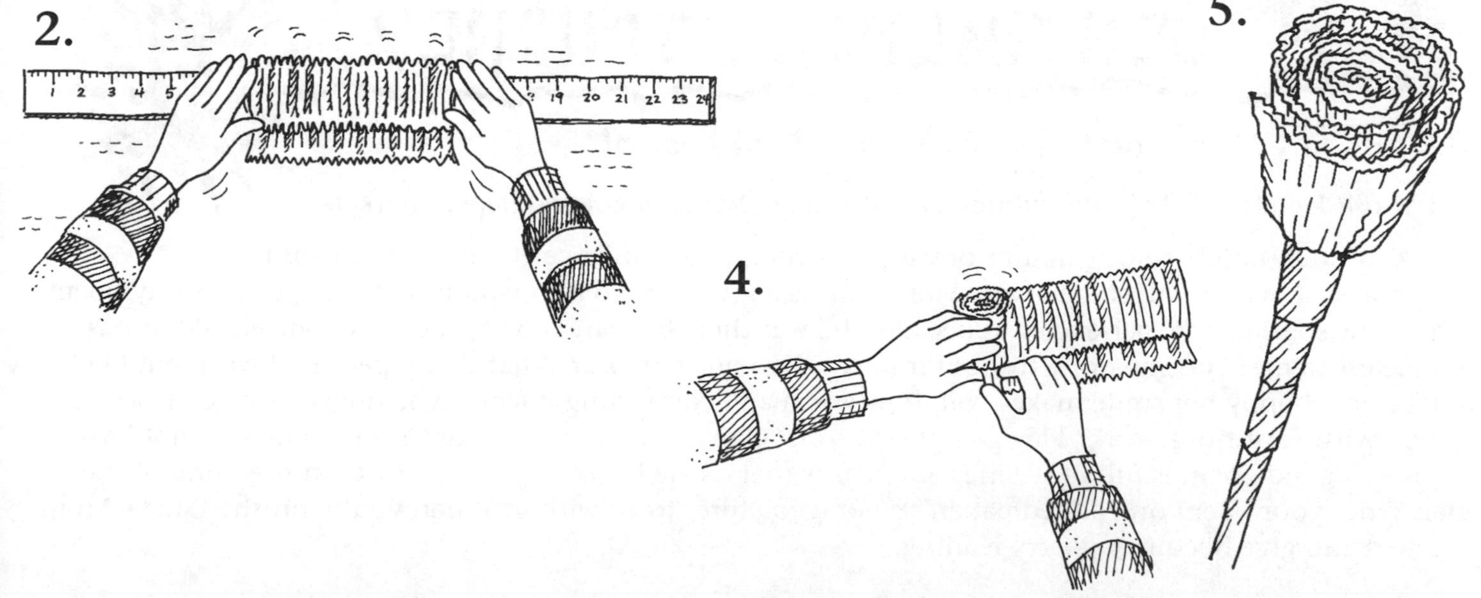

174

Mother's Day

CHOCOLATE SPOONS

Mom will love to stir her coffee with a chocolate spoon.

What You'll Need: ¼ cup semi-sweet chocolate chips, 1½ teaspoons solid shortening, mixing spoon, measuring spoons and cup, 2 plastic spoons, microwave-safe cup, drinking glasses, plastic bags, ribbon

Have an adult help you with this project. Pour the chips into the microwave-safe cup. Add the shortening. Microwave on high for 1 minute. Stir, and continue to microwave for 30 seconds or until the chips are melted. Stir thoroughly. If you don't have a microwave, melt the chocolate in the top of a double boiler on the stove. When all the chocolate has melted, use the mixing spoon to coat the chocolate on the front and back of the plastic spoons. Only coat the spoon part, not the handle. Carefully place the plastic spoon on the rim of a drinking glass to dry. It will probably take about 10 minutes for the chocolate to harden. When the spoons are ready, put them in a plastic bag and tie them with a ribbon. These spoons are best when freshly made. Surprise Mom by placing them next to her coffee cup on Mother's Day morn-

Mother's Day

SENTIMENTAL JOURNEY

175

Tell Mom how much you love her—in an original poem!

What You'll Need: Family photo albums or videotapes, white or colored paper, markers

Look through family photo albums or watch videotapes of family celebrations and trips to remember special events you shared with Mom. This is a great way to get inspiration for a Mother's Day poem. Tell her how special an experience was because she was there to share it with you. Ask yourself: What has Mom meant to me? Has she done things for me that no one else has? What do I especially love about her? Think of how happy her smile makes you, how warm and comforting it feels to be hugged by her. Does she help you with your homework? Play games with you? Cook your favorite foods? Your poem does not have to rhyme. A good poem is full of feelings and words that create lively, colorful pictures in the mind of the reader. Write your poem on colored paper, and draw pictures to go with it. When you're finished, have Mom take a seat and give her a live poetry reading.

176

Mother's Day

BREAKFAST BOUQUET

These flowers will last long after Mother's Day is over.

What You'll Need: Blown eggs, scissors, cardboard egg cartons, construction paper, paint, paintbrushes, glue, poms, wooden beads, chenille stems, florist tape, crepe paper, vase or glass bottle, ribbon

This bouquet will look lovely when set on a Mother's Day breakfast tray. To make the blown eggs for the different flowers, see the instructions for Egg-citing Safari (page 19) or Blown Egg Sachet (page 58). If you want to make a tulip, using very sharp scissors, carefully cut Vs around the small end of a blown egg. Paint the blown egg light pink with darker pink vertical stripes. For a daisy, glue white paper petals around the base of a yellow egg. Cut a cup out of the egg carton to make the base of a tiger lily. Paint it orange, and glue on orange and brown spotted paper petals. Other flowers can be made by painting egg carton cups in pretty colors and gluing a yellow pom or a wooden bead in the center of each. Make stems for your flowers using green chenille stems and florist tape. You can also glue on green crepe paper leaves to your stems. Place the flower arrangement in a vase or clean, empty bottle, and tie it with a colorful ribbon.

Mother's Day

COLORED CANDLEHOLDER

Light up Mom's day with this pretty candleholder.

What You'll Need: Jar that votive candle will fit in, cardboard, pencil, scissors, tape, colored nail polish, salt, ribbon, scented votive candle

Wash and dry a small, empty jar. Draw and cut out a small stencil in the shape of a heart or some other pretty design from the cardboard. Make sure your stencil fits on the jar. Tape the stencil down, and use Mom's favorite color nail polish (with permission!) to paint inside the stencil. Sprinkle salt over the wet polish to make it sparkle when it dries. You may want to paint a design around the whole jar or only the front and back. Be sure to let each side dry thoroughly before you turn the glass over. When the polish is dry, untape the stencil. Tie a colored ribbon around the neck of the jar, and put a small scented candle inside. Make several candleholders, and put them on the table as a centerpiece to add a fragrant scent to your Mother's Day meal.

Mother's Day

GOLDEN JEWELRY

These pins takes patience to make, but Mom's expression will be worth it!

What You'll Need: Animal crackers, oval or oblong crackers, white acrylic spray paint, small paintbrushes, sealer, gold acrylic paint, glue, pin backs, cool-temp glue gun

Pick an animal cracker and an oval cracker for the backing. Brush away all loose crumbs and salt from the front and back of the crackers. Have a grownup spray paint one side of the crackers white. When dry, have the adult spray paint the other side. The crackers should be completely white. Paint sealer on the back of the crackers to seal them. Let them dry. Turn them over to seal the top and sides. Let them dry. Paint the animal and the oval cracker with golden acrylic paint. When dry, glue the animal cracker to the middle of the oval cracker. After the glue has dried, add a another coat of gold paint. When the paint is completely dry, seal it by painting it with a thick coat of sealer. When the sealer is dry, have an adult help you glue the pin to the back.

Mother's Day

COOKIE BOUQUET

179

Is your mother one sweet cookie? Then show her!

What You'll Need: Tube of refrigerated cookie dough, bamboo skewers, a cookie sheet, nonstick cooking spray, florist tape, artificial leaves, ribbons, florist foam

Pick your mother's favorite kind of cookie dough from the tubes of uncooked dough at the grocery store. You can find bamboo skewers in the housewares department. You can find florist foam, florist tape, artificial leaves, and ribbons at a crafts store. Spray the cookie pan with nonstick spray. Cut the cookie dough into 1-inch-thick slices; you can shape the cookies into flower shapes if you'd like. Push a bamboo skewer point first into the bottom of each cookie. The skewer should go in about 1½ inches. Bake the cookies according to directions. Let the cookies cool on the pan. When cool, use a spatula to lift them off the pan. Wrap the bamboo skewer with florist tape, and decorate them with ribbons. Stick the ends of the stems into the florist foam. Cover the foam with artificial leaves.

180

Mother's Day

MOM 'N' ME BOOK

This book is sure to bring tears of joy to Mom's eyes!

What You'll Need: 25 small brown paper bags, scissors, iron, two 9-inch squares heavy cardboard, pencil, metal ruler, clear plastic tape, wrapping paper, white glue, hole punch, 2 clothespins, markers

Along a seam, cut a side of a bag to the bottom. Cut the bottom off the bag. Repeat for all bags. Unfold the bags to make squares. Trim the bags to the size of the cardboard (9-inch squares). Have an adult help you iron the bags with a cool iron to make them flat. Draw a line 1 inch from an edge of each of the cardboard squares. Use the edge of the ruler to bend the cardboard along the line. Bend it back and forth, until it works like a paper hinge. Put a strip of plastic tape on each side of the cardboard covering the hinge. Glue wrapping paper on the cardboard. Punch a hole in the 1 inch section of your covers 2 inches from the top of the book, and another hole 2 inches from the bottom. Punch holes to match in the cut ends of the paper bags. Stack all the bags between the covers and clamp them with the clothespins. Thread the ribbon from the inside to the outside of the cover. Tie ribbon in a knot, and make a bow. Write a title on the front cover, and decorate it. Fill it with thoughts and pictures of Mom.

Mother's Day

COZY CASES

181

Mom will appreciate these soft cases for her glasses and change.

What You'll Need: Old necktie, scissors, ruler, manicure scissors, sticky-backed Velcro dots, clothespins, blue glue gel

For the glasses case, find a necktie wide enough to fit a pair of eyeglasses. Cut a 10-inch piece from the widest end (do not include the pointed part at the tie's bottom in your measurement). If there is a tag inside the tie, carefully cut it out with manicure scissors. Fold the cut edges together, and glue them shut. When that glue is dry, fold the tie in half, bringing the end up to just before the tie starts to narrow. Glue the sides together to create an envelope. Use clothespins to hold the sides together until the glue dries. Make a fastener on the open end of the tie by pressing a sticky-backed Velcro dot on the inside of the pointed end of the tie, folding it over, and placing another Velcro dot on the tie to match up with the first Velcro dot. To make the change purse, cut a 5-inch piece of necktie and follow the instructions for the eyeglass case.

182

Mother's Day

LOVED-ONE LOCKET

Be close to Mom all year long when she wears your photograph inside a pretty locket.

What You'll Need: 2 twist-off bottle caps, colored nail polish, felt scraps, small photo of your face, glue, scissors, silk cord

Locket necklaces are a wonderful way to hold photographs of loved ones. Paint both bottle caps inside and out with a light coat of colored nail polish. Paint one side at a time, use even strokes, and let dry for at least 15 minutes before continuing. You may need to add a second coat to cover the bottle cap well. Cut a small strip of felt in a color that matches the nail polish. Glue one end inside each cap to form a hinge. This will allow the caps to close and form a locket. Cut out and glue another piece of felt inside one cap and glue a picture of your face, also cut to fit, inside the other cap. Make sure the felt hinge is at the top of the locket, and your photo is face-up in the cap that will hang against Mom's neck. You might want to cut out a small felt heart or other decoration to glue to the outside of the locket. When the glue has dried, tie a silk cord around the hinge of the locket. Then tie the ends together to form a loop large enough to fit an adult head. Whenever Mom wears her locket, you'll be close to her heart!

MOM GETS HER DAY

The origins of Mother's Day began in ancient Greece to honor Rhea, mother earth. It wasn't until 1914 that President Woodrow Wilson declared an official day to honor moms. Ana Jarvis started her campaign in 1907 to get moms their special day!

183

Memorial Day

NEIGHBORHOOD PARADE

What would Memorial Day be without a colorful parade?

What You'll Need: Bicycles; skateboards; wagons; red, white, and blue ribbons; hats; clothing; balloons; streamers; banners; homemade drums; rope; fake flowers; chenille stems; kazoos

Get the whole neighborhood involved in this festive march around the block. Gather up your pets, too. Tell everyone to wear clothes that are red, white, and blue. You may want to make or carry flags or flowers. Homemade drums can be made by painting empty coffee cans; beat on the lids with a wooden spoon. Tie wagons together with rope and fill them with stuffed animals and dolls decorated with red, white, and blue ribbons, streamers, and balloons. Weave red, white, and blue streamers into the spokes of your bicycle's wheels. Attach fake flowers to the handlebars with chenille stems. Set a time for your parade to start, and post notices around the neighborhood. When everyone has gathered, pound a beat on one of the drums and lift up those knees in a march.

Memorial Day

FLOAT A FLOWER BOAT

Decorate a homemade toy boat in honor of soldiers who died at sea.

What You'll Need: Paper plate, waterproof markers, pencil, round balloon, small fresh flowers, glue

Every Memorial Day, the navy floats flowers out to sea to honor soldiers who died at sea. Join the tradition by making this balloon boat and floating it away. Draw colorful flowers with waterproof markers on a paper plate. Poke a hole in the center of the plate with a pencil. Poke the open end of a round balloon through the hole. Blow up the balloon (from the back of the plate) until it is full. Knot the balloon. If desired, you can also glue small fresh flowers or wildflowers onto the balloon or plate. Make a few different balloon boats and send them off to "sea" as a beautiful, flowery thank you to the men and women who gave their lives to preserve freedom. (Collect the balloons and discard them after you are done; balloons can be harmful to wildlife.)

185

Memorial Day

PATRIOTIC POPPIES

Memorial Day is also known as Poppy Day.

What You'll Need: Red crepe paper, green chenille stems, scissors, large needle

In the spring, red poppies bloom on European battlefields where thousands of soldiers died in battle. Many veteran's organizations sell poppies to earn money for disabled vets. You can make your own crepe paper poppies. To make each poppy, cut out three 4-inch circles of red crepe paper. Lay the circles on top of each other, and ask an adult to help you use a needle to make 2 holes next to each other in the center (go through all the circles). Put the end of a chenille stem through one hole, bend the chenille stem, and bring the end down through the other hole. Twist the end around the long part of the chenille stem to secure it. Pull the crepe paper petals slightly away from each other to form the poppy.

Memorial Day

TRADITIONAL TATTOOS

186

Show your true colors with these patriotic tattoos.

What You'll Need: Waterbased face paints, small paintbrushes

Memorial Day is a day to remember the men and women who died while fighting for our country's freedom. We often place flowers at the graves of soldiers on this day. Make a hand-painted tattoo to show your support for those who died in battle. Many soldiers got tattoos when they were fighting far from home to remind them of their dedication to their country and the people back home who were missed. Maybe you would like to paint on a flower tattoo in memory of a relative who died in battle. Or perhaps you would like to paint a tattoo of the American flag or a bald eagle to show your patriotism. Wear your tattoos to a Memorial Day picnic or parade, and show them off with pride.

SUMMER

Summer is a blast—all that sunshine, all those outdoor games, all the picnic fun! This chapter gives you even more exciting and interesting things to do and make. There are picnic crafts, games to make and play, delicious recipes to create! Celebrate Summer Solstice, Children's Day, Independence Day, Canada Day, Father's Day, and many more holidays this season!

187

Flag Day (June 1)

PROGRESSIVE MINING FLAG GAME

Play a unique version of this popular Victorian game.

What You'll Need: Small containers, sand, paper, scissors, markers, wooden skewers, glue, plastic straws, empty cups or bowls

This game requires a steady hand while playing. To make the game, fill small containers with sand. These are known as "mines." Cut a 4 × 3-inch square of paper for each of the mines. On each square, draw one of the different stages of the American flag, beginning with the original design, up to our present-day flag. Glue the end of each paper flag to a wooden skewer, and when the glue dries, stick a flag into each of the mines. Cut a little off the end of each straw (one for each player) to make a shovel shape. For every 2 players there must be 1 mine. Players then take turns using the plastic straws to remove a bit of sand and placing it in an empty cup or bowl. Whichever team makes the flag fall while removing sand loses the game.

Children's Day

FACES OF THE WORLD NECKLACE

Make these easy homemade beads into an international piece of jewelry.

What You'll Need: Plastic tub, sand, white glue, measuring cups, spoon, nail, paper plate, old magazines or catalogs, markers, colored cord, tape

You may want to make several of these cheerful necklaces—once your friends see you wearing one, they will want one of their own! To make the beads, in the plastic tub, mix 1 cup sand with ¼ cup white glue to make the dough. Break off a small piece with your fingers, and roll it into a bead. Make the bead large enough for you to later paste a small picture of a child's face onto the front of it. Carefully, or with an adult's help, use the nail to poke a hole through the center. If the dough is too mushy, put the bead back and add a little more sand to the mixture. Make as many beads as you wish. Set the beads to dry on a paper plate until they are hard. While the beads dry, cut small pictures of children's faces from old magazines or catalogs. You can then paste these to the front of the beads. You may want to color the beads with markers, too. Then tape one end of a colored cord that is long enough to go over your head when looped. This will make it easier to string the beads. When you have strung all the beads you want, remove the tape and tie the ends of the cord together. Now wear your new "friends" around the neighborhood, and introduce them to all your best buddies!

A Day for Every Kid

In the United States, Children's Day was started in 1868 by Protestant Churches. It is celebrated on the second Sunday in June. In Japan, Children's Day is May 5. In Thailand, Children's Day is celebrated on the second Saturday in January.

Children's Day

189 SLAMMING CAPS GAME

Play this popular, old-fashioned game of Milk Caps, or Pogs, with your friends.

What You'll Need: Corrugated cardboard, small jar tops, pencil, scissors, copies of school pictures or magazine pictures of children's faces, paints, paintbrush

Back in the 1930s, when milk was delivered in bottles, children collected the milk bottle caps and played a game with them. You can make your own Milk Caps, or Pogs, to use in a special Children's Day game. To make Pogs, trace around a small jar top placed on corrugated cardboard. Cut them out. Glue on either pictures of school friends or children's faces cut from an old magazine or catalog. Leave the other sides of the Pogs blank or paint them a solid color. To play the game, stack 10 or more Pogs in a column. Toss a small jar top, or slammer, at the column. If a Pog lands with the child's face up, the person who tossed the slammer gets 1 point. If the Pog lands with the blank side up, the player gets 0 points. You can also play for Pogs instead of points. Most of the fun of this game is collecting and trading the Pogs. See if you can get an entire set of Pogs with the faces of your classmates!

Children's Day

FAMOUS CHILDREN GAME 190

Do you know the names of famous children? Play this game and find out!

This game will give you and your friends a real mental workout. One player is "It" and must think of a famous child. The famous child could be a movie star, a sports figure, a character in a book or play, or someone that is currently in the news. The famous child must be familiar to everyone playing the game. "It" then says "I'm thinking of a famous child whose name starts with W" (or whatever letter). The other players take turns asking questions about the famous child that can be answered either "yes" or "no." They may ask a total of 20 questions. Whoever guesses correctly gets to be "It" in the next round of the game. Who was the famous child? Tiny Tim in *A Christmas Carol?* Macaulay Culkin in *Home Alone?* Little Red Riding Hood?

Children's Day

INTERNATIONAL DOLL COLLECTION

Welcome these tiny children of the world into your home!

What You'll Need: Stiff paper, small foam balls, scissors, glue, yarn, markers, beads, thin wire, wiggle eyes, fabric and felt scraps, tiny jewels and sequins, cotton balls

Dress these dolls in traditional costumes to show what children might wear in different parts of the world. To make the basic doll body, roll a piece of stiff paper into a cone and flatten the top by folding the point inward. For the doll head, trim the base off a foam ball so that it will fit flat on top of the cone. Glue the head on the cone. Decorate your dolls. For an Native American doll, glue on a braid of black yarn and decorate a strip of paper for a headband. Glue a piece of brown paper with a fringed collar and hem onto the body cone. Make a necklace for around her neck. For a Dutch doll, glue on yellow yarn hair. Draw and cut out the shape of her hat twice, glue the tips together, then glue it on her head. Draw tulips on her dress, and glue a square of fabric on for her apron. Draw faces on your dolls with markers. You can also glue on wiggle eyes and make tiny earrings from sequins. Cotton balls can be pulled apart to make fur trim for a Scandinavian doll. Tiny beads can be strung on thin wire to make necklaces for African dolls. Study pictures of international costumes, and try to copy the fabric patterns on your paper cones. What countries are your dolls from?

DUTCH GO CRAZY FOR TULIPS

Tulips first bloomed in the Netherlands in 1594, and the Dutch loved them. The Netherlands account for more than 90 percent of the world's tulip production!

Children's Day

192 MAGNET MOVIE THEATER

Invite your friends to a movie—right inside your house!

What You'll Need: Shoe box without a lid, construction paper, old magazines or catalogs, scissors, glue, markers, tape, paper clips, magnets, fabric, flashlight

Do you like movies? Have you ever thought of making your own? To celebrate Children's Day, why not make up a science fiction or fantasy movie, such as *The Day of the Disappearing Children* or *The Hundred-Foot Child Who Saved the World*. To make your movie theater, cover a shoe box inside and out with colorful construction paper. You may want to write the name of your movie theater on the sides of the box. Cut out pictures you want for the background of your movie. Does your movie take place in a city? Cut out or draw buildings, and glue them to the inside of the box. If you want something to move—people, animals, clouds, or vehicles—glue a paper clip to the back of the object. Then, when you tell the story of your movie, put your cutout against the background and press a magnet against the back of the shoe box behind the paper clip. When you let go of the cutout, the magnet will hold it up. Slide 2 magnets around the back of the shoe box to make 2 characters move. You can also cut out fabric curtains and glue the top edge to the top of the box. Turn out the lights before your movie starts and have a friend shine a flashlight onto the "screen" just as you flip the curtains up. (Our illustration shows the top cut off the box to better show the inside scene.)

THE CORE OF THE MATTER

The Earth's core is made of iron, and it is like a giant magnet! It helps keep much of the harmful radiation from reaching us here on Earth. But sometimes charged particles get caught in our magnetic field, which creates the Northern and Southern Lights that happen at the North and South Poles!

Children's Day

CARP KITE

193

Celebrate Children's Day—Japanese style!

What You'll Need: Wire coat hanger, tissue paper, tape, construction paper, scissors, markers, spool of string

In Japan on Children's Day, carp kites are flown. The carp is the symbol of strength, courage, and determination because of the way it leaps upstream. These are qualities parents wish for their children. You can draw a carp on a kite to fly on Children's Day. To make the kite, ask an adult to help you bend a coat hanger into a diamond shape. Have them bend the hook part so it won't poke anyone. Then cover the wire by wrapping it with a layer of tissue paper. Tape the ends of the tissue paper to secure it. Cut a diamond shape out of construction paper that is a little larger than the coat-hanger diamond. Draw the carp with the markers. Tape the paper to the coat hanger so that the diamond-shape opening is covered. Ask an adult to help you poke a hole at each of the corners of the diamond. Cut three 20-inch lengths of string. Tie one each to the top and side holes. Tie one end of a spool of string to the bottom hole to make the flying string. Then tie the free ends of the top and side strings to the flying string near where it meets the kite. This will help your kite fly. Take your carp out and run!

STRONG CHILDREN

The Japanese draw carp on their kites because they believe carp are symbols of strength and perseverance since they swim vigorously upstream against strong currents. The Japanese hope that their children will inherit these characteristics.

Children's Day

NEW CHILD WELCOME TRAY

New parents will really appreciate this gift.

What You'll Need: 4 or 5 small jars of different sizes (one with a shaker top for powder), stickers or decals, paints, paintbrushes, round aluminum foil cake pan, ribbon, glue, cotton balls, pins, baby oil, baby powder

Welcome a new child into the world with a special Welcome Tray. Collect some small empty jars of different sizes. You can use jars that once held peanut butter, spices, baby food, mustard, relish, or pickles. Just make sure that they are washed and dried well to get rid of any smell. Decorate the clean jars with stickers or decals, or paint on flowers or other cheery designs. Then label each lid (Cotton Balls, Baby Lotion, Baby Oil, Diaper Pins, etc.) with the new baby supplies that you will put in it. Put baby powder in a spice jar with a shaker top. Next, glue a ribbon around the edge of a foil cake pan. Arrange the jars in the pan and take them over to the new baby's house to welcome her or him into the world.

Children's Day

KID TALK

Put on a special talk show—by kids, for kids, and about kids!

What You'll Need: Chairs, desk or table, video camera or audio cassette player (optional)

What is important to you? Do you think something is unfair? Are there laws that should be changed? Think about the kinds of problems and challenges that children face and what you can do to make life better for children. Write down your ideas, and then act out a TV talk show to discuss them. One person can be the host, and everyone else can be guests or members of the studio audience. One person can videotape, if you have a video camera. Think of a name for your show. You may want to play music while someone announces the beginning of the show. The host can sit at a table with her or his guests. The studio audience can sit in rows of chairs facing the host and guests. The guests can play experts, such as teachers or politicians, or they can play parents and children. The guests might want to discuss what Children's Day means to them. Members of the studio audience can ask questions when the host calls on them. Practice your TV show, and then invite a real audience to watch it!

196

Friendship Day (June 15)

SPECIAL SEED BRACELETS

Let the world see your friendship when you and a friend wear these matching bracelets.

What You'll Need: Watermelon seeds, cookie sheet, large needle, paints, paintbrushes, elastic thread, scissors

Wash lots of watermelon seeds. Use the dark brown seeds; the white ones may not be firm enough. Spread the seeds out on a cookie sheet, and let them dry overnight. When they are dry, have an adult help you carefully poke a hole through the top of each seed with a large needle. To make matching bracelets, decide with your friend what colors you should paint the seeds. You might want to use both of your favorite colors, alternating them when you thread them on the elastic to show how you and your friend always take turns. When you paint the seeds, paint one side of the seeds, and let the paint dry. Then turn the seeds over, and paint the other sides. You can paint each side of your seeds a different color, and you can draw dots or tiny hearts on your seeds. Use your imagination! Thread the seeds onto enough elastic to make a bracelet. Knot the elastic. Each of you slip your bracelets onto your wrists and declare your friendship to be forever.

LIVE LONGER

According to researchers, people who have life-long, meaningful friendships live longer and healthier than those without life-long friends.

197

Friendship Day (June 15)

TOSS AND CATCH GAME

Invite a friend—or a group of friends—to play this special game of catch.

What You'll Need: 2 disposable wooden paint paddles, paints, paintbrushes, 2 paper cups, scissors, glue, tissue paper or Ping-Pong ball

For each player, paint a disposable wooden paint paddle with bright colors and designs. You can write a special friendship message on one side, such as "I'll always be there to catch you when you fall!" Then glue the bottom of a paper cup to the end of each paddle. Let this dry for at least an hour. Crumple tissue paper into a ball or use a Ping-Pong ball. Take your toss-and-catch game outside or where there's lots of room. Put the ball into one of the paper cups and fling it lightly so your friend can catch it in her or his paper cup. Start close together, and take a step back each time the ball is caught. Get a group of friends together and play in a circle. Or 4 players can form a cross and play 2 games at once, trying not to let the 2 balls hit each other.

Friendship Day (June 15)

HOLDING HANDS GAME

Holding hands has never been so much fun!

What You'll Need: 4 dishes, 20 peanuts

Divide the players into 2 equal teams. Have each team line up and clasp hands by weaving their fingers together. Put a dish with 10 peanuts at one end of each line, and an empty dish at the other. The first player in each line picks up a peanut with her or his free hand and then passes it to her other hand (the one that is clasped with the hand of the next player). The next player must use his clasped hand to pass the peanut to his other hand, and so on until the peanut gets to the last person, who drops it in the empty dish with her free hand. As soon as the first player has passed the first peanut, she picks up another peanut and begins again. The team that passes all 10 peanuts into the empty dish first, without unclasping their hands at any time during the game, wins. Hold on tight!

Friendship Day (June 15)

199 BEST FRIEND'S HOUSE GAME

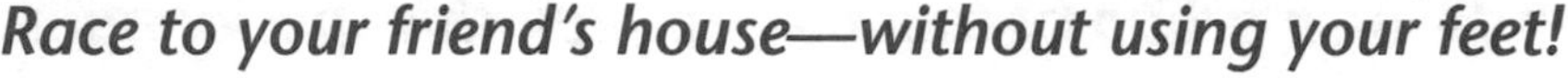

Race to your friend's house—without using your feet!

What You'll Need: 2 shoe box lids, 2 oatmeal carton lids, scissors, construction paper, glue, markers, 6 marbles

This game is great on a rainy day. You and your friend should cut the oatmeal lids on one side to make an opening for the marbles to pass through. After the lid is cut, it should look like a big letter C. Glue this C near one end of the inside of your shoe box lids. If you want, you can first line your lids with colored construction paper. Cut out a 12 × 5-inch rectangle of construction paper and fold it into a square shape to make the walls of a house. Before taping it together, draw on windows and doors, and each of you should write your name and address on your house. Cut out the door so that it will fit over the cutout in the oatmeal lid. Fold another rectangle over the square to make a roof, and tape the roof and the base of the house together. Glue the house over the oatmeal lid, with the door lining up with the opening of the C. Decorate the path to your house with markers. Draw driveways, trees, sidewalks, and people. To play the game, place 3 marbles in each shoe box lid. To start, both of you say "Come on over to my house!" Each person races to get all their marbles into the house by moving their lid.

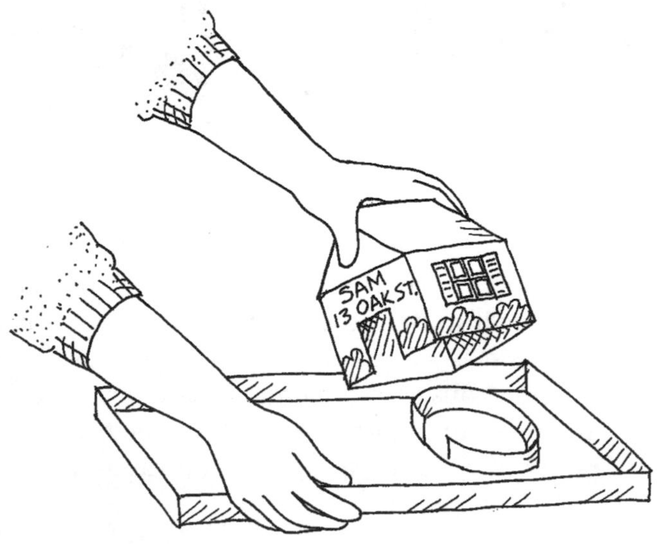

Juneteenth (June 19)

LOGS FOR LINCOLN CAKE

You don't have to be a president to enjoy this cake!

What You'll Need: Coffee can, chocolate cake mix, chocolate frosting, chocolate sprinkles, toasted coconut, construction paper, scissors, marker, toothpicks, tape

Juneteenth celebrates the day East Texas enforced President Lincoln's Emancipation Proclamation that abolished slavery. Share a log-shaped cake with friends to remember this smart and caring president. Have an adult smooth the edges of the coffee can so you won't cut yourself. Wash and dry the empty can. Grease the inside of the can—this will used for the pan to make the cake into a log shape. Follow the directions on the cake mix. Pour the batter into the coffee can. Bake according to the directions on the box, but ask an adult to insert a knife into the center of the cake from time to time to check doneness. If the knife comes out clean, the cake is done. Let cool for 10 minutes, then run a knife around the edges and remove the cake. When the cake has cooled, frost it with chocolate frosting and add chocolate sprinkles and toasted coconut to make the cake look like bark. Cut squares of construction paper, and write on messages such as "Happy Freedom Day!" or "Thanks, President Lincoln!" Tape the signs to toothpicks. Stick the signs in the top of the cake.

Juneteenth (June 19)

LINCOLN'S CABIN

Re-create Lincoln's log cabin for a centerpiece at your Juneteenth party.

What You'll Need: Empty milk carton, brown construction paper, scissors, glue, markers, cardboard, small straight twigs (optional), pencil, tape, plate, leaves

Wash and dry the milk carton; cut off the top half. Glue brown construction paper to cover it inside and out. Cut out windows and doors or draw them on with a marker. Then cut and fold a piece of cardboard in half to form the roof. Attach it to the base of the cabin with tape or glue. Now you are ready to add the logs. You can glue on small straight twigs, or you can make logs by rolling a piece of brown paper around a pencil, taping the paper, and then sliding the pencil out. Glue logs in rows on all the sides of the house, leaving spaces for the windows and doors. Set the cabin on a plate, and surround it with leaves.

202

Juneteenth (June 19)

NUMBER 19 MOBILE

The number 19 is a very lucky number for millions of people!

What You'll Need: Thin cardboard; pencil; scissors; paints; paintbrushes; old magazines; tiny toys, ribbons, shells, stickers, message buttons, small pebbles, feathers, tiny U.S. flags, etc.; markers; glue; large needle; string; plastic-coated hanger

You won't forget what date it is with this giant number hanging around to remind you. Draw and cut out a very large number 1 and a number 9 from thin cardboard. Paint one side of both, let them dry, then paint the other side. While you are waiting for the paint to dry, look through old magazines and find pictures that remind you of freedom, which could include happy faces, birds flying, and people dancing. Gather other decorative objects, such as shells, bits of ribbon, feathers, tiny flags, and other small items. Arrange your pictures and objects in a pleasing design on top of the number 19, and glue them down. Poke a small hole in the tops of the 1 and 9 and tie them to a hanger with string. Draw other figures and objects that remind you of freedom on more cardboard, and cut them out. Poke holes in the tops of these, and tie them onto the hanger with string to make a mobile with number 19 as the middle. How about drawing President Lincoln!

DELAYED FREEDOM

President Lincoln signed the Emancipation Proclamation on January 1, 1863. But Texas didn't receive the news until June 19, 1865, so slavery continued in Texas between those 2 dates. Juneteenth is the oldest known celebration of the abolishment of slavery.

Juneteenth (June 19)

RACE TO FREEDOM GAME

Play this fast-paced game at your Juneteenth picnic.

What You'll Need: Poster board, markers, corncobs, spoons, paper plates

Make a big sign from poster board, and write the word "Freedom" on it. Place it 50 to 100 yards away from the start of the race. Divide players into 2 teams. Players from both teams wait at 10 to 20 yard intervals on the course between the starting line and "Freedom." The first player skates on 2 paper plates while balancing a corncob on a spoon. When this player reaches the next player, he or she hands the skates, corncob, and spoon to the next player on the course, and so on until the final player makes it to "Freedom." If the corncob falls off the spoon at any time, that player must return to the beginning, and his or her team starts again. Whichever team reaches "Freedom" first wins the game!

Juneteenth (June 19)

FREE-FORM FREEDOM RAP

Write a rap song to celebrate Freedom.

What You'll Need: Paper, pencil, wooden blocks

Freedom is something to sing about! Write a rhyming poem, and make up your own freedom rap song. Brainstorm a list of words and ideas that remind you of freedom and the holiday of Juneteenth. Then think of words that rhyme with this list. For example, June and moon, free and honeybee, nineteen and keen. Write rhyming sentences that use these words, such as: "One fine June, I saw a beautiful moon. The date was June nineteen, and it sure was keen. Because now I am free, just like the honeybee!" When you finish your rhyme, clap out a rhythm with wooden blocks, and say it like a rap. Teach it to a friend, and make up a dance to go with it!

205

Juneteenth (June 19)

GODDESS OF LIBERTY CROWN

Be the Goddess of Liberty at the Juneteenth Parade!

What You'll Need: Construction paper, scissors, glue, stapler, markers

A typical Juneteenth parade often has a queen called the Goddess of Liberty. What does she look like? You decide! Make a crown that shows how wonderful it is to be free. Cut out a 10-inch-high piece of construction paper that will be long enough to fit around your head plus a few inches to staple it closed. Cut long, pointed triangle shapes in the long end of the paper to make a crown shape. Cut 2 different-colored pieces of construction paper the same length and with the same pointed triangle shapes at the top. One piece should be 8 inches high, and the other should be 6 inches high. Glue each piece onto the next largest piece, and staple all the ends together. Now you have a beautiful layered crown. Use markers to write Goddess of Liberty on your crown. Decorate it with pretty designs. Put it on your head, and march proudly in the next Juneteenth parade!

GODDESS OF LIBERTY

A TALL LADY

The statue on top of the Capitol Dome in Texas is called the Goddess of Liberty. She holds a sword in her right hand and a gilded star in her left, which she holds up to the sky. The Goddess stands 15 feet, 7 inches tall, which makes the Texas Capitol taller than the U.S. Capitol.

206

Juneteenth (June 19)

FREEDOM FLAG

Wave the flag of freedom high!

What You'll Need: 24 × 18-inch piece of heavy cotton or canvas, glue, stapler, 36-inch length of ½-inch dowel, yarn or ribbons, scissors, felt or fabric scraps, fabric paint, paintbrushes

This flag will look great waving in the Juneteenth parade. To make it, glue or staple the short edge of the fabric to a wooden dowel. Leave 2 inches of dowel showing at the top to tie on yarn or ribbon streamers. The rest of the dowel will be your flag's handle. Decorate your flag by cutting the word "Freedom" out of felt or fabric scraps and gluing them onto the canvas. Paint designs around the word with fabric paint. You might want to draw President Lincoln or the state of Texas on your flag. Think of what Juneteenth means to you and what pictures you can draw to show your feelings. Then wave your flag with pride as you march down the street.

Just like having turkey at Thanksgiving, people celebrating Juneteenth want to eat certain special foods to remind them of their holiday. Barbequing became popular because the smell from the grill reminded people of what their ancestors ate. Also, a custom beverage they drink is strawberry soda pop.

Juneteenth (June 19)

PACK OF LOG SANDWICHES

Make your own picnic basket, and fill it with peanutty sandwiches shaped like logs.

What You'll Need: 2 cereal boxes, scissors, tape, gift wrap, construction paper, glue, yarn, stapler, whole wheat bread (pre-sliced), rolling pin, peanut butter, butter knife, plastic wrap, napkins

It's a beautiful day, and everyone has decided to celebrate Juneteenth with a traditional picnic! To make the picnic basket, take out the inner bags of the cereal boxes, and cut a side panel from each box. Cut off the top flaps from both boxes. Slide one box halfway inside the other. Tape the boxes together where they meet. Cover the boxes with wrapping paper. Glue on cut-out designs such as stars, the word Juneteenth, and the number 19. Staple a length of yarn across the top of the basket to make a handle. To make a log sandwich, flatten a slice of whole wheat bread with a rolling pin. Spread the slice with peanut butter and roll it up into a cylinder shape. Wrap your "logs" in plastic wrap, and stack them inside your picnic basket. Don't forget the napkins!

A STATE HOLIDAY

Al Edwards, a Texas African American state legislator, worked to have Juneteenth declared a state holiday, which happened on January 1, 1980. Many people are working on getting the holiday celebrated in more places than just Texas—in fact, the Smithsonian and the Henry Ford Museum have annual celebrations!

208

Summer Solstice

SUN BREAD

Celebrate the sun with a sunny treat!

What You'll Need: 2 tablespoons margarine, 1 cup maple syrup, 1 egg, ¾ cup orange juice, 2 tablespoons grated orange rind, 1 tablespoon baking powder, ½ teaspoon salt, 2 cups whole wheat flour, 1 cup sunflower seeds, loaf pan, electric mixer, 2 mixing bowls, mixing spoon

To make this delicious bread, ask an adult to preheat the oven to 325 degrees. Beat the margarine, maple syrup, and egg for 1 minute at medium speed. Mix the other ingredients together in a separate bowl. Add the dry ingredients to the wet ones, and mix with a spoon until smooth. Pour the batter into a greased loaf pan and bake for 1 hour. Let the bread cool for about 15 minutes, then remove it from the pan to finish cooling. Gently press more sunflower seeds onto the top of your bread to make a sunflower design. Serve with peanut butter or jam, and don't forget to wear your sunglasses while you eat!

209

Summer Solstice

FLAME-JUMPING CONTEST

Play this old-fashioned game, and try not to get "burned"!

What You'll Need: Scissors, ruler, pencil, markers, corrugated cardboard, clothespins, masking tape

This is a popular Midsummer's Eve game. Draw and cut out a cardboard flame 15 inches high by 10 inches wide. Decorate the flame with markers. Cut out and decorate another piece of cardboard that is 20 inches square. Fold this piece in half to make a stand 10 inches high. To play the game, fasten the cardboard flame with clothespins to the cardboard stand. Start by pinning the flame so that its bottom is level with the bottom of the stand. Each player must then jump over it without knocking it over or touching it and getting "burned." Each time all the players have successfully leapt over the flame, the flame is repinned an inch higher. How high can you jump? If this flame game is too easy for you, make a taller flame!

Summer Solstice

210 CLOWNY CONES

These cool, sweet clowns bring the circus right to your summer solstice party.

What You'll Need: Paper doily, paper plate, ice cream, ice cream scooper, gum drops, chocolate chips, round hard candies, sugar ice cream cone

For each clown, put a paper doily on a small paper plate. Place a scoop of ice cream on top of the doily. Use gum drops or chocolate chips for the clown's eyes and nose. Carefully break a round hard candy in half for a smiling mouth. You can also use the whole candy if you want your clown to look surprised. You can use 2 more round candy halves for eyebrows. Give your clown a sugar cone hat with a gumdrop stuck on the tip. Keep your clowns in the freezer until you are ready to serve them. Your party guests will be laughing all the way to the table!

JUST DEWY DEAR

In Lithuania, the summer solstice celebration is called Rasa, which means dew. In the region of Svencionis, young women would get up early and wash with the dew on the grass. They would then go back to sleep to dream of their future mate!

211

Summer Solstice

SCULPTURES OF ICE

Here's a fun way to make your own sculpture and cool off at the same time!

What You'll Need: Empty plastic containers or milk cartons, water, food coloring, garbage bags

Add a few drops of food coloring to water that you have put into empty plastic containers or milk cartons. Freeze overnight. The next day, spread large garbage bags on a picnic table (in the shade!), and put a frozen container on each. Peel off or have an adult cut away the containers. Now you are ready to sculpt. Use your hands and your mouth to make wild and crazy shapes. Even the family dog might enjoy cooling off while licking one of these ice sculptures!

Summer Solstice

FUZZY FLOWERS

These flowers don't ever need watering—and they'll remind you of summer long after the solstice has passed!

What You'll Need: Heavy worsted yarn in different colors, rolling pin or dowel at least 2 inches in diameter, scissors, chenille stems, ribbon

These pinwheel-shaped flowers are cozy and soft. To make one, lay a piece of yarn (about 4 inches long) straight along the length of the dowel or rolling pin. Next, wind another piece of yarn around the dowel and the first piece of yarn about 30 times. Tie the ends of the 4-inch piece of yarn together—which will hold the wound yarn together. Slide the yarn off the dowel. Now you have a round yarn flower! To make a stem for your flower, bend the end of a chenille stem and hook it into the flower and twist the end. Make a bunch of these fuzzy flowers, and tie them together with a ribbon or put them in a vase to make a fantastic, fuzzy bouquet!

213

Summer Solstice

ICY ANIMAL WAGON

Hurry up and eat this wagon before it melts in all that sunshine!

What You'll Need: Brick of Neapolitan ice cream, knife, round chocolate mints, animal crackers, small plastic figures of animals

A wagon made of ice cream? Why not? This is another cool treat for a long, hot summer day. Cut a square of Neapolitan ice cream. Use 4 round mints for the wheels, and put 2 animal cracker elephants or horses at the front to pull the wagon. You can add other small plastic animals to ride on top of the ice cream wagon (but be sure people know these are not to be eaten!). This makes a cheerful centerpiece, but don't wait too long to eat it!

Summer Solstice

IF IT RAINS GAME

Whatever the weather, you'll be ready to play!

What You'll Need: Rubber-tipped child's umbrella, Ping-Pong balls

Don't worry if the sun is hiding on summer solstice—you can still invite your friends over for a great time. If it rains, that just means there will be lots of umbrellas around to play this fun game. All you need is an open umbrella, set upside down on a bare floor. A carpeted area will not work for this game. Each player is given a Ping-Pong ball and must stand 5 feet from the umbrella. One at a time, players try to bounce their ball once before it lands in the umbrella. A player scores 1 point for each ball that stays without bouncing out again. Be sure to use an umbrella with rubber-tipped spines so no one gets poked!

Summer Solstice

MUD PEOPLE

Have some earthy summer fun!

What You'll Need: Old clothes, dirt, pail of water, small spade, leaves, twigs, pebbles, flower tops

On a sunny day, put on your oldest clothes that you are allowed to get dirty. Grab a pail of water and a spade, and head for a place where it is okay to dig. A great way to celebrate the longest day of summer is to make some friends to join in the fun. Your new friends will be made of mud, but that won't be a problem—until it rains! Dig up a nice pile of earth, and add enough water to make clay. Roll balls to make heads, and roll out longer shapes to make bodies. Give your mud people arms and legs made of stiff leaf stems or tiny twigs. You can add flower tops for hair, and stick on bits of leaves and grass for clothes. Find tiny pebbles to use for eyes and noses. Line up your mud people in a circle and pick a bunch of wildflowers to put in the center. Before heading back to the house, make sure you clean up so all that nice summer mud stays outside where it belongs!

Father's Day

MOUSE MITT

Protect Dad's mouse from dust—and cats!

What You'll Need: Felt, scissors, stapler, glue

Ask your Mom for permission to make a cover for Dad's computer mouse. To make your Mouse Mitt, place the computer mouse on a piece of felt that is Dad's favorite color. Draw a large computer mouse shape around it. Make your shape about twice the size of the real computer mouse. Cut out the shape, and then cut another one from a second piece of felt that is Dad's other favorite color. Put the computer mouse between the 2 pieces and staple all the sides together except for the one with the mouse's "tail" (computer cord) poking out. Now cut out shapes from felt to glue onto your Mouse Mitt. You can cut out the word "Dad" or make the face of an animal. Now Dad's mouse won't get dirty (or run away) while it's waiting for him to use it!

217

Father's Day

MINI GOLF

If your dad is a golfer, he'll love having his own golf course!

What You'll Need: Long stick, new sponge, colored tape, empty juice cans, paint, paintbrushes, oatmeal containers, scissors, shoe boxes, hula hoop, sand, corrugated cardboard, blocks, foil pie plates, small rocks, golf ball

The only limit to the challenge of this golf course is your imagination. You can make the course inside or outside your house. Generally, there are either 9 or 18 holes in a course, but make yours as large as you have space for. To make a golf club, attach a new sponge with colored tape to the end of a long stick. To make the course, you will want to set up obstacles before each of the holes. To make a hole, lay a small empty can on its side. Paint the can, and write the number of the hole on it. You can make the obstacles in lots of different ways. For example, a tunnel can be made by cutting the bottoms from lidless oatmeal containers and taping them together. Turn a shoe box upside down, and cut an arch on either side of it big enough for the golf ball to pass through. If you are outdoors, you can pour sand inside a hula hoop to make a sand trap. Make tents of corrugated cardboard and build towers from blocks. Set up foil pie plates in a daisy pattern with just enough room for a golf ball to pass through the petals. Use small rocks to hold things down if you are outdoors and it is a windy day. Keep score to see how many strokes it takes to get your golf ball in each of the holes. Challenge Dad to get a birdie—or a hole in one!

218

Father's Day

DAD SNACK

Even dads like a snack now and then!

What You'll Need: Unsweetened dry cereal, pretzel sticks, mixed nuts, goldfish or small rice crackers, seasoning salt, garlic salt, Worcestershire sauce, margarine, oil, bowl, spoon, measuring cup and spoon, saucepan, baking sheet, saucepan, jar, stickers, ribbon

Make Dad a jar of delicious Dad Snack. It's easy and guaranteed to be a tasty hit. Just mix 1 box of cereal with handfuls of pretzel sticks, nuts, and small crackers. How much you use depends on how large your jar is. Add 1 tablespoon each of seasoning salt, garlic salt, and Worcestershire sauce. Add the seasonings a little at a time, tasting to make sure the mix is not too salty. Remember, you can always add more seasoning later. Have an adult help you with the stove. Melt ½ cup margarine with ½ cup oil in a saucepan over low heat. When the margarine melts, pour it over the cereal mixture. Then spread the mix on a baking sheet, and put it in the oven for 1½ hours at 250 degrees. Stir the mixture every 15 minutes or so. When the mix has cooled, fill a clean jar with it. Decorate the jar with stickers. Tie a ribbon around the jar's neck, and leave it beside Dad's favorite chair.

Father's Day

A HUG FOR YOU CARD

219

Give your dad a double hug—one for real and one he can carry around with him all day.

What You'll Need: Construction paper, scissors, markers, glue

Give Dad a card that is also a hug! To make the card, cut out a large plate-sized head shape and draw on hair and a face so that it looks like you. Cut out an 18 × 4-inch rectangle. This will be the arms. Glue the head to the middle of the arms. Now trace around your hands on a separate sheet of paper, and cut out the hand shapes. Glue a hand to the end of each arm. Fold the arms in so that the hands overlap. Inside the arms write a message for Dad, such as "Here is a big loving hug for you on Father's Day!"

Father's Day

BEST DAD BADGE

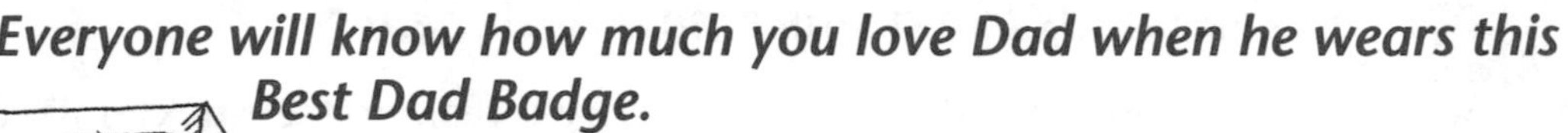

Everyone will know how much you love Dad when he wears this Best Dad Badge.

What You'll Need: Dried alphabet macaroni, stiff cardboard, scissors, paints, paintbrushes, glue, markers, large safety pin, tape

Alphabet noodles are fun to eat, and they are also great 3-dimensional letters to write things with. You can use them to write "Best Dad" or other messages on these easy-to-make Father's Day badges. Cut a 4 × 1-inch rectangle out of stiff cardboard. Paint one side, let it dry, then paint the other side. Glue the alphabet noodles to one side of the cardboard to spell out your message. You can use markers to color the noodles. When the glue dries, turn the cardboard over, and tape a large safety pin to the back (be sure the pin can be opened before you tape it down). Pin the badge to a dad-sized T-shirt, and place it somewhere Dad will find it. Bet he gives you a big Best Dad smile!

Father's Day

I LOVE DAD GAME

Watch Dad's smile grow bigger and bigger as this game goes on and on.

What You'll Need: Dictionary (optional)

Here's a game that's also like a show—just for Dad. Gather your family members together. Dad will be the audience. The first player says, "I love Dad with an A because he is so Athletic" (or whatever nice thing you want to say about Dad that starts with A). The next player repeats what the first player says and then says, "I love Dad with a B because he is so Brave" (or another word that starts with a B). Players keep repeating what has already been said and adding to it until they have gone all the way to Z. (When you get to the letter X, you can cheat a little and say something like "because he is so X-tra great"). You might want to have a dictionary handy, just in case. This will surely be one of the best shows Dad has ever seen!

Father's Day

222 ALL ABOUT DAD POSTER

Dad will be so surprised to find out how much you know about him.

What You'll Need: Construction paper, scissors, markers, cardboard, gold or silver foil, ribbon, glue, snapshots, old magazines and catalogs, poster board

There's an old saying about gifts: It's the thought that counts. Well, to make this gift you are sure to be thinking a lot about Dad. What do you know about him? Is he funny? Serious? Loving? Do you remember times when he did something really nice or brave? Did he scare away a bear from a family picnic? Did he rescue a kitten from a tree? Does he make delicious pancakes for Sunday breakfast? Think of all the things you love about your dad, and write them down on pieces of colored paper cut into different shapes. Make medals by covering cardboard circles with foil and gluing ribbon to the back. Cut out a smaller circle of paper to glue on the foil and write what the medal is for, such as "Best Hugger" or "Best Gardener." Gather up extra snapshots of Dad, or ask an adult to make photocopies of them. Cut out pictures of Dad's favorite things from old magazines or catalogs. Draw pictures of the 2 of you together, having a good time. When you have gathered or made all the things you want to put on your poster, lay them out in different arrangements on your poster board. After you find a pattern you like, glue the pieces down and write the words "ALL ABOUT DAD" at the top. Add the date and your own message to Dad in one of the bottom corners, such as "Happy Father's Day!"

DAD GETS HIS DAY!

Father's Day took much longer to become a national holiday than Mother's Day, though people began celebrating them about the same time. It wasn't until 1956 that the U.S. Congress recognized Father's Day, and not until 1966 that President Lyndon Johnson signed a presidential proclamation declaring the third Sunday in June as Father's Day. President Richard Nixon, in 1972, established the national holiday.

223

Father's Day

DAD'S SHADOW PICTURE

Have Dad sit for this special silhouette portrait.

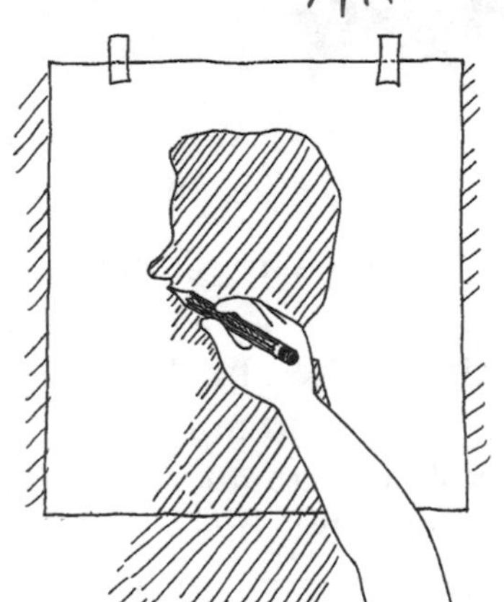

What You'll Need: Large white paper, tape, clip light, pencil, scissors, large black paper

There is something magical and mysterious about a silhouette. It's like a shadow you can keep forever. Tell Dad you are going to give him his shadow for a Father's Day present. He won't believe it, but you can assure him that what you say is true. Attach a large piece of white paper to a wall. Place a chair several feet away from it. Invite Dad to sit in the chair so that you have a side view of his face. Turn off the lights in the room, and shine the clip light on Dad so that the shadow of his profile falls onto the white paper. Now trace around the shadow. When you finish, cut out the outline of Dad's shadow and lay it on a piece of black paper. Then cut out the shape from the black paper to give Dad his shadow!

Father's Day

GIANT DAD COOKIES

224

Make Dad's day a little sweeter with these cookies painted with love.

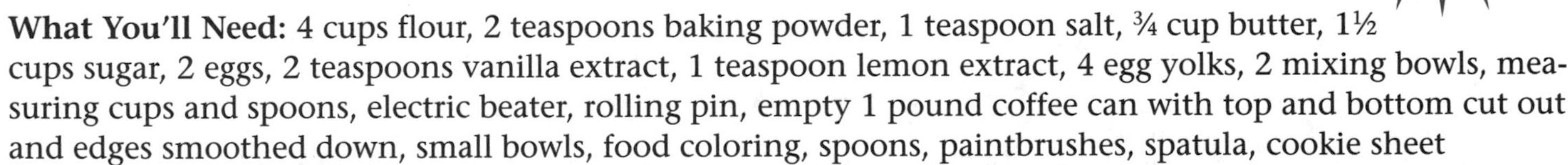

What You'll Need: 4 cups flour, 2 teaspoons baking powder, 1 teaspoon salt, ¾ cup butter, 1½ cups sugar, 2 eggs, 2 teaspoons vanilla extract, 1 teaspoon lemon extract, 4 egg yolks, 2 mixing bowls, measuring cups and spoons, electric beater, rolling pin, empty 1 pound coffee can with top and bottom cut out and edges smoothed down, small bowls, food coloring, spoons, paintbrushes, spatula, cookie sheet

Have an adult help you preheat the oven to 375 degrees. Mix together the flour, baking powder, and salt. In another bowl, cream the butter and sugar together with an electric beater until it is fluffy. Add the flour mixture a little at a time, and stir until everything is well blended. Roll out the dough on a clean counter. Use a coffee can to cut out large circles—make sure an adult has smoothed down the edges of the can so you don't cut yourself. To make the cookie paint, put an egg yolk in a small bowl with a few drops of food coloring. Stir until well mixed. For each color you want, you will need another egg yolk in a separate bowl. Now write sweet messages and paint pictures on your giant cookies. Write things such as "I Love My Dad," "Best Dad," and "My Dad Is Great!" Then carefully lift the cookies with a spatula and bake them on a cookie sheet for about 10 minutes or until they are just slightly brown. When the cookies have cooled, serve Dad a sweet message on his special day.

225

Father's Day

HAPPY FAMILY DOLLS

These dolls always land on their feet!

What You'll Need: Small rubber ball, craft knife, plaster of Paris, disposable container, construction paper, markers, scissors, tape, glue

Ask an adult to cut the ball in half to form 2 bowl shapes. Prepare the plaster of Paris in the disposable container according to the package instructions. Pour plaster into each ball half, and let it harden. (Dispose of unused plaster of Paris in the trash!) While you are waiting, draw and cut out 2 faces from construction paper. Make 1 face to look like your Dad and 1 face to look like you. Make 2 paper cones (choose colors that will contrast with the faces) to fit on top of the rubber balls—they will look like upside-down ice cream cones. Close the cones with tape, and glue them onto each half of the rubber balls. Glue a face onto each of the cones. These happy dolls are made like a Japanese folk toy called the *daruma*. "Wishing" darumas are made without eyes. If you want, don't draw eyes on your Dad's doll right away. Have your Dad make a wish, and then draw one eye. When his wish comes true, he can draw on the other eye. In the meantime, just have fun playing with your happy dolls.

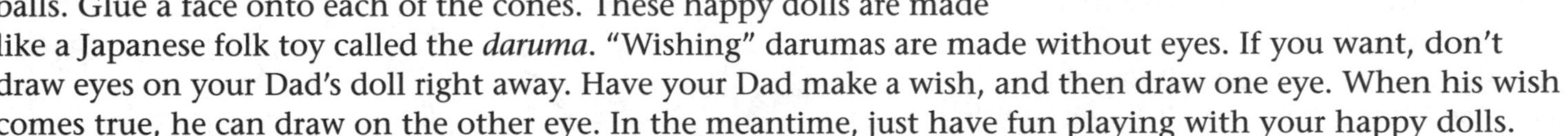

DAD'S FLOWERS

The official flower for Father's Day is either a white or red rose. The white rose honors a father who is deceased; a red rose is for a father who is living.

226

Father's Day

GREATEST DAD STATUE

Dad will get a big kick out of seeing a statue of himself right in your own yard!

What You'll Need: Full-length photo of Dad, scissors, pencil, thin cardboard, glue, thin wooden skewer, tape, plaster of Paris, water, bowl, empty container 6 to 8 inches high, paints, paintbrushes, small towel

Find a full-length photograph of your dad, and cut it out. Lay it on thin cardboard. Trace around the figure, cut out the shape, and glue the photo and cardboard together. Tape the figure to a wooden skewer. Mix 2 parts plaster of Paris to 1 part water in a plastic bowl. Pour the mixture into an empty plastic or cardboard container. When the mixture reaches the top of the container, smooth it flat with a piece of cardboard. Poke the wooden skewer into the center of the plaster of Paris mixture. In about an hour, the plaster should be dry. Then remove the container. Paint the base of the statue, and write "Greatest Dad" on it. Erect your statue in the backyard, and invite Dad out to the big unveiling! (Throw unused plaster of Paris into the trash. Never pour it down a drain—it will clog it!) If it rains, don't forget to bring your statue inside!

LET'S HONOR DADS!

Father's Day began when Sonora Smart Dodd, of Spokane, Washington, wanted to honor her father. Her father raised her, along with her five brothers and sisters, after her mother died. Dodd proposed the idea in 1909, and she wanted Father's Day to be celebrated around his birthday, June 19.

227

Father's Day

BOTTLE FISHING GAME

Even if you live in the middle of the desert, you can still go fishing!

What You'll Need: Long wooden stick, paint, paintbrush, string, scissors, small plastic lid, colored tape, clear plastic soda bottle, markers, water, blue food coloring

Offer to take Dad fishing on Father's Day—right in your own backyard. To make a fishing rod, paint a long, thin wooden stick or branch, and tie a 24-inch piece of string to one end. Cut out the middle of a small plastic lid (a pint-sized yogurt container works great) until just the outer ring is left. Cover the ring with colored tape, and tie it onto the free end of your string. (You could make 2 rods—one for you and one for your dad!) Use more colored tape to decorate a few large plastic soda bottles. Cut out fish shapes and other sea creatures to put on them. Use markers to color in their faces. When you are done decorating the bottles, fill them with water and a few drops of blue food coloring. When you are ready to go fishing with Dad, tell him to keep one hand behind his back while he tries to fit the plastic ring over a bottle's neck. You and Dad might also want to each put one hand on the fishing rod to see how many fish the 2 of you can catch together!

SHOCKING COMMUNICATIONS

The Elephant Nose fish communicates with other fish of its kind by sending electrical pulses through the water. The fish is from Africa, and it grows to about 10 inches long.

228

Father's Day

PAPER CUP RACE

Make this homemade paper cup race game and play it with Dad on his day.

What You'll Need: Large cardboard box, scissors, paints, paintbrushes, paper cups, table, tape, string

This game will get you breathing hard! Remove the top of a large cardboard box. Paint the box lots of bright colors, and write the words "Happy Father's Day" on the bottom of the inside. Let the paint dry. Poke a hole in the bottom of 2 paper cups. Paint the cups or use some that have colorful designs already on them. Set the box on its side on a table. Make sure that the open end is several inches away from the edge of the table. Tape a length of string to the top of the left side of the box. The string should be long enough so that it reaches the table edge. Thread a paper cup onto the string, with the open part facing you. Tape the other end of the string to the table edge. Repeat with another string and paper cup on the top of the right side of the box. Now you are ready to race with Dad! The paper cups should be resting on the table edge with the openings facing you. At the count of 3, blow into the cups and see who can make their cup reach the top of the box first. Is Dad winning? Well, that's what Father's Day is all about!

Canada Day (July 12)

RED AND WHITE GAME

229

This is a good memory game—once you play, you'll always remember the colors of Canada!

What You'll Need: Pencils, paper, timer, Canadian flag (optional)

You can play this game with a big group or just 2 people. Hang up a big red and white Canadian flag to get everyone in the mood. Then have all the players make a list of all the red or white things they can think of in 5 minutes. It can be anything as long as it is mostly red or white or both. Each player reads her or his list aloud and by crosses off items that everyone else has listed (everyone has to cross them off, too). One point is gained for things that another player has listed (as long as it's not on everyone's list). 2 points are gained for things no one else has listed. The player with the most points wins the game.

Canada Day (July 1)

230 MAPLE LEAF TOSS

Here's a great way to use all those unmatched socks!

What You'll Need: Large cardboard box, red and white paint, paintbrush, red and white socks, sand, red fabric paint

To make the game, first decorate a big cardboard box to look like the Canadian flag. Gather up all the unmatched white or red socks that you can find, and fill them with sand. Tie the end of the sock securely. If you only have white socks, you can paint a red maple leaf on some. To start the game, players stand 5 feet away from the box and toss the socks in. Players score 1 point for each white sock and 2 points for each red sock that they get into the box without tipping it over. After each turn, players move back 1 foot. Keep playing until someone reaches 50 points. This is an outdoor game—Mom and Dad won't appreciate sand in the house!

Independence Day (July 4)

INDEPENDENT NOSES 231

Be as nosey as you like when you play this game!

What You'll Need: Old white bed sheet, scissors, red and blue nontoxic face paints

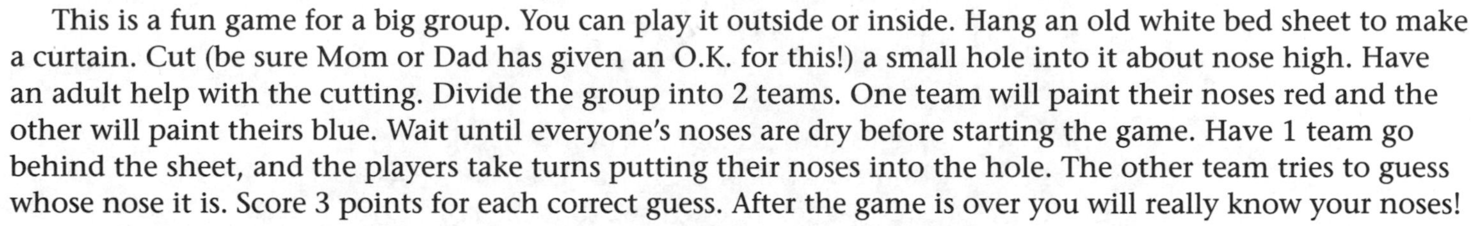

This is a fun game for a big group. You can play it outside or inside. Hang an old white bed sheet to make a curtain. Cut (be sure Mom or Dad has given an O.K. for this!) a small hole into it about nose high. Have an adult help with the cutting. Divide the group into 2 teams. One team will paint their noses red and the other will paint theirs blue. Wait until everyone's noses are dry before starting the game. Have 1 team go behind the sheet, and the players take turns putting their noses into the hole. The other team tries to guess whose nose it is. Score 3 points for each correct guess. After the game is over you will really know your noses!

232

Independence Day (July 4)

FLAG WINDSOCK

You'll feel free as the breeze when you catch the wind in this decorative windsock.

What You'll Need: Tissue paper, scissors, glue stick, large plastic dry-cleaner's bag, plastic-coated hangers or thick wire, tape, pole, ribbons (optional)

This windsock will be tons of fun to play with at your July 4th picnic. It looks pretty, too! To make it, cut out a large square of blue tissue paper. Draw and cut out white tissue-paper stars, and glue them to the blue background. Glue this onto a plastic dry-cleaner's bag. Cut out red and white tissue paper stripes, and glue these to the bag to make the American flag. Make a large hoop from a plastic-coated hanger or thick wire. Have an adult help you with this. Fold about 2 inches of the bag over the loop and tape it. Attach the windsock to a pole with loose wire loops so your windsock can change direction in the wind. Tie long red, white, and blue ribbons to the top of the pole to make streamers if you'd like. This windsock works best on a breezy day, but if you run with it, the bag will fill with air and float as you create your own wind. (Keep plastic bags away from small children—plastic is a choking hazard!)

Sign on the Dotted Line

Only 2 people signed the Declaration of Independence on July 4: John Hancock and Charles Thomson. Most of the rest signed on August 2, but the last signature wasn't added until 5 years later.

233

Independence Day (July 4)

WATERMELON SLUSH

This cool and refreshing drink is as fun to make as it is to drink!

What You'll Need: 8 ice cubes, 2 cups seedless watermelon, 1 teaspoon honey, blender, spoon, measuring cup and spoon, glasses, marshmallows, blueberries, toothpicks

The sun is hot, and everyone is extra thirsty. A nice juicy slice of watermelon would taste great, but why not take that watermelon and try something new? Put the ice cubes in a blender, and turn it on high. Have an adult help you get the ice thoroughly crushed by turning the blender off and mixing the ice with a spoon before turning it on again. Add chunks of watermelon. Make sure you have taken out all the seeds. Add the honey, and blend well. Pour into tall glasses that you have chilled in the freezer. Garnish each drink with a marshmallow sandwiched between 2 blueberries on a toothpick. Lay the toothpick across the rim.

FIGHT FOR INDEPENDENCE GAME

234

Even bad weather can't spoil the fun of this game.

What You'll Need: Thick cardboard, ruler, pencil, paint, paintbrushes, thin cardboard, scissors

Here's a great 2-person game for a rainy day. To make the game board, cut a piece of thick cardboard into a 20 × 20-inch square. Mark off 25 squares, 5 across and 5 down, so that the board looks like a checkerboard. Paint the squares different colors. Then draw and cut 20 thin cardboard circles a little smaller than the size of a square. Paint 10 markers blue with a white star, and paint 10 markers white with a red cross. The blue markers will represent the United States (1 player) and the red will represent Great Britain (the other player). Players line up their markers in 2 rows closest to them. Each player takes a turn moving 1 marker at a time. Markers can move forward, backward, and diagonally, but only to an empty square. If a player's marker is fenced in so it cannot move, the other player gets 5 points. The first player to get all their markers into the other player's 2 rows wins 10 points. Play until someone gets 50 points.

Independence Day (July 4)

235 FLYING HIGH ROCKET

Launch a patriotic rocket in your own backyard!

What You'll Need: Plastic drinking straws; scissors; long red, white, and blue balloons; rubber bands; paper; markers; pencil

This balloon rocket will fly high up in the air just like fireworks. To make it, cut a straw in half. Fold the tip of one straw and insert it into the end of the other until it is all the way inside. Slide the neck of a balloon over 1 end of your double straw, and secure it with a rubber band. Cut a 3-inch square piece of paper, and fold it in half. This will be your rocket's fin, which you can decorate with patriotic designs. Use a pencil to poke a hole through the middle of the fin, and slide it over the double straw. To make your rocket fly, hold the rubber band around the balloon's neck and blow through the straw. When the balloon is full, let your rocket go! Make sure that no one is in the way before you let go. Your rocket should fly high. Experiment with different shapes and sizes of rocket fins. The fin controls the rocket's path. Get your friends together for some high-flying fun! (Balloons are choking hazards—keep them away from small children!)

THE FATHER OF ROCKETS

Robert Goddard, born in 1882, forecasted that rockets would one day go to the Moon—but the press in his day ridiculed him. He launched the world's first liquid-fuel rocket in 1926. When he died in 1945, he held over 200 patents about rockets!

Independence Day (July 4)

236 YANKEE DOODLE BELL GAME

Dress up as a Yankee Doodle Dandy, and try your skill at ringing the liberty bell!

What You'll Need: Paper bag, old newspapers, paints, paintbrushes, yarn, scissors, glue, old broomstick, tape, construction paper, bell with string attached, beanbag

Make Yankee Doodle's hobby horse by stuffing a paper bag with newspaper and painting on a face. Glue on yarn for the horse's mane, then tape the end of the bag around the broomstick. Fold a piece of construction paper into a tricornered cap, and draw and cut out a feather to stick in it. Then take turns being Yankee Doodle Dandy by wearing the hat while you ride the hobby horse. Tie the bell to the limb of a tree. As Yankee Doodle Dandy rides by, she or he must try to ring the bell by tossing a bean bag at it without stopping. Each Yankee Doodle Dandy gets 3 tries. You get 2 points each time you ring the bell. Whoever gets 10 points first wins the game.

WHICH STATE SONG?

"Yankee Doodle" is the official state song of Connecticut, which is also known as the Constitution State. One of the unofficial nicknames of the state is the Nutmeg State.

Independence Day (July 4)

237

PATRIOTIC WIGGLE STARS

These gelatin stars make a shimmering red, white, and blue holiday dessert.

What You'll Need: Packages of raspberry and blueberry gelatin, 2 mixing bowls, 2 glass baking pans, star cookie cutters, spatula, whipped cream, large serving platter

These colorful stars are almost too pretty to eat. Mix up separate batches of red and blue gelatin, and pour them into shallow baking pans. (Have an adult help you with the hot water.) Set the pans in the refrigerator for several hours until the gelatin is firm. Use a star-shaped cookie cutter to make stars, and gently lift the stars out of the pans with a spatula. Arrange the stars in alternating rows of red and blue stars on a large serving platter. Squirt a button of whipped cream in the center of each star. People say that the stars and stripes will last forever, but once everyone sees these stars, forever will be just a spoon away!

Independence Day (July 4)

UNITED STATES CELERY

Can a vegetable be patriotic? Do this experiment and find out!

What You'll Need: Celery stalks with white part attached, 3 glasses, water, red and blue food coloring, knife

Tell your friends that you know a vegetable that can celebrate Independence Day by turning the colors of the American flag. Ask an adult to help you make several slits in the lower part of 3 celery stalks (choose celery stalks that are not much taller than the glasses you are going to use). Fill 3 glasses with water. Put a few drops of red food coloring in the first glass, a few drops of blue in the second, and leave the third glass clear. Place a stalk of celery into each of the glasses. One celery stalk will turn red, 1 will turn blue, and 1 will remain white (choose one of the center, light-colored stalks to put in this glass). When you're done with the experiment, you can have an all-American snack!

239

Independence Day (July 4)

PATRIOTIC EYEGLASSES

You'll have perfect red-and-blue vision when you wear these fancy eyeglasses.

What You'll Need: Ruler, thin white cardboard, pencil, scissors, red and blue cellophane, glue, red and blue markers, white chenille stems, glitter glue

Can't decide what to wear for your July 4 party? How about a pair of red, white, and blue eyeglasses? Make enough for the whole family for an insightfully good time! Measure the width of your face, and cut out a cardboard rectangle a little longer than that. Your rectangle should be at least 2 inches deep. Your glasses can be any shape you want—circles, squares, triangles, or big Independence Day stars. Draw 2 eye holes on the glasses and cut them out. Cut out a piece of red and a piece of blue cellophane a little larger than each eye hole. Glue a piece of cellophane over the inside of each eye hole to make the colored lenses. Next, poke a small hole at either end of the eyeglasses, and fasten a chenille stem in each. Hook the free ends of the stems over your ears. Use red and blue markers to decorate your eyeglass frames. Use glitter glue for sparkly fireworks. These eyeglasses are guaranteed to be a real blast!

ROCKET'S RED GLARE

Although Francis Scott Key wrote "The Star Spangled Banner" in 1814, it did not become the official anthem of the United States until 1931. By then, the Army and the Navy had already adopted it.

240

Independence Day (July 4)

Won't everyone be surprised when they see the Statue of Liberty marching down their street?

What You'll Need: Green yarn, green headband, green poster board, stapler, brown construction paper, tape, cotton, orange spray paint, glue, nontoxic green face paint, green bedsheet, sandals, green notebook

In 1886, the country of France gave the United States a beautiful lady as a gift. This beautiful lady, the Statue of Liberty, was the first thing millions of immigrants saw on their way to a new life of freedom as their ships came into the New York harbor. Dress up like the Statue of Liberty and celebrate the joys of independence. Make a long green wig from yarn held in place by a green headband. Make a crown (the base should be long enough to go around your head) out of green poster board, staple the ends, and tuck the base of the crown into the headband to hold it more tightly in place. Roll brown construction paper into a cone and tape it in place for a torch. Have an adult help you spray paint the cotton orange, and glue it to the top of the torch. Paint your face and arms with nontoxic green face paint. Wrap a green bedsheet around you like a sari or a toga, pull on a pair of sandals, grab a green notebook to use as a stone tablet (the original tablet is inscribed with the Declaration of Independence), and march down the street holding your torch high!

The Statue of Liberty was given to the United States by France in 1886 to celebrate America's 100 years of independence. Gustave Eiffel built the iron framework for the structure, and sculptor Frederic-Auguste Bartholdi molded 452 sheets of copper onto the frame.

Independence Day (July 4)

RED, WHITE, AND BLUE BUGS

You won't mind having these cute bugs at your Independence Day picnic.

What You'll Need: Peanuts in the shell; red, white, and blue paint; paintbrushes; wiggle eyes; dried maple seeds; glue; hairpins; wire cutters; hat pins

These patriotic bugs can sit at your Independence Day picnic table without bugging anyone. To make the body, paint a whole peanut shell red, white, and blue. Glue on 2 wiggle eyes and 2 dried maple seeds for the wings. (If you don't have maple seeds, cut wings from construction paper.) Ask an adult to cut hairpins in half to make 6 legs. Bend the ends of the hairpins to make feet. Then poke the legs into the sides of the peanut body. Carefully poke 2 hat pins into the bug's head for its antennae. Make a whole line of bugs leading up to a big cake centerpiece!

Bastille Day (July 14)

CRÊPES BASTILLE 242

Oo la la! What a delicious treat!

What You'll Need: 1 cup flour, 1 tablespoon sugar, ¼ teaspoon salt, 1 cup milk, ⅓ cup water, 3 eggs, 3 tablespoons melted butter, raspberry and blueberry preserves, powdered sugar, electric beater, nonstick skillet

Before the French Revolution, the colors of the French flag were white and blue. After the revolution, the flag's colors were changed to red, blue, and white. These crepes will remind everyone how sweet freedom can be! Have an adult help you make these light, sweet pancakes—especially with the cooking. Mix the flour, sugar, and salt. Add the milk, water, eggs, and butter. Mix with an electric beater until smooth. Heat a heavy nonstick skillet until it is very hot. Pour in a few tablespoons of the batter, then quickly tilt the pan so that the batter is evenly spread. Cook about 30 seconds until the crepe is light brown, then flip and cook another 20 seconds. Fill each crepe with raspberry and blueberry preserves, then roll them up. Sprinkle with powdered sugar, and enjoy!

Bastille Day (July 14)

243 STEAL THE BASTILLE GAME

Have great fun playing a game while collecting money for children in need!

What You'll Need: Large heavy drawing paper, markers, 2 rubber bands, large outdoor play area, red and blue bandannas (enough for each player to wear 1), pennies

The Bastille was a French prison that was dismantled in the first serious act of the French Revolution. To play a game of Steal the Bastille, have 2 teams each draw a large picture of the Bastille. A great place to play the game would be a large backyard or field with lots of trees and bushes to hide behind. Before beginning play, the players on 1 team tie red bandannas around their heads. The other team's players tie blue bandannas around their heads. Each team stakes out a prison and a safe territory, which should be marked and shown to both teams. Clearly mark a dividing line between the 2 territories. Clearly mark outer boundaries, too. Outer boundaries are lines that cannot be crossed. Now each team should hide their Bastille picture somewhere on their territory by rolling it up and putting a rubber band around it. The picture may need to be weighted down with stones if it is a windy day. Once the game begins, players must try to find and steal each other's Bastille. If a player is tagged in the other team's territory, he or she is captured and must stay in prison until another of his team members finds and tags him. Once the Bastille picture is found, it must be torn up by the team that finds it and resold to the team it was stolen from for a penny a piece. (When the original Bastille was dismantled, the pieces were sold as souvenirs.) You can donate the pennies to UNICEF for children in need!

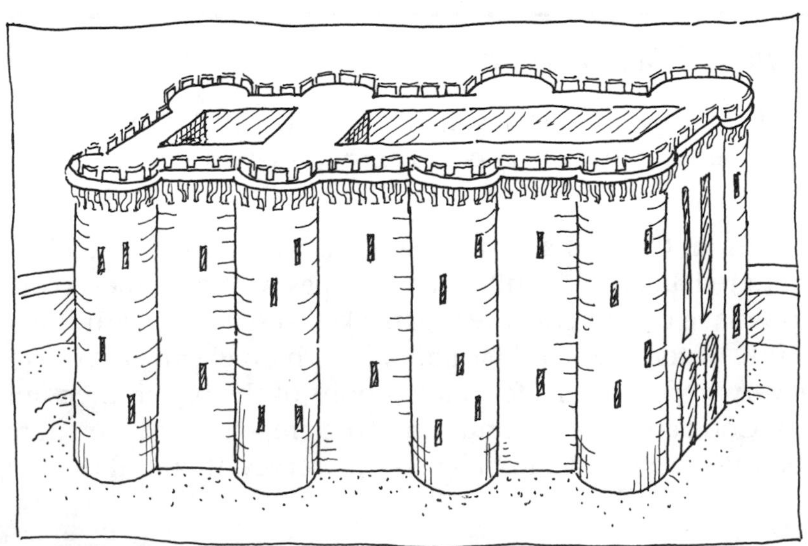

244

Ice Cream Day

PURPLE COW PARTY

Say a big thanks to all the cows at this special party.

What You'll Need: Construction paper, purple markers or crayons, purple balloons and streamers, purple nontoxic face paint, vanilla ice cream, ripe bananas, grape juice, blender, glasses

Make invitations for a purple cow party. Use a purple marker and draw lots of purple pictures on the invitations. Ask your guests to wear only purple clothes! Decorate your party room with purple balloons and streamers. When each guest arrives, paint their face with purple face paint. For each purple cow shake, put one scoop of vanilla ice cream, ½ ripe banana, and ¼ cup purple grape juice into a blender. Blend until all the ingredients are mixed, and pour it into a glass. Say the purple cow rhyme as you serve each shake: "I never saw a purple cow, I never hope to see one. But I can tell you, anyhow, I'd rather see than be one!"

Ice Cream Day

ICE CREAM CONE NECKLACE

245

Here's an ice cream cone you can wear!

What You'll Need: Box of sugar cones, clear varnish, disposable paintbrush, waxed paper, shoe box with lid, scissors, 2-inch craft foam balls, glue, staples, modeling paste, butter knife, paints, paintbrushes, embroidery thread

Paint sugar cones with varnish inside and out—have an adult help you, and do this in a well-ventilated area. Lay the cones on waxed paper to dry overnight. Cut 1-inch holes in the lid of a shoe box, and put the lid back onto the shoe box. This is the stand. The next day, run glue around the rims of the cones, and carefully press a foam ball onto each one. Put a tiny bit of glue onto the ends of staples and push one into the top of each ball. Make sure you leave a little room for the embroidery thread cord to pass easily underneath the staple. Put the cones into the stand until they are dry. Use a butter knife to swirl modeling paste over each foam ball. Make sure not to cover the staples. The modeling paste will make the balls look more like real ice cream. Put the cones back into the stand to dry. Paint the ice cream in the colors of your favorite flavors. When the paint is dry, thread embroidery thread through the staples to finish your ice cream necklace. These cones are guaranteed to make everybody scream for ice cream!

Moon Day (July 20)

246 MOON WALK

Use homemade foot paint to mark your "moon" jumps.

What You'll Need: ½ cup dry laundry starch, 2 cups cold water, saucepan, wooden spoon, ½ cup mild soap flakes, 1 tablespoon tempera paint, 2 large foil baking pans, long butcher paper, duct tape, measuring tape

When an astronaut takes a step on the moon, each step equals a distance of 6 feet! See how many "earth" steps it takes you to make a moon step. Stir the laundry starch and cold water together in a saucepan. Have an adult help you cook this over medium heat. Keep stirring the mixture until it is thick and shiny. Take the pan off the heat, and quickly stir in the soap flakes and paint. When the mix has cooled, pour it into the large foil baking pans that have been set outside. Tape a very long piece of butcher paper to your driveway with duct tape. Make sure that the foil pans are close to the paper. Take off your shoes and socks, and step into the pans. This paint will feel great between your toes, but don't forget to come out and jump onto the paper. Measure your footsteps to see how many equal a "moon" step. (Wash feet before going inside the house!)

Moon Day (July 20)

MOON ROCK RELAY 247

Step quickly on these moon rocks to race to the moon and back.

What You'll Need: Brown cardboard, scissors, black marker

Cut 6 large rock shapes out of cardboard, and color them with a black marker to look like moon rocks. Divide players into 2 teams. Mark the start of the racecourse with a cardboard sign that says "Earth." Place another sign that says "Moon" about 20 feet away. The first player on each team has to toss out 3 moon rocks and step on them, each time picking up the back rock and moving it forward to the Moon. The players can only move forward by stepping on the moon rocks. When the player reaches the Moon, she or he picks up the moon rocks, tosses them out again, and repeats the process to get back to Earth. When the first player gets safely back to Earth, it's time for the next player to go to the Moon and back. When all the astronauts on a team have gone to the Moon and come back, they are the winners.

Family Day

CHILDHOOD HOME

You'll always remember the place you grew up when you look at this homey model.

What You'll Need: Construction paper the color of your house, old home-decorating magazines and catalogs, glue, scissors, markers

Homes are the places that families create together. In the home, a family eats, sleeps, laughs, cries, and plays together. Memories are created there every day. To form a house, fold in the 2 sides of a large sheet of construction paper to meet at the middle, so that each side opens and closes. You might need to tape a few sheets together to get a piece that is large enough. Cut a triangle-shaped roof for your house, and glue it to the top of the flaps of the closed house. (If you live in an apartment building, you might not have a roof like this.) Then cut up from the bottom of the triangle to the point so that the roof will open and close with the flaps. Cut out and glue on a chimney as well. Use colors that match your actual house.

Find pictures of doors, windows, outside shrubbery and flowers, front steps, and other details in old home-decorating magazines. Cut these out and glue them to the outside of your house. Then open your house, and divide it into the number of rooms that are in your house. You might want to leave space for a staircase if you have more than one floor. Cut out furnishings from the home-decorating magazine, and glue them in the rooms they belong. Find rugs, beds, tables, chairs, curtains, and plants that look similar to things you have in your house. You can change the color of objects with markers. If you want, write the names of the people who live in your house in the different rooms. Or you might want to write a sentence or 2 telling what the people in the house are likely to do in each room. As you get older, you will always want to remember this special place where you shared so much with your loved ones.

249

Family Day

FAMILY SHOES GAME

The family can get to know one another better with this thoughtful game.

What You'll Need: Cardboard box large enough for 1 shoe of each family member, paints, paintbrushes, family members and their shoes, scarf

Here is the perfect activity for Family Day. In fact, your family may like it so much, it could be a weekly event. The day before Family Day, decorate a large cardboard box by painting it in bright colors. Each family member might want to contribute to part of the design. Let the box dry overnight. On Family Day, have each member put one of their shoes into the box. Use a scarf to blindfold family members one at a time, and have them reach into the box and pick out a shoe. If they pick their own shoe, they should put it back and try again. When everyone has picked someone else's shoe, they have to think of 3 nice surprises they can do for the shoe's owner on Family Day. Dad may like a helping hand around the house. Grandma may need help mowing her lawn!

Family Day

FAMILY PAPER DOLLS

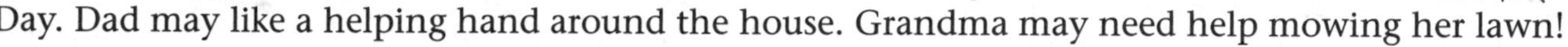

Make everyone in your family into a doll!

What You'll Need: Construction paper, pencil, scissors, family photographs, glue, markers, old wrapping paper

Surprise the whole family with a set of paper dolls that look just like them. Draw the head and body shape of each member of your family on construction paper that matches their skin tone. The dolls will probably be different sizes, just like the members of your family. Cut out the dolls. Find photographs of family members' heads that will be the right size for the cutout bodies (make sure it is all right to cut these photos). Carefully cut out the heads, and glue them onto the dolls. Use markers to draw underclothes on the dolls. Trace around each doll on wrapping paper to make clothing and shoes. Before you cut out the clothes and shoes, add small tabs that can be folded over the doll's body to attach them. You can make lots of different outfits for your family. Does each family member have a favorite outfit? Draw and color it on white construction paper. Then dress up your doll family, and invite your real family to meet themselves!

Family Day

TREE OF HANDS

This special family tree will win a place in everyone's heart—hands down!

What You'll Need: Large poster board, paints, paintbrushes, construction paper, pencil, scissors, glue, marker

Family trees are a great way to remember the names and birthdays of everyone in the family. It will be neat to see all the different hand sizes of family members in this unique family tree. Paint a large brown tree trunk on a poster board. Add branches on both sides, enough for every member of the family to have their own branch. You can add more at the bottom for later generations. Trace each family members hand on different colored construction paper and cut out. When the paint on the poster board has dried, glue the construction paper hands onto the branches, starting with the oldest members of the family at the top branches and working your way down. Have each family member sign their name and write their birth date on their paper hand. When everyone is finished, you may want to decorate the background around the tree. Hang your family tree in the family room, and add more names as more people are born into the family.

Night of the Falling Stars (August 11)

STAR-FALL SLEEP OVER

252

Before movie stars or TV stars, there were other stars—heroes, monsters, and animals—who marched across the night sky.

What You'll Need: Sleeping bags, pillows, flashlights, red cellophane, rubber bands, star chart, mythology book

Invite your friends for a special camp out—and plan to stay up very late. Before the day of your camp out arrives, read about the origin of constellation names—you can tell the exciting stories to your friends while you wait for falling stars! If you can, spend the night at least 20 miles from the nearest large city. You will be able to see the stars more clearly. Before dark, put red cellophane over your flashlights. This will help your eyes stay adjusted to the dark so you can see the stars better. The biggest, best, and brightest falling stars will probably be seen between midnight and 2:00 A.M. No bright lights or campfires allowed!

253

Night of the Falling Stars (August 11)

FALLING STARS

For ages untold, humans have looked up at the summer night sky in amazement as the stars themselves seemed to fall from the sky!

What You'll Need: Waxed paper, white glue in bottle with a pointed top, glitter, string

Ancient people didn't know what we do now—that once a year the earth's orbit passes though a giant field of space rocks called the Perseids (rocks left in the wake of a passing comet). They are called the Perseids because they seem to come from the constellation Perseus. The rocks burn up as they smash into our atmosphere—and we call them falling stars. You don't have to wait until dark to fill your room with falling stars! Draw 5-pointed star outlines, including 3 lines for a "tail," on waxed paper with glue. Make the glue lines wide and thick. Sprinkle the glue with glitter until the lines are completely covered. Let your stars dry for 2 days. When completely dry, peel the stars off the waxed paper and hang up your falling stars with string.

STARRY DWARF?

The sun, our closest star, is a huge, glowing mass that is 860,000 miles in diameter. Though it seems big to us, it is designated a dwarf star by astronomers. There are stars that have diameters a thousand times larger!

254

National Aviation Day (August 19)

FLYING MACHINES

People have dreamed of flying ever since... well, ever since there have been people. Now it's your turn to make a flying machine!

What You'll Need: 2-liter soda bottle with black base and a cap, craft knife, small stuffed animal, tape, paints, paintbrush, plastic coffee can lid, a straight pin with a ball head, cool-temp glue gun

Why not invent your own incredible machines? They won't really fly, but they will be fun! Here's one that's easy to make: Pull the black bottom off a 2-liter soda bottle. Have an adult cut the bottle in half with the craft knife. Set a stuffed animal "pilot" in the top of the bottle. Push the top of the soda bottle into the base to make the body of your flying machine (with the pilot inside). Wrap tape around the seam between the top and the base. Paint the machine, leaving the front half clear for the windshield. Cut 4 sections out of the coffee can lid, but don't cut the rim! (Have an adult help you with the craft knife and glue gun!) Push the pin through the center of the coffee can lid and into the center of the soda pop lid. Paint and then glue the plastic cutouts on as wings for your airplane. Happy flying!

255

National Aviation Day (August 19)

HELICOPTERS

This helicopter can help you figure out how propellers work.

What You'll Need: 6-inch wood or plastic propellers (from hobby store), unsharpened pencil, drill, glue

Buy a wood or plastic propeller at the hobby store. Have an adult help you drill out the hole in the center of the propeller until a pencil will just fit inside. It must be a tight fit. Push the pencil into the propeller. Make a little mark on the top of the propeller so you will know which end was up when you took your test flight. Now you're ready for the test. When the blades of the propeller turn they will either push down on the air, making the helicopter go up, or they will push up on the air, making the helicopter go down. Hold the pencil between your hands and slide the palm of one hand quickly across the palm of the other to make the pencil and propeller turn. Let go. Did the helicopter go up or down? If it went down, pull the propeller off the pencil and turn it over. Try again. When you have the propeller on the correct way, glue it in place.

256

National Aviation Day (August 19)

UP, UP, AND AWAY RALLY

Invite your friends over for an Up, Up, and Away Rally. Make paper planes or fancy flyers; the only rule is they must really fly!

What You'll Need: Construction paper, ruler, pencil, scissors, tape, drinking straw, large trash bag, hula hoop, marker, duct tape

Here are a few fancy flying machines to make:

Baby UFO: Cut 2 strips of construction paper, one ¾ × 6½ inches and the other ½ × 5½ inches. Make both into a loop. When you make the loops, overlap the ends ¾ of an inch. Tape the ends of the strip on the inside and on the outside. Insert the ends of a drinking straw into the space between the overlapping ends. Fasten the straw to the loops with tape. Hold the UFO horizontally, with the small loop in front, and toss.

Mama UFO: Cut along 1 side of the trash bag, and open it up. Lay the hula hoop on it. Trace around the outside of the hoop with a marker. Cut out the circle. Tape it to the hula hoop with duct tape. Fly it like a giant flying disk!

How many fancy planes or flying machines can you invent?

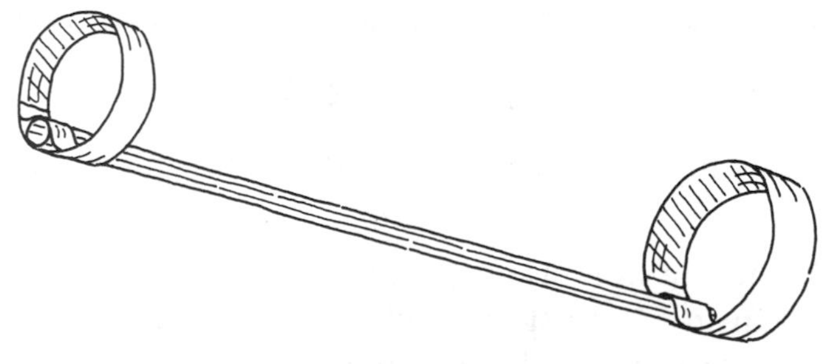

257

National Aviation Day (August 19)

STRING ROCKET RACES

Invite some friends over for rocket races.

What You'll Need: Small milk carton, scissors, glue, aluminum foil, markers, soda straw, masking tape, kite string, long balloons

Cut the bottom (the square end) off a small milk carton and discard. Spread glue on the outside of the remaining milk carton, and cover it with aluminum foil. Smooth the foil with your fingers to make sure it's all stuck down. Use markers to draw windows on your rocket, with an astronaut looking out. Cut a 1-inch piece of soda straw. Tape it on top of the milk carton. Thread the string through the straw. Tie one end of the string to a tree limb 10 to 20 feet away. Tie the other end of the string to a chair or limb. Put a balloon in the rocket, with the nozzle facing back. Blow up the balloon as big as you can. Release, and watch your rocket go! For rocket races, set up 2 string rockets. (Balloons are choking hazards—keep them away from small children!)

National Aviation Day (August 19)

STABILE MOBILE

258

These planes are in the air, but they won't fly away.

What You'll Need: Plaster of Paris, small can, wire coat hangers, origami paper, paints, paintbrushes, chenille stems, thread, glue

A stabile mobile is like a mobile, but you don't need to hang it from the ceiling. Prepare the plaster of Paris. Fill a can with the plaster, and, while it is still wet, stick 2 curved pieces of wire coat hanger in it to set. While the plaster is drying, fold 8 small airplanes from the origami paper. Paint the outside of the can after the plaster has hardened. Tie 2 chenille stems together with thread to form a cross, and repeat for another cross. Tie the crosses to the coat hangers. Glue thread to the airplanes, and tie them to the chenille stem ends. Place your mobile near an open window or on an outside table, and watch your airplanes fly!

FALL

Crisp leaves crunching underfoot, buying new clothes for school, going apple picking, deciding on the best Halloween costume ever—this season is full of fun and excitement. During this season we celebrate Grandparent's Day, Native American Day, Labor Day, Thanksgiving, and so much more! And let's not forget spooky Halloween! So get crafting, cooking, making, and baking for these great holidays!

259

Labor Day

BUTTER CHURN

Work your muscles the old-fashioned way by making your own butter.

What You'll Need: Whipping cream, jar with tight-fitting lid, bread or crackers, butter knife

Not too long ago, people in this country couldn't just drive to the store to buy a pound of butter. They had to make the butter themselves! Here's your chance to experience some good old-fashioned labor and make yourself some delicious, creamy butter. It's easy, but hard work, so have lots of friends around to help. To start, let a pint of whipping cream sit at room temperature for about an hour. Cold whipping cream cannot be used for this recipe. When the cream is ready, pour it into a jar with a very tight-fitting lid. Have an adult help you close the jar if you aren't sure it is tight enough. Taking turns with your friends, shake the jar as hard as you can. After a little while, the butterfat in the cream will start to clump together and form a lump. There may be a little watery liquid left over. This is known as the buttermilk. When a large lump has formed, put the jar in the refrigerator until the butter is firm. You can drain off the buttermilk into a glass and drink it. Then set the butter on the table and serve it with some fresh bread or crackers. See? All that hard work was worth it!

260

Labor Day

"GOOD WORK" SIGN

Remind your favorite worker of the good work they've done.

What You'll Need: Embroidery canvas, different-colored raffia, wool needle, pencil, scissors, thin cardboard, glue

Write the words "Good Work" on a piece of embroidery canvas. You can add other simple line drawings if you wish, such as stars to show that a job has been done well. Then sew the words and pictures with different-colored strands of raffia. Use long stitches for straight lines and small stitches for going around curves, such as for letters in the word "Good." Cut a piece of thin cardboard into a frame shape, and glue it over your canvas so it frames your artwork. Glue another piece of cardboard to the back. When dry, give the sign to your favorite worker to hang in his or her workplace.

Labor Day

FIELD HOLLER

You'll be surprised how fast your chores get done once you start singing while you work.

Lots of people sing or whistle while they work to make the time go faster. Workers in the fields used to set up a steady rhythm and sing about the jobs they were doing. You can set up your own chant or "field holler" to sing while you work by first deciding on a beat. You might want to use a One, Two, One-Two-Three rhythm or maybe use a simple sing-song One-and-Two-and-Three-and-Four. If you are cleaning a room with a friend, sing about the tasks that you both are doing, such as: *"You are dusting and I will sweep, getting rid of dirt we sure won't keep! I will wash the windows today, and you will throw all the trash away!"* You can make up three or four different verses and repeat them over and over, changing the melody or volume every couple of verses. Try whispering the lyrics or harmonizing. Before you know it, your chores will be over—but you'll still be singing!

262

Labor Day

APPLE WALK GAME

Apples are not just for eating!

What You'll Need: Apples, 2 large empty buckets

This is a relay race for 2 teams. For each team, set an empty bucket 20 feet away from the players. The first player on each team puts an apple between his or her knees, runs or walks to the bucket, and drops it in. The first player then picks up the apple and runs back to hand it to the next player. That player must do the same thing the first player did, and so on until everyone has had a turn. The first team to finish wins the game. Make sure you have plenty of apples to snack on—after all that hard labor, you're bound to be hungry!

263

Grandparent's Day

CUP OF LOVE

You'll make the nicest "drink" anyone could have!

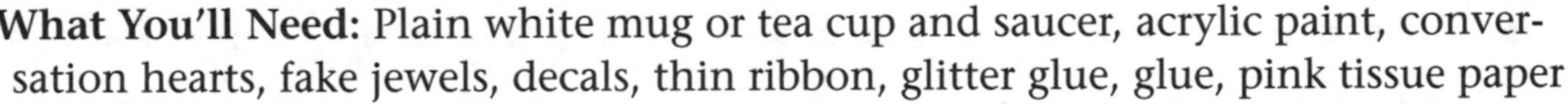

What You'll Need: Plain white mug or tea cup and saucer, acrylic paint, conversation hearts, fake jewels, decals, thin ribbon, glitter glue, glue, pink tissue paper

Your grandparents will really know you love them when you give them this special cup. Paint the cup with the words and phrases that tell your grandparents how you feel about them. You can write surprise messages of love on the inside of the cup and underneath it. Write short things, such as "I Love You" or "You're Nice." Paint pretty designs on the cup or glue on conversation hearts, jewels, decals, ribbons, and glitter. When the paint and glue dry, fill the cup with a froth of pink tissue paper and more conversation hearts to look as though it is overflowing with love.

264

Grandparent's Day

YOUR BIGGEST FAN

Help Grandma beat the heat with this pretty, lacy fan.

What You'll Need: 10-inch length of 1-inch-wide edging lace (3 yard package of lace seam binding), liquid starch, small container, 2 pieces of shiny 4 × 10-inch wrapping paper, small paintbrush, glue, ruler, pencil, paper clips, 14-inch length of ¼-inch-wide velvet or satin ribbon, scissors

1. To make the fan, first dip the lace in liquid starch, smooth it out, and hang it to dry.

2. When the lace is dry, brush on ¼-inch-wide line of glue along one 10-inch edge of paper on the wrong side. Lay the bottom, straight edge of lace along the glued edge, and press it flat.

3. When the glue is dry, brush slightly thinned glue over the wrong sides of both pieces of paper. Press them together, smoothing the paper carefully. You might want to put a book on top until the glue is dry.

4. When dry, measure and draw very light pencil lines on the paper to make ½-inch-wide sections. Fold along the pencil lines to make accordion pleats.

5. Then brush a ½-inch line of glue along the edge opposite the lace. Press the pleats together at this point and fold the bottom up against the rest of the fan to make a little handle.

6. Glue the folded part to the fan and clamp with a paper clip until the glue dries. Tie a bow with the ribbon, and glue it to the bottom of the fan. Won't Grandma feel cool now?

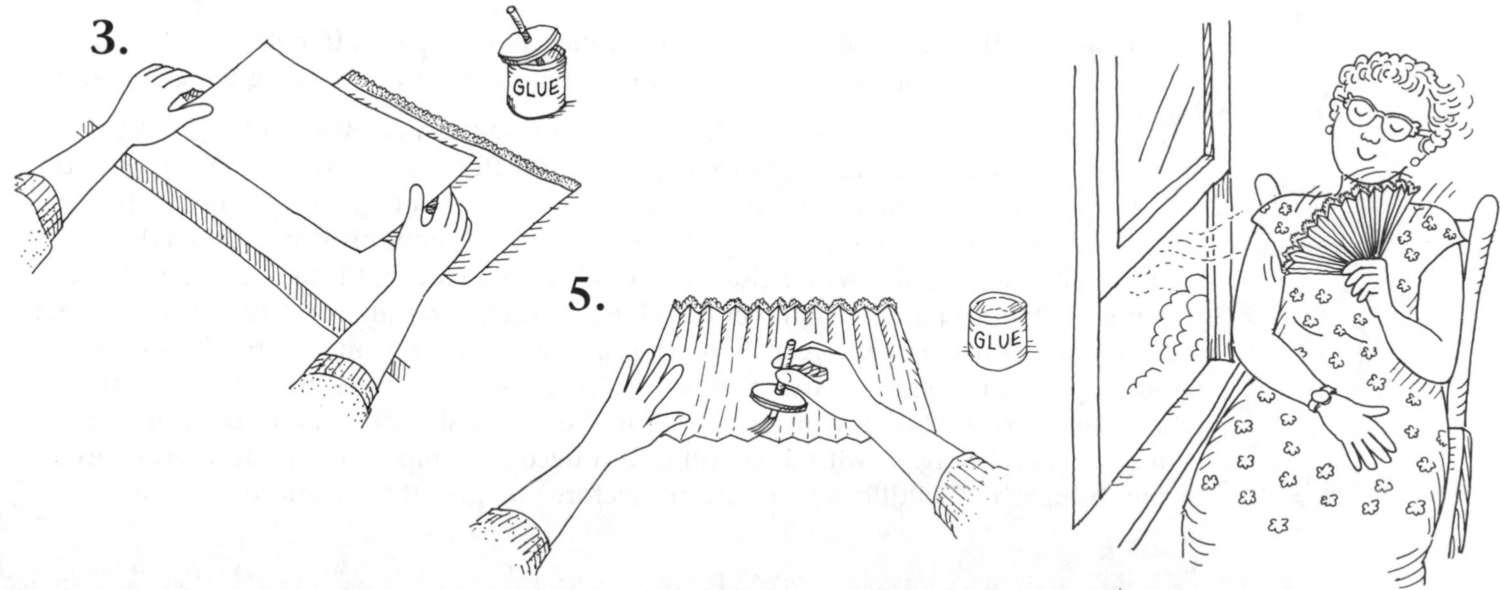

Grandparent's Day

DRESSY HANKY

Paint one of your Grandma's or Grandpa's favorite things on this special hanky.

What You'll Need: Plain white handkerchief, wax crayons, damp towels, iron

To make one of these dressy hankies, draw a design on a plain white handkerchief with a wax crayon. Press firmly so the wax really sticks to the fabric. Think of a design your grandma or grandpa would really like. Do they have a favorite color? A favorite pet or flower? Draw something that will make them know you are really thinking about them. You might want to write their name and sign yours with a message, too. When you are satisfied with your design, put the handkerchief between 2 damp towels, and ask an adult to help you press it with a warm iron. The wax will melt, and most of the dye from the crayons will stay in the cloth for a permanent design. A homemade hanky is a thoughtful and personal gift. It's useful, too!

Grandparent's Day

GOLDEN VASE

266

These vases are so attractive—even without flowers!

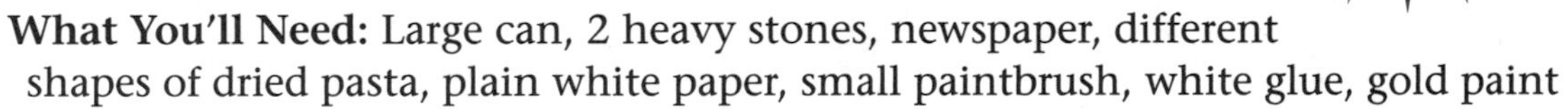

What You'll Need: Large can, 2 heavy stones, newspaper, different shapes of dried pasta, plain white paper, small paintbrush, white glue, gold paint

Turn pasta into gold—a golden vase. To make the vase, wash a large coffee or juice can with soap, and remove paper labels. After you dry the can, prop it up on its side between the heavy stones on a few sheets of newspaper. Try out different arrangements of pasta shapes on a piece of plain white paper until you find a design that you like. Then paint white glue on the side of the can that is facing up, and cover the glue with your pasta design. Let the glue dry, then carefully roll the can to the next section you want to cover. Again, prop the can between the stones to hold it in place. Glue on pasta in the same pattern as before. Let it dry, and repeat the process until the whole can is covered with your design. Prop the can upside down, and paint it gold. Let it dry, and paint it again with a second coat if needed. Wrap your vase in pretty paper, or pick a bunch of wildflowers to put in it before you give it to Grandma or Grandpa.

Grandparent's Day

VISIT ME GUEST SOAPS

Make Grandma and Grandpa's visit sweet and bubbly with these pretty guest soaps!

What You'll Need: Soap flakes, measuring cup, mixing bowl, food coloring, water, fun-shaped cookie cutters, decorative stickers or labels, clear or colored plastic wrap, ribbon

Put 2 cups of soap flakes into a mixing bowl. Squeeze a few drops of food coloring into ½ cup of water and add it to the soap flakes. Use your hands to mix it until the soap is evenly colored. If the mixture is sticky, add a little more soap. If it is dry and crumbly, add a little more water. When it is smooth like clay, form small balls and press them down on a clean counter. You can cut fancy soap shapes with cookie cutters, then put soap shapes on a plate to harden for 2 days. If you want, you can decorate each soap with a sticker or a label with a special message written on it, such as "Thanks for Visiting!" Wrap each soap with plastic wrap, and tie it with a pretty ribbon. Show your grandparents what a thoughtful host you are by putting a group of soaps into a bowl in their room the next time they come to visit.

Grandparent's Day

WHEN I WAS YOUNG BOOK

Show your grandparents how much you care with this book.

What You'll Need: Construction paper, stapler, markers, old magazines, scissors, glue

Your grandparents have led a long and full life. They probably have had experiences that seem unbelievable to you. What did your grandparents do for fun when they were your age? What sorts of clothes did they wear? What did they dream they would be when they grew up? Get to know your grandparents. Ask them to tell you stories about their lives when they were your age, and take notes or tape record the conversation. Then staple folded sheets of construction paper together to make a book. Write a story inside about some of the things your grandparents told you. Draw or cut out pictures from old magazines to illustrate their story. Write a title on the cover of your book, such as "When I Was Young" or "The Story of Grandpa and Grandma." This is one book that the whole family will cherish forever!

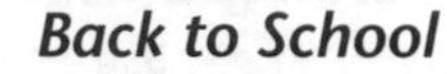

Back to School

269 BACK-TO-SCHOOL NEWSPAPER

Find out all the school news that's fit to print!

What You'll Need: Paper, pen and markers (or typewriter or computer), copy machine

To get your stories, interview classmates and teachers to find out what they did over the summer and what they hope to accomplish this year at school. Remember that a good newspaper story always answers the questions who, what, when, where, why (and sometimes how). You can write your stories by hand or use a typewriter or computer. Illustrate your stories with funny cartoons that you draw or use cutouts from old magazines. If you have a camera, you could also take pictures of the people who are in the stories. Think of a name for your newspaper, and write it across the top of the first page in big, bold letters. Give all your stories headlines, such as "Mrs. Sellars Builds Sailboat Over Summer." You may also want to include a "Letters to the Editor" column, a joke corner, or a weather report. Ask an adult to copy your newspaper so you have one for everyone in your class. Staple the pages together, and hand them out.

Back to School

270 SHAPE IT UP

Teach your favorite young child about different shapes.

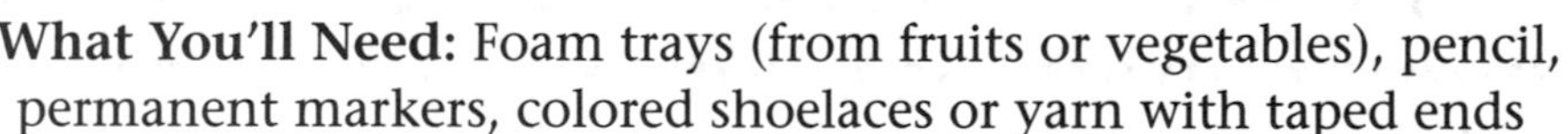

What You'll Need: Foam trays (from fruits or vegetables), pencil, permanent markers, colored shoelaces or yarn with taped ends

You can be a real teacher when you help some young friends learn about circles, squares, triangles, and other shapes. First wash some foam deli trays well with hot water and soap. You may want to have an adult help you do this because the trays must be really clean. Dry the trays. Use a pencil to poke out the outlines of various shapes (triangle, circle, square, etc.). Leave ¼ to ½ inch between each hole, depending on the size of the shape you want. Use a marker to write the name of the shape on each tray underneath the shape. To teach younger children the names of the shapes, help them lace up the outline with a piece of yarn or a shoelace. Show them the name of the shape that you have written. Make sure you tell your young students what a great job they did! (Be sure that young children do not play with yarn or shoelaces without supervision!)

271

Back to School

STYLING BOOK COVERS

These covers make schoolbooks look great.

What You'll Need: Thin cardboard, felt, fabric, glue, scissors, elastic strips, needle and thread

For each book you want to cover, open the book and lay it flat with the back and front covers facing you. Cut a piece of thin cardboard to fit over the book's surface. Cut your piece about ½ inch larger at the sides. Make 2 creases in the middle of the cardboard (the width of the spine) so that it will bend easily when the book is opened and closed. Glue a piece of fabric or felt onto the cardboard. Make sure the cloth is at least 1 inch larger than the cardboard all around. Fold the extra fabric on the other side of the cardboard, and glue it in place. Cover the remaining cardboard by gluing another piece of felt or fabric onto it. A couple inches from either end, sew an elastic strip top to bottom on the inside of the book cover you just made—be sure the elastic is stretched a bit so the book cover stays in place. Slide the front and back covers of your schoolbook into these strips to hold the book in place. Decorate the outside of your new book cover with felt cutouts. This year, go back to school in style!

Back to School

SCHOOL BUS GAME

272

This is one exciting bus ride!

What You'll Need: Half as many chairs as there are players, table, a slip of paper for each player, pencil

Play this game at home or at school. To set up the game, put the chairs in rows, like on a bus. Write the names of all the players on the slips of paper, and put them on a table across the room from the chairs. One player is the school bus driver. She or he says: "The school bus is here. Let's all be on time. Pick up your tickets over there, so we can be in school by nine." After this is said, the other players run to the table to find the ticket with their name on it. If they find it, they run to the bus and get a seat. Whoever is left cannot ride the bus. Play the game over and over and keep score for perfect school bus attendance. Whoever first reaches a perfect score of 5 (for the 5 school days of the week), gets to be the bus driver for the next round.

Rosh Hoshanah

273 BLOW YOUR OWN SHOFAR

Ring in the New Year with this colorful shofar!

What You'll Need: Plastic funnel, colored tape, 30-inch length of rubber hose, scissors, colored cord with tassel

You need a lot of practice to be able to blow a shofar. Here's an easy way you can make those holiday sounds with a shofar of your own. Decorate the funnel with colored tape. You might want to wind strips around the funnel to cover it entirely, or you could use little cutout shapes. Cut a 1-inch slit in one end of the hose. Push the funnel into this slit, and tape it in place. Then make a large loop in the hose, and tape it in place—be sure you have a few straight inches left over for the part where you hold the horn and blow. Wind strips of colored tape around the hose to decorate it. Wind a couple inches of colored tape at the mouthpiece at the straight end of the hose opposite the funnel. Now you are ready to blow! Just hold the horn, and blow into the mouthpiece end, making your lips vibrate against it. Blow hard or softly to make different tones. Make your lips tighter, and see what sort of a shofar sound comes out now!

Rosh Hoshanah

DRIED APPLES 274

These leftover apple slices are dried and enjoyed for weeks into the New Year.

What You'll Need: Apples, knife, string, coat hangers, tape

Long ago, people preserved their food without refrigerators. Here's a great way to use up any leftover Rosh Hoshanah apples that didn't get eaten. Ask an adult to help you peel, core, and slice the apples. Then loop pieces of string through the circular apple slices. Tape or tie the other ends of the string to a coat hanger and hang in a warm, dry place. In 2 weeks, the apples will have dried out and will be a sweet and chewy treat!

275

Rosh Hoshanah

APPLE OF HOPE

Make a giant papier mâché apple, and fill it with messages telling of your hopes for the New Year.

What You'll Need: Balloon, rubber band, newspaper, liquid starch, bowl, paper towels, stiff cardboard, scissors, paints, paintbrushes, glue, green construction paper, paper, pen

To make the apple, blow up a large, round balloon. Fasten the end with a rubber band. Tear newspaper into strips that are 1 to 2 inches wide. Soak the strips in liquid starch for 10 minutes. Then paste the strips onto the balloon until the whole balloon is covered. Let paper dry. Add 3 more layers of newspaper strips—letting each layer dry before adding the next. Each time you add a layer, change the direction of the strips to make your apple strong. Soak 1- to 2-inch strips of paper towels in the liquid starch, and add 2 layers of these strips to form more of an apple shape. Cut a 1 × 4-inch piece of stiff cardboard for the stem. Wrap starched newspaper strips around it. Let your apple and stem dry for a few days. Release the rubber band, and the balloon inside will lose its air. Then draw a line all around the top third of the apple. Cut along this line. Cut a hole in the top half that is a little smaller than the stem you made. Wedge the stem in the hole so that it forms a tight seal and can be used as a handle. Paint the stem brown and the apple a rosy red color. You could even glue on some green construction paper leaves. Paint the inside of your apple white. Have family and friends write messages telling their hopes for the New Year, and put them inside the apple. Take turns reading the messages aloud at the Rosh Hoshanah seder.

A Sweet Year

Apples, honey, and carrots are eaten at Rosh Hoshanah to symbolize the sweetness and good fortune of the coming year. The Rosh Hoshanah meal is begun by dipping apples and challah (a special bread) in honey.

Rosh Hoshanah

276 HONEY CARDS

Send out lots of these honey-sweet New Year's cards.

What You'll Need: Heavy paper, permanent markers, felt, glue, scissors

It's traditional to send out New Year's cards at Rosh Hoshanah wishing your friends and family a sweet year. To make a honey of a card, draw a large honey jar along the edge of a folded piece of heavy paper. Cut out the honey jar shape on all the edges except the folded one. Trace the jar shape on a piece of felt and cut out 2 felt jar shapes that you can glue onto the front and back of your card. Cut an oval shape out of felt to use as the honey jar's label. Write the word "HONEY" on it with a marker. Inside the card, draw pictures and write the message, "May your New Year be as sweet as honey!" Everyone will agree that this is one sweet card!

Yom Kippur

277 CHAI CHARM

Three cheers for life!

What You'll Need: Self-hardening clay, sandpaper, pencil, craft stick, gold or silver paint, paintbrush, clear varnish or nail polish, thin leather cord

In ancient times, many Jewish people cut stones to make seals for traders, farmers, and merchants. They also cut stones to make charms to wear around the neck or wrist. You can practice an ancient tradition and make a Chai charm. Chai is the symbol for life and is a traditional New Year's symbol. To make your charm, roll a piece of self-hardening clay into a ball and flatten it to the size of a half dollar. Poke a hole at the top for the cord. Lightly trace the Chai symbol onto one side of the clay. With a craft stick, carefully shape the clay around this symbol so that the Chai is slightly raised up from the rest of the clay. Let the clay dry. Paint the Chai with gold or silver paint. When dry, coat the charm with clear varnish. Thread a thin leather cord through the hole, and wear your charm for a lucky life.

278

Citizenship Day (September 17)

AMERICAN MEDALS

Present your favorite American with a patriotic medal.

What You'll Need: Plaster of Paris, water, empty plastic tub, disposable plastic cups, pencil, markers or paints, clear nail polish, cord

Citizenship Day is a time to celebrate new citizens of the United States. It is also a day to remind us of our rights and privileges that have been guaranteed by the United States Constitution. You can present a new citizen with one of these homemade medals, or simply wear the medal yourself and celebrate your pride in being an American. Mix plaster of Paris and water in an empty plastic tub until it is thick and smooth. Pour ½ inch of the mix into a small plastic cup. Quickly poke a pencil at one edge to make a hole to thread the necklace cord through. When the plaster has dried, peel away the plastic cup. Paint your medal on both sides, and let it dry. You can now draw or paint patriotic messages such as "I Am an American," "U.S.A. All the Way!," or "Life, Liberty, and Happiness." Protect your medal with a coat of clear nail polish after the paint has dried. Thread enough cord through the hole to make a loop large enough for your head to pass through. You are now ready to wear or give away your medal with pride.

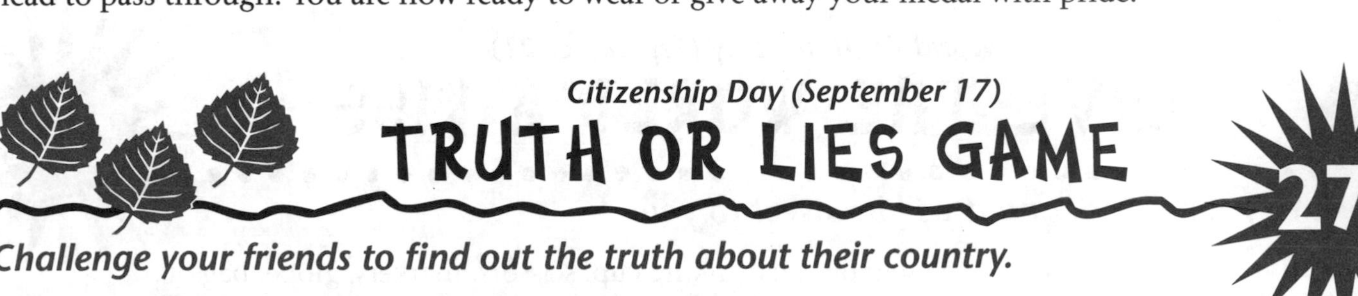

Citizenship Day (September 17)

TRUTH OR LIES GAME

279

Challenge your friends to find out the truth about their country.

What You'll Need: Prewritten true and false facts about America

How much do you and your friends really know about the United States? Play this truth or lies game and find out. The leader of the game must write a list of facts about America. For example: There are 50 states in America. Native Americans were the first people to live in this country. The first president of the U.S. was George Washington. The leader should also write a list of lies about America. For example: France is the name of an American state. Each president has 2 vice presidents. When the leader has a list of around 20 facts and lies, the game is ready to begin. The leader quickly calls out facts from the lists. It is good if the leader can call out the facts in a kind of rhythm, like a rap. Players respond by clapping in rhythm 3 times if the statement is true, and not at all if the statement is false. Keep the pace lively. Anyone who claps at the wrong time is out, and the last one left is the leader next time around.

World Gratitude Day (September 21)

WORLD ON A PENCIL

Keep the whole world in mind as you write.

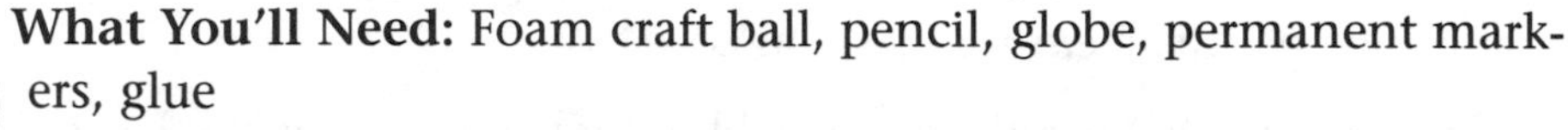

What You'll Need: Foam craft ball, pencil, globe, permanent markers, glue

These special pencils will remind you what a fantastic planet you live on. To make one, copy the outline of the continents onto the foam ball. Use a globe to help you get the shapes right. When you finish, outline the continents with a black, fine-tipped marker. Color them with different colors. Color the space around them blue to make seas and oceans. Poke the end of a pencil into the bottom of your model world—add a little glue to keep the world on. Now you have a nifty way to write pen pals all around the world.

World Gratitude Day (September 21)

281 GIVE THE WORLD A KISS

Be sweet to your world, and it will be sweet to you.

What You'll Need: Thin cardboard, pencil, plastic drinking cup, scissors, markers, globe, bag of chocolate Kisses, tape

On cardboard, trace around a plastic drinking cup to make circles and cut them out. Then color each to look like a part of the world. Use a globe to help you remember what different parts of the world look like. Tape a wrapped chocolate Kiss in the center of each part of the world, and place them here and there around the house. This will be a really sweet reminder for people to love their world today.

Autumnal Equinox

282 APPLE BREAD

The tastes of fall harvest are mixed together in this yummy bread.

What You'll Need: 2 cups whole wheat flour, 1 cup cornmeal, ½ teaspoon salt, 1 teaspoon baking soda, 1 cup water, 1 cup maple syrup, ¾ cup unsweetened applesauce, ¾ cup raisins, ½ cup chopped walnuts, measuring cups and spoons, mixing bowl, mixing spoon, loaf pan, butter knife

Have an adult preheat the oven to 350 degrees. Mix the flour, cornmeal, salt, and baking soda together in a bowl. Add the water and the maple syrup and mix everything until it is smooth. Fold in the applesauce, raisins, and nuts. Pour the batter into a greased loaf pan and bake for about 35 minutes. Have an adult stick a butter knife in the center of the bread to tell if it is done. If the knife comes out clean, take the pan out of the oven. If not, let the bread cook a few minutes longer. This bread is nice when served with baked beans and a big green salad. Or, have it with a little cinnamon butter for dessert!

Autumnal Equinox

AUTUMN JEWEL BRACELETS 283

You can make this bracelet only during the autumn season.

What You'll Need: Roll of wide masking tape, nature

Take a walk and make a bracelet at the same time! Pick a nice, sunny day for your walk. Ask a grown-up friend to walk with you out in the woods or in a field where there are lots of little natural "gems" (such as baby pinecones, leaves, little pebbles, seed pods, and moss) to collect for your bracelet. Before leaving on your walk, have your friend attach a loop of wide masking tape, sticky side out, around your wrist. Then, as you walk, pick up pretty bits of nature and stick them onto the tape. Make a bracelet of tiny wild flowers and acorn tops or small feathers and fuzzy grass!

Autumnal Equinox

284 SWEET SQUASH SOUP

This sweet and creamy soup is so good on a cool, autumn day.

What You'll Need: 1 butternut and 1 acorn squash, water, 1 chopped onion, 1 tablespoon oil, 1 vegetable bouillon cube, ½ teaspoon basil, ¼ teaspoon cinnamon, ¼ teaspoon nutmeg, lowfat milk, knife, measuring spoons, vegetable peeler, saucepan, frying pan, blender

Have an adult help you peel the squash, remove the seeds, and cut it into chunks. When that is done, place the squash chunks in a large saucepan, cover them with water, and cook them over a medium flame for about 20 minutes or until mushy. Do not drain the liquid out of the pot. While the squash is cooking, have an adult help you brown the onion in the oil. Then put the squash, bouillon cube, and some of the cooked liquid into a blender. Blend it until smooth, and pour it back into the pan. Mix in the onions and the seasonings and enough lowfat milk to make the soup as thick or thin as you like. Stir and heat—then it's time to eat!

Autumnal Equinox

AUTUMN TREASURE BOX 285

Display nature's treasures!

What You'll Need: Clear plastic utility box with separate compartments and clear lid, acrylic paint, paintbrush, pebbles, dried seed husks, dried berries, other found nature treasures

With different colors, lightly paint the squares of each compartment of a plastic utility box and set aside. While you are waiting for the paint to dry, go on a nature walk and collect small treasures to put in each compartment. Look for unusual pebbles, seeds, and dried berries or leaves. Try to get an assortment of shapes and colors. Then arrange your treasures in the painted box in a pleasant display. Set the box on a windowsill so light can shine through. The paint will make the box look like stained glass.

Native American Day

TERRIFIC TOTEMS

Choose from a variety of totem figures to make your own totem pole.

What You'll Need: Corks, spools, egg cartons, shoe boxes, oatmeal containers, cardboard tubes, stones, shells, leaves, craft feathers, construction paper, paints, paintbrushes, glue

Some Native American tribes carved animals, fish, birds, and other objects in wood to make these decorative poles. Totem poles symbolize the harmony of people and nature. You can make your own totem pole by stacking empty shoe boxes, oatmeal containers, corks, spools, and egg cartons, and gluing them together. If your pole is a little tippy, weigh the bottom container with a few stones. Paint your pole in bright colors. You can paint on different Native American designs or glue on construction paper cutouts. Glue on small rocks, feathers, leaves, and shells. Here are some ideas to choose from and what they symbolize to Native Americans: beaver=water, canoe paddle=transportation, deer=food and clothing, fiery flames=campfire, handshake=friendship, thunderbird=tribal crest. What things in nature do you especially love? Make up your own ideas for what these things symbolize, and add them to your totem pole.

HOW'D THEY MAKE THOSE COLORS?

The three main colors used by the S'Kallam tribe from the Puget Bay area in Washington were red, blue-green, and black. Red was created by mixing iron oxide or red ochre from the soil with salmon eggs. The blue-green was created using copper or a type of clay available in the area with salmon eggs. Black was created by grinding together salmon eggs, cedar, and charcoal.

287

Native American Day

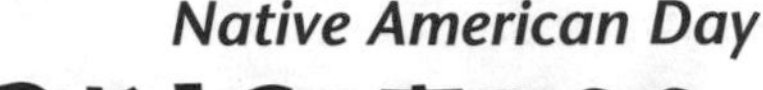

RING TOSS TOY

This was a favorite toy among the Sioux and Cheyenne Indians.

What You'll Need: Cardboard, pencil, scissors, 1-inch wooden dowel, crayons or markers, colored tape, 12-inch piece of colored string, small plastic ring, paint (optional), needle

You can carry this game with you and play it just about anywhere. From cardboard, draw and cut out a round head with horns and a neck. Make sure the neck is as wide as the wooden dowel you want to use, but narrower than the head. Decorate the head to look like a fierce bull. Tape the neck to the top of the wooden dowel (you can paint the dowel first or you can leave it plain). Tie a small plastic ring to one end of a string. Poke a small hole in the top of the bull's head, and thread the other end of the string through the hole and knot it. Now try to flick the ring so that it lands on one of the horns. Keep score by yourself or with a friend by counting the number of flicks it takes to ring the horn. This time, the lowest score wins!

Native American Day

NATIVE AMERICAN LEAF MOSAICS

288

Use nature to "paint" a nature scene.

What You'll Need: Dried leaves of different colors, glue, pencil, white construction paper

You will need to collect and press leaves to dry them. Put the leaves in heavy books, and leave them alone for a week or two until they are dry. While you are waiting, you can draw different Native American scenes, such as a tepee on a river bank with a canoe parked out front. Draw only the outlines of the things in your scene, because you are going to "color" them in and add details by using bits and pieces of dried leaves. When the leaves are dry, tear them into small pieces. Glue the bits inside the lines to fill in the shapes. Use many different-colored bits and make sure none of the paper shows through. Don't worry if the colors don't match the things that you have drawn. Instead of a blue or green river, why not "paint" a yellow or orange one?

289

Native American Day

COMANCHE DART GAME

Make your own darts, and hit the moving target—if you can!

What You'll Need: Toothpicks, corks, paints, pencil, construction paper, scissors, tape, outdoor hill, rubber ball

This dart game was especially popular with Comanche children. You can make your own darts by sticking a toothpick in a cork and painting it in a bright color. Draw and cut out a construction paper feather and tape it onto the toothpick. Make lots of darts! To play the game, one person rolls a ball down a hill while the other players try to hit the ball with their darts. Each time someone hits the ball, they score 10 points. Play until someone reaches 100 points, then play again. Hold a Comanche dart tournament!

Native American Day

CORN AND BEAN FRY CAKES

290

Make a delicious meal from two traditional Native American foods.

What You'll Need: 2 cups cornmeal, ½ teaspoon salt, 2 cups boiling water, 1 cup cooked pinto beans, 1 tablespoon miso, ¼ cup oil, sour cream or plain yogurt, chopped scallions, measuring cups and spoons, large frying pan, wooden spoon, waxed paper, bowl, masher or fork, paper towels

Ask an adult to help you fry up these delicious little cakes for lunch or dinner. Mix the cornmeal and salt in a pan. Have the adult slowly stir in the boiling water. It is important to stir slowly so the batter doesn't get lumpy. Cook the mixture over low heat for about 5 to 10 minutes, until it is thick. Drop 8 equal-sized portions of the cornmeal mix onto a piece of waxed paper. Let them sit until they are cool enough to touch. Divide each portion in half, and, with your hands, make a little round cake out of each half. Put the beans and the miso in a bowl, and mash them together until you have a fairly smooth paste. It's okay if there are a few lumps in this. Place 2 tablespoons of the bean mixture on 8 of the cornmeal cakes. Put the other 8 cakes on top to make little bean sandwiches. Press around the edges with a fork to seal so that the bean mix is hidden inside the cornmeal cakes. Pour the oil in the frying pan, and have the adult heat the oil on medium high heat until the oil is sizzling. Have an adult fry the cornmeal cakes until golden brown. Flip them over and brown the other side. Add more oil if you need to. Let the cakes drain on a plate covered with paper towels. Top each with a dab of sour cream or plain yogurt and a sprinkle of chopped scallions.

291

Native American Day

NATIVE NECKLACE

Make traditional jewelry for boys and girls.

What You'll Need: Ravel-free burlap scraps, scissors, embroidery thread and needle, thin wire, beads, ribbon

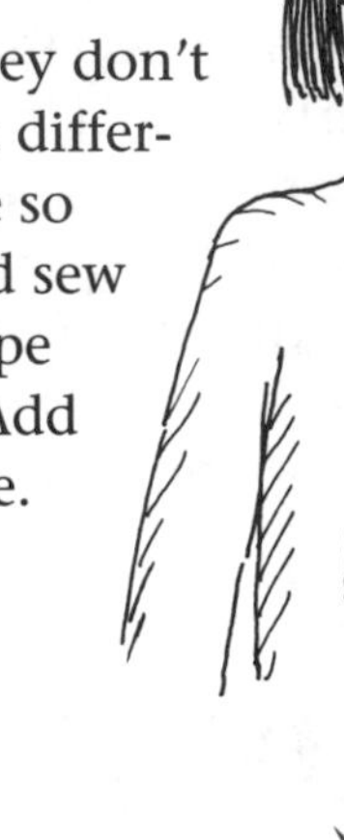

Cut 4 different geometric shapes out of burlap. Sew around the edges so they don't unravel. Embroider the shapes with cross-stitches in geometric patterns. Use a different bright-colored thread for each pattern. Attach the burlap shapes with wire so that they hang down in a long line. Cut a piece of wide ribbon into fringe and sew on the bottom of the last shape. Sew a thin ribbon to each side of the top shape and tie in a knot; make sure the loop is long enough to pass over your head. Add more beads to hang down from the shapes with short pieces of wire if you like. Experiment with different shapes, and make necklaces for all your friends to wear for this special day.

Native American Day

SNAKEY STICK GAME

292

Toss the sticks and try your luck!

What You'll Need: 3 ice cream sticks or craft sticks, red and blue markers

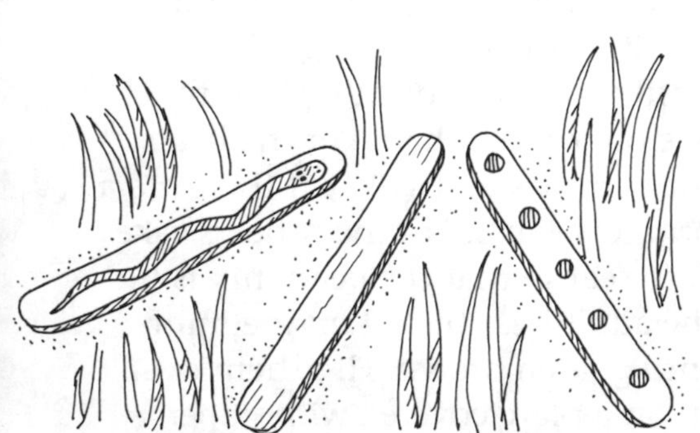

Here's a traditional Native American game that the whole family will enjoy. Draw a red snake pattern on one side of 2 of the craft sticks. These are the snake sticks. Draw a blue dot pattern on one side of the other stick. This stick is the man stick. Now you are ready to play. Hold the sticks in one hand and toss them up into the air. If all the patterned sides land face up, score 4 points. If all the plain sides land face up, score 4 points. If you get 2 snakes and 1 plain facing up, score 6 points. If you get 2 plain and 1 snake facing up, score 6 points. If you get a man and 2 snakes, score 3 points. If you get a plain, a snake, and a man face up, score 0 points.

Native American Day

OWNER STICKS

The Crow Indians used sticks like these to identify the belongings of tribal members.

What You'll Need: Craft sticks, markers, colored tape, craft feathers, colored string, beads, scrap pieces of soft leather or suede

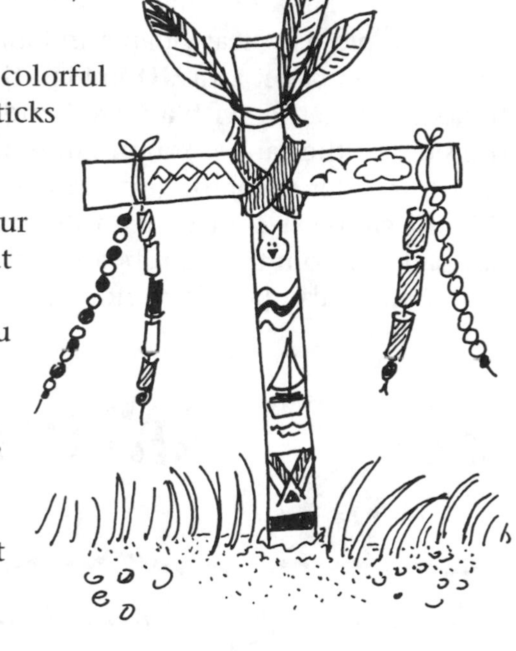

Instead of using name tags to identify your belongings, why not use colorful "owner sticks," as the Crow Indians of Montana did. Sometimes these sticks were driven into the ground to mark outdoor piles of firewood or deer hides. These sticks were usually about 2 feet long, but you can make smaller versions using wooden craft sticks to keep on your desk or in your backpack. To make your owner sticks, draw symbols that best show what you are like, such as a lion if you feel you are a brave person or a flower if you think you are sweet. Draw lots of different symbols on 1 stick. You can also tape on craft feathers and strings of beads. Wind soft pieces of leather or suede around your sticks. Make a cross by taping 2 sticks together with colored tape. Decorate your owner stick however you like, but make sure that it really shows how unique you are. You may want to make up an Indian name, such as Little Running Deer, and sign it on your stick. If you go camping, drive your owner stick in the ground next to your tent to let everyone know you're there!

CHIEF PLENTY COUPS

Plenty Coups, or "Bull Who Goes Into the Wind," had a dream when he was a child about the destruction of the Crow way of life and the buffalo herds his people needed for survival. He grew up to become the leader of the Crow Nation, and he led his people through the hard times that he had seen in his dream.

294

Native American Day

LITTLE CANOE

This canoe will make you dream of deep rivers and wide lakes!

What You'll Need: 8 × 12-inch piece of heavy paper, scissors, needle and embroidery thread, markers, toothpicks, thin cardboard, pencil

Fold a piece of heavy paper in half lengthwise. Draw a canoe shape on it and cut the extra paper away. Don't cut the fold, however. Sew each pair of ends of the canoe together with an overhand stitch. Draw Native American designs on the sides of the canoe. You might draw the sun, the moon, a bow and arrow, or a deer. After decorating the canoe, insert 2 or 3 toothpicks horizontally inside the canoe at 2- or 3-inch intervals to hold the sides apart. Draw and cut out paddles from thin cardboard. You can also draw and cut out a couple of Native American people to ride in the canoe.

Native American Day

NATIVE AMERICAN WALL HANGING

295

This wall hanging is easy to make, and it looks so authentic!

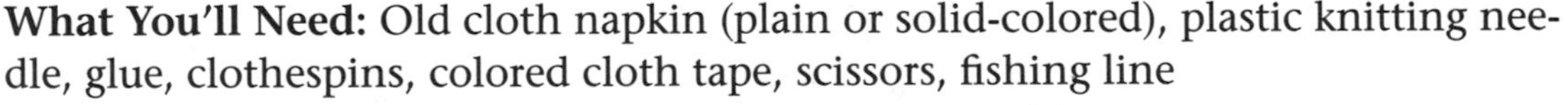

What You'll Need: Old cloth napkin (plain or solid-colored), plastic knitting needle, glue, clothespins, colored cloth tape, scissors, fishing line

Native Americans often decorate their homes with beautiful wall hangings that were either painted or woven in traditional designs. To make a hanging for your wall at home, run glue along the top border of a cloth napkin and fold the edge over a knitting needle. You can use clothespins to hold the napkin while the glue dries. Cut different geometric shapes from colored tape. Use triangles, squares, rectangles, and hexagons, and form symmetrical patterns with them on the napkin. Lots of traditional Native American designs have one pattern that repeats over and over in a pleasing way. Look through books to find patterns that you want to copy, or make up one of your own. Tie fishing line to either end of the knitting needle to make a hanging loop. Hang your design to brighten your home!

296

Native American Day

DREAM CATCHER

Make all your good dreams come true!

What You'll Need: Plastic coffee can lid, scissors, ribbon, glue, embroidery thread and needle, thin leather cord, beads, feathers

Cut out the middle of a plastic coffee can lid to make a ring. You may need some adult help for this part. Wind the ribbon several times around the ring until it is totally covered and nicely padded; glue the ends in place. Loosely wrap embroidery thread around the plastic ring to form 8 small loops. Use a needle to weave the thread in and out of the loops around the ring. Loosely knot the thread to each loop. Then sew each loop with its opposite loop to make a web. Hold a bead in the center and pass the thread through it each time you sew 2 loops together. To finish, tie loops of thin leather cord to the top and bottom of the ring. Cut the bottom loop so 2 lengths of cord hang down. Thread beads and glue feathers to these ends. Hang the Dream Catcher over your bed using the top loop. All your bad dreams will get caught in the web, but all your good dreams will pass through the center and come true!

297

Native American Day

KICK STICK GAME

You'll need fast feet to play this Zuni Indian game.

What You'll Need: 12-inch wooden dowels or branches, paint, paintbrush, white cornmeal (optional)

This is a great outdoor game. If you are camping, you may want to use real branches instead of dowels, just as the Zuni's did. The branches must be straight, about 12 inches long, and 1 inch thick. Peel off some of the bark from one of the branches so that they look different. If you are using dowels, paint one red and one green. To make the Kick Stick playing field, have a group of your friends stand in a large circle or make a circle of white cornmeal on a large area of pavement or dirt. Both players then stand back to back at a point on the circle. When someone else shouts "Go!," the 2 players must kick their sticks around the circle in opposite directions until they return to the starting point. If a player kicks her or his stick out of the circle, or if the stick touches the other player's stick or another person, they must start again. When the game is over, the players shake hands.

298

Oktoberfest

HOT CANDY APPLES

These apples make a fiery fall treat!

What You'll Need: 1½ cups sugar, ½ cup corn syrup, ½ cup hot cinnamon candies, ¾ cup water, ¼ teaspoon salt, 1 teaspoon red food coloring, 1 teaspoon cinnamon, 1 teaspoon ginger, 6 wooden skewers, 6 tart apples, measuring cups and spoons, saucepan, baking pan, waxed paper, spoon, bowl

You'll need adult help to make this sweet and hot apple treat. Mix sugar, syrup, cinnamon candies, water, and salt in a saucepan. Stir over medium heat until it comes to a boil. You must stir the mixture constantly so it doesn't burn. After the mix boils, stop stirring and wait until the syrup forms a solid ball when a bit is dropped into cold water. Remove the saucepan from the stove, and carefully place the saucepan in a pan of very hot water. Add the food coloring and dry spices, and stir. Stick a skewer into the bottom of each apple. Swirl the apple into the syrup until it is entirely covered. Let the apples harden on waxed paper. Serve these at an Oktoberfest gathering with plenty of ice cold apple cider.

Oktoberfest

APPLE GIRL

299

Not only does she have apple cheeks, her whole head's an apple!

What You'll Need: Apple, knife, craft stick or wooden skewer, tissue paper, embroidery thread, glue, yarn, child's sock, colored pom

To make this doll, peel a medium-size apple (you may need adult help for this). Use your fingers to press in eyes, a nose, and a mouth. Let the apple dry in a cool, dry place for about 2 weeks until it is brown and small. When it is ready, poke a stick into the bottom of the apple. To make the doll's dress, fold 3 pieces of tissue paper in half and make a little hole in the middle. Slide the tissues onto the stick. To make the doll's arms, roll up 2 or 3 pieces of tissue paper, and tie the ends with embroidery thread. Slip the arms up horizontally underneath the dress, then tie the dress at the waist with thread so the arms stay in place. You can glue on yarn hair and make a hat from a tiny sock with a pom glued to the top. Name your doll, and introduce her to your friends. Can they guess what her head is made of?

300

Oktoberfest

PUMPKIN-HEAD TWIRLERS

This pumpkin-head person never tires of going round and round.

What You'll Need: Thin cardboard, pencil, markers, scissors, plastic drinking straws, chenille stems, tape

This is an amusing and acrobatic toy. To make it, draw a little person about 4 inches tall on a piece of thin cardboard. Instead of the usual head, draw a pumpkin with a face on it. Give it a funny hat if you want. Use the markers to decorate it. Cut out the pumpkin-head person, and tape chenille stems to its back to form arms and legs. Use 1 horseshoe-shaped piece for both arms, and another horseshoe-shaped piece for both legs. Wrap the ends of the arms around a drinking straw so your pumpkin-head person is holding on like a trapeze artist. When you twirl the ends of the straw, watch the tricks begin! Make another pumpkin-head person, and wrap the ends of its legs around the straw. Make a whole circus of pumpkin-head performers!

THAT'S ONE BIG PARTY!

Munich has the largest Oktoberfest celebration in the world. The first Oktoberfest in Munich was held in 1810. Today, Oktoberfest in Munich has over 7 million visitors during the 16-day celebration!

Oktoberfest

301 SILLY APPLESAUCE FACES

These silly faces are quite yummy.

What You'll Need: Applesauce, plain yogurt, nuts, raisins, toasted coconut, cinnamon candies, dried fruit, bowls, spoon, measuring cup

October is the best apple season! It's a great time for picking apples, jumping into leaves, and working up a big appetite. When you and your friends are really hungry, invite them in for a silly snack. Measure 1 cup of applesauce into a bowl, and add 1 cup of yogurt. Stir the mixture until it is smooth. Then divide it evenly into 3 bowls. Gently add raisins and nuts to make a silly face. Use a spoon to sprinkle cinnamon freckles. Toasted coconut makes great moustaches, beards, eyebrows, and hair. Add a cluster of cinnamon candies on each cheek to give your silly face a rosy autumn glow!

Oktoberfest

LEAFY LETTERS 302

Use the beautiful autumn leaves to make your own stationery.

What You'll Need: Leaves, food coloring, small paper plates, paper

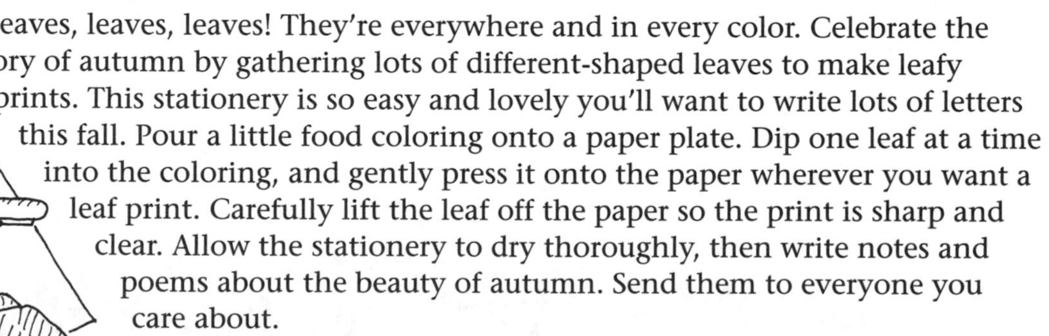

Leaves, leaves, leaves! They're everywhere and in every color. Celebrate the glory of autumn by gathering lots of different-shaped leaves to make leafy prints. This stationery is so easy and lovely you'll want to write lots of letters this fall. Pour a little food coloring onto a paper plate. Dip one leaf at a time into the coloring, and gently press it onto the paper wherever you want a leaf print. Carefully lift the leaf off the paper so the print is sharp and clear. Allow the stationery to dry thoroughly, then write notes and poems about the beauty of autumn. Send them to everyone you care about.

303

Columbus Day

RACE TO THE NEW WORLD

Who will win the race? The Nina, the Pinta, or the Santa Maria?

What You'll Need: Large plastic tub, adhesive vinyl paper in various colors, clear adhesive vinyl, scissors, waterproof markers, foam blocks, toothpicks

Here's a fun game to play outside in nice weather. To make the game, draw the scenes of Columbus's journey from the Old World to the New World on adhesive paper. You may first want to stick a strip of blue adhesive paper around the top 4 to 5 inches of a deep plastic tub to look like the sky. Then you can draw things like islands with palm trees, clouds, birds, fish jumping into the air, sailboats, and pirate ships on more adhesive paper. Do some research to find out what else Columbus might have seen on his journey. Cut out the figures you drew, and stick them onto the blue paper. Label one side "Old World" and the opposite side "New World" with waterproof markers. When you have finished creating your scene, cover the whole thing with clear adhesive paper. Then fill the tub with water to just a little below the bottom edge of the adhesive paper. Make Columbus's boats next: the Nina, the Pinta, and the Santa Maria. Make each boat by poking a toothpick into a small foam block. You can use more adhesive paper to cut a sail for each boat. Label each boat with its name. If you like, decorate the boats with waterproof markers or more adhesive paper. Now you are ready to race. Line up the boats in the Old World and blow them over to the New. Which boat will get there first?

304

Columbus Day

BIG ROUND WORLD BOX

This box is a great gift for your favorite explorer.

What You'll Need: Large round balloon, rubber band, newspapers, liquid starch, large bowl, map or globe, paints, paintbrush, markers, chalk, craft knife, small metal can, construction paper, glue or tape

Blow up a large, round balloon, and fasten the end with a rubber band. Tear newspaper into strips that are 1 to 2 inches wide. Soak the strips in liquid starch for 10 minutes. Paste the strips onto the balloon until the whole balloon is covered. Dry between layers. Add 3 more layers of newspaper strips. Each time you add a layer, change the direction of the strips to make your globe strong. Let your globe dry for a couple of days. Release the rubber band, and the balloon inside will lose its air. Copy the shapes of the different countries from a map or another globe onto your globe. Paint the countries different colors and label them. Label the oceans, too. (Try not to have any lettering near the center of the globe because you are going to make a cut there). Then draw a light chalk line all around the middle of the globe. Cut along this line to make the halves of your Big Round World Box (have an adult help you). Paint the inside of your box a solid color. Glue colored construction paper around a can to make a stand.

Columbus Day

DISCOVER IT GAME

305

This is an exciting race against time!

What You'll Need: Thin cardboard, black and colored felt, glue, fine-tipped marker, scissors, timer

Glue a square of black felt onto a 20 × 20-inch piece of cardboard. Use a fine-tipped marker to draw simple shapes, such as Spain, North America, Columbus's ships, Columbus, spice bottles, the sun, and ocean waves on the colored felt. Cut out each shape, and then cut each shape again into 2 or 3 pieces. To play the game, one player makes a simple scene by putting the shapes on the black felt board (they will stick). The other player studies the scene for a few minutes. The first player then takes the scene away and scrambles the pieces. Set the timer for 5 minutes. The other player must put the felt pieces back together to make the scene before the timer runs out. Make 2 games, and race each other to see who can discover faster.

Sweetest Day

YOU'RE SWEET TARTS

Bake someone nice a delicious goody.

What You'll Need: 1 cup flour, ⅓ cup butter, 2 tablespoons water, ¼ teaspoon salt, fruit preserves, nuts, powdered sugar, measuring cup and spoons, bowl, spoon, small muffin tin, construction paper, scissors, markers, tape, toothpicks

Spread some scrumptious cheer to people who have been kind to you lately. Ask an adult to preheat the oven to 350 degrees. Cream the flour and butter together. Add the water and salt, and blend well. Roll the dough into small balls, and press each one into a muffin tin cup with your fingers. Bake about 10 minutes or until the tart crust is a light, golden brown. When the crust has cooled, spoon fruit preserves into each until the tarts are full. Sprinkle nuts and powdered sugar on top. Draw and cut out heart shapes, and tape them onto toothpicks. Write messages for the people you want to give the tarts to, such as "Thanks for being so nice." They'll be glad they were!

Sweetest Day

TINY SECRET BOX

307

These miniature scenes will touch someone's heart.

What You'll Need: Empty sliding matchbox, construction paper, fabric scraps, scissors, magazines, glue, markers

There is something irresistible about a miniature scene hidden away in a tiny box. It's almost as though you are telling someone a lovely little secret. Maybe you know someone who has been sick in bed or a senior citizen who lives alone. These tiny secret boxes would be a really sweet way to help them celebrate this Sweetest Day. Slide the top off an empty matchbox. Line the box with pretty paper or a square of soft fabric. Cut out or draw tiny pictures to make a little scene to glue inside the box. Does the person you are giving this gift to love the ocean? Make a cheery beach scene inside your box. Finish your box by gluing construction paper to the outside of the matchbox and writing a little message to your friend, such as "You're Sweet" or "I'll Never Forget You."

308

Sweetest Day

SUGAR CUBE SCULPTURES

Sugar is sweet—but it can also be art!

What You'll Need: Cardboard, scissors, markers, old newspapers, sugar cubes, thick poster paints, paintbrushes, glue

Sweetest Day started as a way to remember the orphans and shut-ins who felt forgotten or neglected. One small kind act or gift can mean so much to a person who needs attention—a homemade gift is always especially appreciated. These sugar cube sculptures will make a unique present for someone you want to remember. Cut a square or circle of cardboard to make the base for your sculpture. You can also write a message to the person you are giving the sculpture to on this base. Cover your work area with old newspapers. Paint sugar cubes in a variety of colors; let them dry. When they are ready, glue the cubes together to make interesting shapes on top of the base. You might want to build a little sugar cube house or castle, or stack the sugar cubes in a pattern of repeating colors. Think about who you are giving your sculpture to, and let thoughts of them guide your imagination to create a truly original work of art. (Don't eat the sugar cubes. They are for your art project, not for eating!)

Sweetest Day

FLOWER OF CANDY

The center of this big paper flower is made of sweet, colorful candy.

What You'll Need: Crepe paper, scissors, small bowl, wrapped candies

Whoever receives this colorful flower will not soon forget it—or you! To make a big flower of candy, fold a 6-inch-wide strip of crepe paper in half lengthwise. Cut petal shapes all along the edge that is not folded. Arrange the petals in a small bowl. Fill the center of the flower with pretty candies. Give this sweet flower to someone sweet. Delicious!

United Nations Day (October 24)

WORLD COLORING BOOK

Add color to all the places in the world that you would like to visit!

What You'll Need: Encyclopedias and other research books, white paper, black marker, stapler

This coloring book will not be the only one in the world—but it will be all about the world! Use encyclopedias to research facts about different countries that you would like to visit. Staple together 10 or 12 sheets of white paper to make a book. For each page, write a short caption that includes a fact you have learned during your research. Then draw a simple outline of something that relates to the caption. Give your book as a present to a friend so they can color in your outlines. If you researched France, you can draw the Eiffel Tower. Underneath it you can write, "The Eiffel Tower was built for the Paris International Exhibition and was designed by Alexandre Gustave Eiffel."

United Nations Day (October 24)

TERRIFIC TRADING CARDS

Make your own trading cards to trade with your friends.

What You'll Need: Thin cardboard, playing card, pencil, scissors, tracing paper, map, markers or colored pencils, research books

The United Nations is the peacekeeper for the world. This organization believes that only through international cooperation can humans live together in peace. Trading is one way in which people cooperate. You can make these fun, colorful cards and trade them with your friends. Lay a playing card on cardboard, trace around it, and cut it out. Repeat this for as many cards as you want to make. Then trace the outline of a country or a state by placing tracing paper over a map. Transfer the outline by placing the tracing paper on the cardboard and pressing down hard with a pen. Remove the tracing paper, and go over the indentations you made with the pen on the cardboard. Write the name of the country or state inside the outline. Color the card with markers or colored pencils. On the back of the card, draw pictures that show something found in that country or state, such as official trees, birds, or special foods that are prepared there. Write interesting facts about this place under your pictures. Trade these cards with your friends, and collect the world!

WATCHING OVER THE WORLD

The idea of having an organization where all nations could work toward peace began in 1942, during the Second World War. President Franklin D. Roosevelt came up with the name, "United Nations." Fifty countries signed the original United Nations Charter, with Poland signing later to become one of the original 51 countries of the United Nations. The organization came into being on October 24, 1945.

312

United Nations Day (October 24)

UNITED BUTTONS

Make your own international fashion statement.

What You'll Need: Reference books, strong craft foam squares, ruler, pencil, scissors, permanent markers, craft knife

Add miniature flags to your favorite button-down shirt. Look in reference books to find pictures of flags from different countries. Trace and cut out 2 × 1-inch rectangles from strong craft foam. Make a rectangle for each button you want to cover. Use permanent markers to color each button cover like a different flag. Then take a pencil and mark the width of the button holes from your shirt in the middle of each button cover (on the unpainted side). Have an adult cut slits for the buttons on the lines you just drew. Put on your shirt, and button it. Slip the button covers over the buttons, and unite all the nations!

UNICEF Day (October 31)

COLORFUL COLLECTION BOX

313

This collection box is so pretty everyone will want to put something in it.

What You'll Need: Shoe box or other small box with lid, paints, paintbrushes, old magazines and catalogs, scissors, glue

Do you know what UNICEF (United Nations Children's Fund) does? They collect money to give to needy children all over the world. That's a pretty big job! Lots of people help UNICEF by doing some of the money collecting for the organization. It's easy to make your own collection box. Just use a shoe box or a cigar box and cut a small slot in the lid. Paint the box a pretty color inside and out. When the paint is dry, decorate your box by cutting out pictures of children from magazines and catalogs. Glue the pictures all over the box. Cut out large letters that spell the word UNICEF, and glue these to the top of the box. Put the box on your dining-room table. Whenever you find a coin, you can put it in the box. Whenever you or your family members feel grateful for all you have, you can put in money to send to UNICEF.

314

UNICEF Day (October 31)

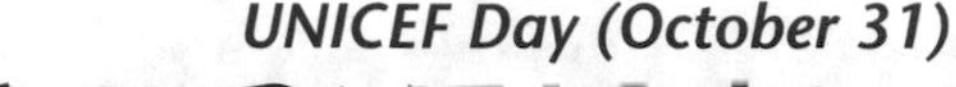

PAPERWEIGHT FACES

These smiling children's faces hold down everyone's papers.

What You'll Need: Smooth, flat stones; paints; paintbrushes; marker; clear varnish; shoe box

Everyone needs a paperweight—especially one as charming as these smiling children paperweights! Gather some smooth, flat stones. Try to find ones that are round or oval-shaped. Paint each one of your stones a different skin tone. There are so many different colors of skin to choose from! Give each face different colored eyes, and all kinds of hairstyles, colors, and textures. The variety is endless! When the fronts of your stones have a smiling child's face on them, let them dry. Then paint the back a pretty color, let it dry, and use a marker to write the words "I Gave to UNICEF" on it. Let the stone dry, and then paint one or more coats of clear varnish on it to protect the paint. Carefully arrange the paperweights in a shoe box. Now you are ready to sell your paperweights to friends and family. Donate your profits to UNICEF!

I Gave to UNICEF!

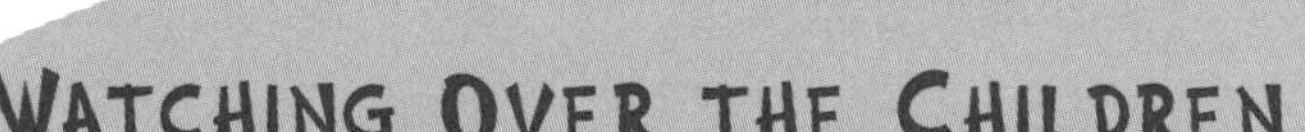

WATCHING OVER THE CHILDREN

UNICEF was founded in 1946, the year after the United Nations began, to help the children of the world. They keep track of statistics of children around the world, such as the percentage of children in a country that reach grade 5. In the U.S., 99 percent of the children reach grade 5, but in Papua New Guinea it is only 59 percent, in Haiti it is 47 percent, and in Afghanistan it is 43 percent.

Halloween (October 31)

315 SPOOKY SPIDER

Hang a few of these spiders around the house to spook up your Halloween!

What You'll Need: Foam egg carton cup, scissors, chenille stems, black permanent marker, pencil, needle, black thread

Spiders look scary, but most are great to have around because they eat pesky bugs. You can make your spider look scary or friendly or silly or even sad! To make it, cut out an egg cup from a foam egg carton. Draw the spider's face on one of the sides. Then poke 4 black chenille stems through one side and out the other. Bend them so that your spider can stand up. Have an adult help you sew a thread up through the inside of the spider's head. Leave the free end of the thread long enough to hang your spider. Your spider may even fool a few bugs!

Halloween (October 31)

MUMMY PIN 316

Wear this silly, scary pin when you go trick or treating.

What You'll Need: Wooden craft stick, white embroidery thread, glue, 2 wiggle eyes, jewelry pin, scissors

You can make this pin almost as quickly as you can say the word "Mummy." Wind white embroidery thread around a craft stick over and over. The more thread you wind on, the fatter your mummy will be! Make sure you wrap more thread around the part that is supposed to be the head. When finished winding, use glue to fasten the thread to the back of the pin. Glue 2 wiggle eyes to the front and a jewelry pin on the back. Make a whole group of mummy pins, and pin them in a big "M" shape on the back of your Halloween costume. M is for Mummy!

I Want My Mummy!

The earliest Egyptian mummies found date back to around 3200 B.C. Back then, people prepared the body by covering it with a natural salt to help dry it out; it was then wrapped in bandages soaked in a type of resin. The organs were removed, and the body was immersed in baking soda for about 40 days. After that, the body was washed, adorned with spices, and wrapped in bandages. The whole process took about 70 days!

317

Halloween (October 31)

BAKED WITCH'S FINGERS

These witchy fingers magically point out how hungry you are!

What You'll Need: 1½ cups warm water, 1 package dry yeast, 1 teaspoon salt, 1 tablespoon sugar, 5 cups white flour, 1 egg, coarse salt, jam, 2 cookie sheets, bowl, measuring cups and spoons, small jar, pastry brush, metal spatula

Make long and crooked witchy fingers, and serve them at your next Halloween party. Have an adult preheat the oven to 350 degrees. Grease 2 cookie sheets. Mix together the warm water and the yeast. Stir in the salt, sugar, and flour to make dough. On a floured surface, pull off pieces of the dough and roll them between your palms to make ropes. Shape each rope into the long, crooked finger of a witch. Make the tip of the finger as pointy as you can. Lay the fingers on the cookie sheets so that they don't touch each other. Put the egg and 1 tablespoon of water into a tightly closed jar, and shake it up very hard. Use a pastry brush to brush this egg glaze onto each finger. Sprinkle the glaze with coarse salt and bake for 25 minutes. Loosen the fingers with a metal spatula. When the witch's fingers have cooled, paint red jam fingernails on their pointy tips!

Halloween (October 31)

BLOOD-RED EYEBALLS

It's your party—you can scream if you want to!

What You'll Need: Maraschino cherries, white chocolate, dark chocolate, 2 small pans, waxed paper, plate

Your friends will be the ones who will be screaming when they see this plate of blood-red eyeballs staring up at them! They will be shocked and horrified! But not too shocked and horrified to gobble up the gruesome orbs and beg for more! With an adult's help, heat the white chocolate until it is melted. Hold a maraschino cherry by the stem, and dip it ⅔ of the way into the chocolate. Dip it several times, so that the chocolate coating is nice and thick and the red of the cherry doesn't show through. Set it on the waxed paper while the chocolate cools. When the white chocolate is cool, melt the dark chocolate. Pull the stems from the cherries, and, using a spoon, fill the hole with an "iris" of dark chocolate. Arrange all the eyes on the plate. Just try not to think about all those eyeballs following your every move!

Halloween (October 31)

OGRE COSTUME

Even your best friend won't recognize you in this scary getup!

What You'll Need: Ratty jeans, mismatched shoes and socks, small towel, string, sweater, old oversized T-shirt, fabric markers, rope, cold cream, sweet corn syrup, cotton balls, liquid foundation, eye pencil, face paint, burlap bag, reflective tape, old woolen ski cap

Every Halloween party should have at least one ogre around to liven things up. You will need to wear old, mismatched clothes and shoes. If your father has a pair of old shoes, wear those and stuff them with newspapers so that your feet don't slip out. Ogres are some of the world's worst dressers! You might even want to wear the shoes on the wrong feet because ogres are not too smart, either. For the ogre's hump, fold a small towel in quarters and tie it up. Put the towel on your shoulder and tie more string around it and your shoulders to hold it in place. Put on a tight sweater to keep your hump really secure. To make the ogre's tunic, cut the sleeves off an old T-shirt that is too big for you. The dirtier and more full of holes, the better! You can also paint blood or snakes on it with fabric markers. Use a rope to belt it around your waist. To make a lumpy ogre face, apply a thin layer of cold cream. Then glue thin wisps of cotton to your face with sweet corn syrup. Put the lumps on your nose and cheeks. Carefully dab liquid foundation on the cotton and then over the rest of your face. When the makeup dries, use an eye pencil to draw a scary third eye in the middle of your forehead. Smudge green face paint around your real eyes. You can also draw thin red lines above and below all 3 eyes for a really sickly ogre look. Draw black scar lines with dots on either side of the lines to look like stitch marks. Color your lips gray. Use a burlap bag for your trick-or-treat bag. Put reflective tape on the front and back of your costume for safety if you are going to be walking around in the dark. Finish off your costume by tucking all your hair up in an old woolen ski cap. Have some twigs and leaves sticking out so it looks like you've been doing scary ogre things in the deep, dark woods!

320

Halloween (October 31)

REALLY HAUNTED HOUSE

Create a house of horrors, and give your friends a silly scare!

What You'll Need: Blindfold; small tables, chairs, or boxes; large sheet; rubber creatures; tape; cold, cooked noodles; peeled grapes; old mop head; chilled, greased broccoli; rubber gloves filled with wet sand; wet string; chopped gelatin, flashlight, sound-effects tapes; feather

For a realistic Halloween, create a haunted house. Lead your blindfolded friends one by one through this scary room. To make a first-class scary haunted house, cover folding chairs and tables or boxes with a big, open sheet to make a long tunnel. Tape rubber spiders and bats to the inside for your friends to feel while a scary tape plays. Outside the tunnel, place bowls of clammy substances to dip your guests' hands into, such as cold, cooked noodles, peeled grapes, an old mop head, greased broccoli, rubber gloves filled with wet sand, wet string, and chopped gelatin—which can feel like intestines, eyeballs, witch hair, brains, hearts, and monster hands. Flick a flashlight on and off, and play scary tapes of cackles and screeches that you have prerecorded. Tickle your friends' arms with a feather, and tell them that it is a vampire bat. Have them walk through a curtain of hanging strings—tell them that it is a spider web. When you finish, take off the blindfold and let them see just how scary the haunted house really is. You'll all have a good, long cackle.

Halloween (October 31)

MARVELOUS MONSTER

Beware! There are monsters everywhere!

What You'll Need: Tennis ball; craft knife; black, green, and orange felt; scissors; white glue; pencil; yarn; small candies or toys

Ask an adult to cut a 2½-inch slit in the middle of the tennis ball. Cut 2 triangle-shaped mouth pieces from felt—the base of the triangles should be 2½ inches wide. Put glue on the top and bottom edges of the ball's slit. Glue the edges of the triangles into the slit to form a beak. Slide a pencil into the slit to keep it open while the glue dries. Cut eyes from felt, and glue them in place. Use felt or yarn tentacles to decorate your monster. When the glue is dry, squeeze the monster's sides to make it open its mouth. Fill it up with wrapped candy or toys!

322

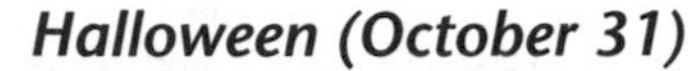

Halloween (October 31)

SPIDER BALL

On Halloween—when werewolves howl and crazed creatures crawl—ghosties and ghoulies play spider ball! Play it by yourself, or with a fiend . . . er, friend.

What You'll Need: Large plastic lid from a coffee can (or any large plastic lid), scissors, black and white yarn, Ping-Pong ball, black and red markers

To make a spider's web paddle, cut the center out of the plastic lid, leaving a 1-inch rim all the way around. Tie black yarn to the ring, leaving a 2-inch tail. Wrap the ring with yarn until it is completely covered. Be sure the tail is not covered! Tie the yarn, and trim the end. Tie the white yarn to the 2-inch tail. Stretch the yarn across the ring to the other side, and pull it fairly tight. Wrap it around and tie a knot, then stretch it across in a different direction and repeat to form a web. Repeat until you have a nice tight web. Now, using the markers, draw a big, black spider (with red eyes) on top of the Ping-Pong ball. Her long, black legs should wrap around the "egg-sack" ball. Bounce the spider ball on the web. How many times can you bounce it in a row?

Halloween (October 31)

FLOATING GHOSTS GAME

323

Watch out for low-flying ghosts when you play this game.

What You'll Need: Black construction paper, tape, white balloons, black permanent marker

Your party guests can each make their own ghost to use in this fun game. Give each player a piece of black construction paper, and have them tape it to make a tube. Have everyone blow up a white balloon. Younger children may need an adult to help them do this. Each player draws a silly or scary ghost face on their balloon with a black marker. To play the game, players lie on their backs with their ghost balloon on top of their black tube. When someone says "Go," players have to blow through their tubes. Whoever keeps their ghost up in the air (it can't touch the tube) for the longest time is the winner. (Balloons are choking hazards for small children—be sure they are supervised when playing with balloons!)

Halloween (October 31)

324 IT'S IMPOSSIBLE

Practice makes perfect before you perform this tricky trick.

What You'll Need: Catsup bottle with cap, checkers or poker chips, strip of paper 1½ × 3 inches

You may want to wear the magician's costume (see next page) you made for this trick. Before you perform it, however, you will need to practice. To set up the trick, place a strip of paper on top of a closed catsup bottle so that one end of the paper hangs over longer than the other side. Stack checkers or poker chips on top of the paper. The higher the stack, the more impressed your audience will be. Start practicing with just a few checkers or chips though, and work your way up. To remove the strip without knocking the checkers or chips off the bottle, lick your index finger so that it will stick to the paper. Grasp the longer end of the paper between your index finger and your thumb. Quickly bring your hand down toward the table. You must remove the paper as quickly as possible. If you hesitate, the stack will fall! When you are ready to perform your trick, tell your audience that you have special powers on Halloween. Show them how you set up the trick and how easy it is to knock the stack over. Challenge a member of the audience to perform the trick. The stack will crash. Then you, the powerful Halloween magician, will show them your magic!

Halloween (October 31)

MAGIC GLOVE 325

To your audience, this is no ordinary glove. Only you know the real truth.

What You'll Need: Long shiny glove, ring, toothpick, playing cards, table

Before doing this trick, tell your audience that the glove on your hand has magic Halloween powers. Lay your gloved hand on a table, and push a card under it. Keep pushing cards under it until there are 10 cards. Say "Abracadabra," and slowly lift your hand. All the cards will raise up with your hand! How did you do it? Everyone will want to know. Your secret is this: The ring you are wearing on the middle finger of your glove has a toothpick stuck in it along the underside of your hand. The toothpick holds the first card, and the rest of the cards hold the others as you push them in one by one. Now that's magic!

326

Halloween (October 31)

MAGICIAN COSTUME

Wear this costume while you perform some Halloween magic.

What You'll Need: Two 15 × 4-inch strips of shiny material, 2 fake jewels pins, black crepe paper, needle and thread, black ribbon

If you want to put on a magic show this Halloween, you'll need to be dressed in the right costume. To make a magician's turban, drape a strip of the shiny material over your head so that the middle of the fabric is in the middle of your head and the ends hang down on either side of your body. Bring the ends up over the top of your head and cross them in front to make a big X. Tuck the ends into the back of the fabric where it meets your head. If you have a big jeweled pin, attach it to the middle of your turban. To make a sash, tie another strip of fabric around your waist and let the ends hang off to one side. Make a cape from crepe paper; use a bath towel for a pattern by laying it on the crepe paper and cutting around it. Fasten the cape around your neck with another large, jeweled pin, or sew a black ribbon to each of the top corners of the cape, and tie them in a bow around your neck. Now you're ready to do some hocus pocus!

WHAT'S IN A NAME?

Perhaps one of the most famous early magicians was escape artist Harry Houdini. His actual name was Ehrich Weiss, but he changed it after reading an autobiography by the French magician Jean Robert-Houdin. He wanted to be just like Robert-Houdin, so he added the letter I, which means "like," to his name; so he became Houdini.

Halloween (October 31)

SCARY SOUNDS

Disguise your voice and fool the witch in this scary party game.

What You'll Need: Blindfold, witch hat, 4 or more players

See how good you are at making monster sounds when you try to fool the witch. The game begins with one person wearing a witch hat and a blindfold. This person is the "witch" and must be seated facing away from the rest of the players. The rest of the players are the "monsters." Each monster takes a turn creeping up to the witch and disguising their voice to make scary monster sounds. They can also say scary monster sayings such as "I'm coming to get you!" The witch must try to guess who each monster is. If the monster gets caught, he or she must take the witch's place.

Halloween (October 31)

PAPER PLATE MONSTER

328

Keep this big-mouthed monster away from all your Halloween treats, or else!

What You'll Need: White paper plate, poster board, scissors, glue, chenille stems, crayons or markers, ribbon

To make this scary decoration, fold a dinner-sized paper plate in half for the giant mouth. Cut out a few 3-inch-long, arch-shaped eyes—remember, monsters can have more than 2 eyes! Carefully cut slits in the top half of the mouth, and stick the eyes into the slits. Fold the bottom edge of the slit, and glue it to the inside of the mouth to hold the eyes in place. Make antennae or horns, and attach them to the mouth in the same way as you did the eyes. Cut out arms, legs, or tentacles. Glue them to the underside of the mouth so that they stick out. Color your monster with wild colors. You might want to glue a long ribbon inside the mouth for the monster's tongue. Put your monster on the kitchen table, and tell everyone to watch their treats!

Halloween (October 31)

329 ALIEN EGGS

One look at these eggs and you will know they could never have been laid by an earthy creature!

What You'll Need: Wrapped candies, Halloween toys (creepy bugs and monsters), 12-inch balloons, white glue, water, measuring cup, string

Push 3 to 4 large wrapped candies and a medium-sized toy inside a deflated balloon. (Important: Don't use small candies or toys! Make sure that the candies and toys are too big to fit back through the nozzle of the balloon—so you have no danger of inhaling the objects. You should have to stretch the nozzle to get them inside.) Blow up the balloon until it is about 6 inches across. Tie the balloon. Mix ½ cup white glue and ¼ cup water. Put the string in the glue/water mixture. Pull the string between your fingers to squeeze out some of the glue; wrap the balloon in a spider's web of string. Allow to dry in a warm place for at least a day. When the glue is thoroughly dry, pop the balloon. Carefully take out the broken balloon pieces. (Balloons are choking hazards—keep them away from small children!)

Halloween (October 31)

330 SPOOKY PICTURES

These are the scariest pictures you'll ever make by blowing through a straw!

What You'll Need: Newspaper, drawing paper, teaspoon, thinned tempera paint, drinking straw

These spooky pictures can be a little messy to make, so cover your table with newspaper before you begin. For each picture, pour a teaspoon of tempera paint onto a piece of paper. Gently blow at it through a drinking straw to make weird, scary shapes. If you want, you can add teaspoons of different colors of paint to blow on top of the first color. These pictures will always be a big surprise. Is that a spider? Is that a witch riding a broom? Take turns with your friends describing the things you see in each picture.

Halloween (October 31)

GHOSTLY GOBBLE GAME

This is a tasty way to turn yourself into a ghost!

What You'll Need: Powdered donuts, strings, coat hangers

This game is a silly way to serve dessert after a Halloween dinner. Attach strings to coat hangers that are hung in your Halloween party room. Tie a powdered donut to the end of each string. (You may want to cover the floor with an old shower curtain or newspapers, or do this game outside—it can get a little messy). Invite your guests to eat the donuts while keeping their hands behind their backs. The powdered sugar will get all over everyone's faces and turn them into ghostly gobblers!

Halloween (October 31)

COLORED FACE POWDER

Mix up a batch of makeup for your favorite ghoul.

What You'll Need: Colored nontoxic chalk, plastic bags, rolling pin, 2 nesting metal bowls, cornstarch, measuring cup, talcum powder, cup, food coloring, spoon, cotton balls

Here's how you can mix up your own Halloween makeup. To make face powder, wrap a piece of colored chalk in a plastic bag. Pound it with a rolling pin. Be careful that you do not break the plastic bag. When you have broken the chalk into small pieces, pour it into the larger of two nesting metal bowls. Put the smaller bowl inside the larger one and move it around in circles to grind the chalk into a fine powder. You will need to press fairly hard to do this. After the chalk is ground into an even powder, mix in ½ cup of cornstarch. You can experiment with different amounts of chalk and cornstarch to see which feels best on your skin. You can make another kind of powder by putting 1 tablespoon of talcum powder into a cup and mixing in 5 or 6 drops of food coloring. Mix the food coloring well, so that it is spread evenly in the powder. Use the cotton balls to apply your ghoulish powders—look great from head to toe in your Halloween costume!

Halloween (October 31)

DRACULA COSTUME

Your neighbors will scream when the famous Count Dracula shows up at their house!

What You'll Need: White dress shirt; dark pants, shoes, socks, bow tie; 2 yards black material; scissors; sewing supplies; black ribbon; 2 large rubber bands; reflective tape; hair gel; nontoxic face paints; fangs; fake blood; black bag

Count Dracula may be a monster, but he is also a snazzy dresser. Put on a white dress shirt, and dark pants, shoes, socks, and bow tie. Cut out a cape—make the bottom of the cape scalloped, just like bat wings. Sew black ribbons at the top corners to tie the cape around your neck. Sew a rubber band on each side where the cape hits your wrist so the fabric will swirl nicely when you move your arms. Put a V for vampire or write "The Count" on the back of your cape with reflective tape. Slick back your hair with hair gel, and paint your face with white face paint. Smudge dark circles under your eyes—Count Dracula is always up all night! Slip some plastic fangs in your mouth, and drip a little fake blood down your chin or the corners of your lips to show everyone just what the Count has been drinking. Color your lips black and then add a coat of red. Don't forget your trick or treat bag—black, of course!

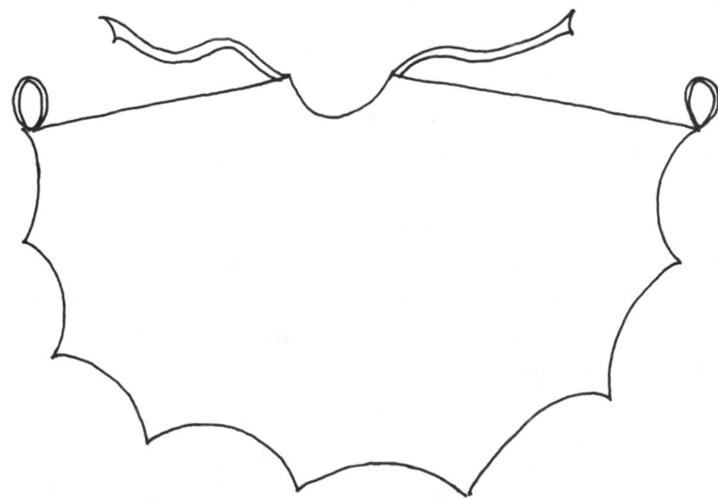

334

Halloween (October 31)

SCARY BONE HUNT

Hunt for bones, and make them into scary glowing "bone" people.

What You'll Need: White cardboard, scissors, glow-in-the-dark paint and markers, paintbrushes, newspapers

Invite your friends to a scary bone hunt this Halloween. First draw and cut out lots of different-sized bones from cardboard. Hide them around the Halloween party room. Be creative with your hiding places—bones can be tucked inside books, under rugs and chair cushions, even slipped inside a bushy plant. If you are having your bone hunt outdoors, you might want to weight the bones down with small pebbles so they don't blow away. When all of the bones have been found, lay out newspapers and paint the bones with glow-in-the-dark paint. When the paint is dry, use glow-in-the-dark paints and markers to make faces on the bones. These scary bone people are great party favors for your guests to take home.

Halloween (October 31)

GHOSTLY FINGERS PUNCH

A ghostly hand floats in a punch bowl!

What You'll Need: Disposable gloves, yellow food coloring, lemonade, orange juice, carbonated water, punch bowl, scissors

Serve this punch at your next Halloween party and watch the surprise on your friends' faces. Wash a pair of disposable gloves inside and out. Fill them with water, add a few drops of yellow food coloring to the water, and knot the opening closed. Freeze your gloves for several hours or overnight. Just before the party, pour enough lemonade, orange juice, and carbonated water to fill a large punch bowl. Then take your frozen gloves from the freezer and cut away the gloves. Place the frozen hands into the punch, and let the party begin.

336

Halloween (October 31)

ZOMBIE COSTUME

On Halloween night, dress up like one of the walking dead!

What You'll Need: Ratty old shirt, fabric paint, old dark pants that can get smeared with dirt, old beat-up shoes and socks, cold cream, gray eye shadow, black eye crayon, white eye crayon, blue and red makeup sticks, cold spaghetti, lightweight chains, burlap bag, silver reflective tape

Turn into a scary zombie for Halloween. Start with an old, torn-up shirt and draw a jagged, "bloody" slit over the chest. Dribble more red paint down from the slit so it looks like dried blood. If anyone asks how you were killed, tell them in a scary voice that someone stabbed you! Put on old dark pants and smear them with dirt. Dirty up some old shoes and socks and put those on, too. Remember, zombies have to climb through 6 feet of earth to get out of a grave! For the zombie face, cover your face with a thin layer of cold cream; then smooth on gray eye shadow. Color your nostrils and lips black, and smudge more black all around your eyes. You can add white circles around your eyes, too. To make a scar, draw a crooked smudge of blue and dark red. Draw a thin black line through it and tiny black dots on either side to look like the holes left by stitches. You can also paint your hands gray. Make it look like you have maggots crawling all over you by putting short pieces of cold, cooked spaghetti in your hair and on your costume. Drape some lightweight chains around you, and rattle them as you walk. Your trick or treat bag can be a burlap sack. Have someone put some reflective tape on the front and back of your costume so you can have a safe as well as a scary Halloween.

Halloween (October 31)

SCARY BUG GAME

All the bug lovers in the house will have fun playing this scary game of chance.

What You'll Need: Die, paper, scissors, markers, tape

This game will be fun during a Halloween party. Cut small squares of paper to cover a die. Mark each square with one of these letters: B, H, L, E, A, T. These letters stand for body, head, legs, eyes, antennae, and tail of the Scary Bug. Tape each square onto one side of the die. Then give each player a piece of drawing paper. Have a lot of colored markers for them to choose from. To play the game, a player rolls the die. That player draws the body part starting with whichever letter is face up. The next player rolls the die and draws whatever body part that starts with the letter rolled. Play continues until someone draws the entire Scary Bug to win the game. At the end of the game, everyone can color their bug drawings and hang them up as Halloween decorations.

Halloween (October 31)

DANCING JACK-O'-LANTERN

Put on a Halloween show for the trick-or-treaters with this dancing pumpkin pal!

What You'll Need: Poster board, scissors, paintbrush, glow-in-the-dark paints, paper fasteners, dark clothes

To make a dancing jack-o'-lantern, cut out a round pumpkin shape for the body and a smaller pumpkin shape for the head. Cut out rectangles for the arms and legs. Cut out small pumpkin shapes for the hands and feet. Paint all of the shapes with glow-in-the-dark paint, adding jack-o'-lantern faces on the head and hands. Using the paper fasteners, attach the hands to the arms and the legs to the feet. Then attach arms and legs to the body. Charge up the glow paint by shining a light on it. Turn off all the lights, and stand in front of the window with the curtains drawn behind you. Wear black or dark clothes, gloves, and a hat so you are almost invisible. Move the jack-o'-lantern's head, arms, and legs to make him dance. Anyone who looks in the window will see something very spooky!

Halloween (October 31)

BUTTERFLY MASK

People will be wondering who's behind this mask long after you have flown away.

What You'll Need: Cardboard egg carton, scissors, poster board, paints, paintbrushes, markers, glue, sequins, glitter, feathers, needle, elastic string

Not all Halloween costumes are scary—some are actually quite beautiful. To transform yourself into a beautiful butterfly, cut out a 2-cup section from an egg carton for the eye mask. Make holes in the bottoms of the cups so you can see through them. Cut out 2 butterfly wings (add tabs to the inside of the wings to attach them to the mask) from poster board. Paint the wings and the eye mask pretty colors, and glue on sequins, glitter (on the wings only), and feathers in an attractive design. To attach the wings to the eye mask, carefully cut a small slit on the top of each egg cup just large enough for you to snugly fit the tabs of the butterfly wings into. Glue the tabs in place. Ask an adult to poke a tiny hole on the side of each egg cup with the needle. Thread the elastic string through the holes. Knot the ends of the string in the holes. You don't need a lot of elastic because it will stretch—you may need to experiment with different lengths to see what best fits your head. Put on your mask, and flap your wings!

A JACK O' WHAT?

In Ireland, where the first jack-o'-lantern was carved, people used rutabagas, potatoes, turnips, and beets! Pumpkins weren't used until the jack-o'-lantern was brought to the United States.

340

Halloween (October 31)

VISIBLE/INVISIBLE GAME

You won't believe your eyes in this secret game of camouflage!

What You'll Need: 12 small objects (piece of embroidery thread, nail, marble, button, piece of ribbon, thimble, postage stamp, pencil, etc.), list of objects and pencil for each player, timer

You and your Halloween guests won't be the only ones in disguise during this exciting game. Ordinary household objects will seem to disappear once you know how to "disguise" them. To set up the game, all the players except one must leave the room. That one player then places a dozen small objects in plain sight near other objects that can camouflage them. For example, she or he might put a piece of thread on a curtain that is the same color or place a pencil along the bottom edge of a cabinet. When all the objects are hidden, the player who hid them gives each of the other players a list of what they must find. The players race to find the objects but when they spy one, they don't tell anyone. They write down on their list where they saw it hidden. After 5 minutes, all the players stop looking. Whoever found the most objects is the winner. (Hint: Whoever is hiding the objects should keep a list for her or himself to remember where the objects are hidden!)

Halloween (October 31)

WRIGGLING SNAKE

341

This snake isn't dangerous—until it gets out of your pocket!

What You'll Need: 5-inch piece of stretchy plastic wrap, large paper clip

Here's a great Halloween "trick" to perform when earning "treats." Tell your audience that you have a live snake in your pocket. Sometime before the trick, hold one end of a piece of plastic wrap and twist the other end into a rope shape. Make sure when you are twisting the wrap that you wind it very tight. Roll the twisted wrap up so it forms a round, flat coil. For the snake's head, make a small knot in the free end of the coil. Hold the coil together with a large paper clip. When you are about to let your snake out of your pocket, reach your hand in and remove the paper clip, but hold the coil so it doesn't unwind. Once the snake is in your hand without the paper clip, it will wriggle and writhe as it unwinds. Getting the clip off in secret will take a little practice. This trick looks very good with colored plastic wrap!

342

All Saints' Day (November 1)

SOULING

On All Souls' Day—a day when lost souls wander the earth—people used to go Souling—a game that was half trick-or-treat and half truth-or-dare.

What You'll Need: Shortbread cookies or candies, small napkins, 2 masks, 2 sheets, straws

Invite your friends over for a medieval costume party. Put a treat—any special candy or cookie will do—on a small napkin by their plate. Warn them not to eat it! When the meal is done, draw straws to see who will be the wandering souls. The 2 guests who draw the short straws must put on masks, or smudge their faces with soot, and wrap up in a sheet. As they walk around the table, the soulers chant: "A soul cake, a soul cake, please, give us a soul cake, one for Peter, two for Paul, three for Him who made us all. If you haven't got a soul cake, a half-penny will do, if you haven't got a half-penny, then God bless you!" When they say "you!" they tap someone on the shoulder. That person can either give them the treat on the napkin or keep it for themselves. If they keep it, however, the wandering souls can command them to do something funny or tell a secret.

NOW THAT'S A CEILING!

One of the most amazing pieces of art was unveiled on All Saints' Day in 1541. Michelangelo's "Creation," on the Sistine Chapel ceiling, was uncovered that day.

All Saints' Day (November 1)

343 LACE CANDLE

In many countries, people light candles to remember the saints. Make a special lace candle for All Saints' Day.

What You'll Need: 1 quart milk carton, pencil, white candle wax, old saucepan, long white candle, ice

Poke lots of holes in the sides and bottom of the milk carton with the pencil. Have an adult help you melt the wax. Put the long white candle in the middle of the milk carton. Hold the candle in place, and fill the carton with ice. Have the adult pour the hot wax into the carton over the ice. When the hot wax melts the ice, the water will run out the holes you made in the sides. Don't stop pouring until the wax reaches the top of the carton. Let the wax cool. Peel the carton off. Set your lace candle in the center of the table at dinner time.

Veteran's Day (November 1)

VICTORIOUS VETERAN PINS

Award these colorful pins to the brave veterans at the parade!

What You'll Need: Large safety pins, colored beads to fit on pins, white glue, waxed paper, ribbon, scissors

It is traditional to honor brave soldiers with medals, pins, and ribbons. Long after the war, you can show veterans that you have not forgotten their courageous acts. Make these victory pins, and give them to your local veteran's association to distribute. To make one, thread colored beads onto the pin side of a large safety pin. You could use only red, white, and blue beads for a patriotic flair! Or you can use purple for a Purple Heart pin, or use white beads for peace. Glue the beads onto the pin. Let them dry on waxed paper. Tie a little ribbon onto the other arm of each pin. Don't forget to make a pin for your shirt, too!

345

Veteran's Day (November 11)

WOODEN SPOON SOLDIERS

This army will be sure to protect all the ice cream at your holiday party!

What You'll Need: Wooden ice cream spoons, markers, construction paper, scissors, glue, aluminum foil, ribbon

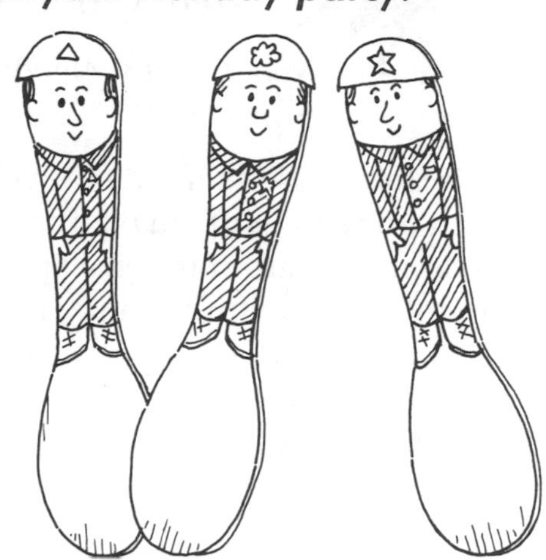

Bring this army to your Veteran's Day picnic to protect the food and decorate the table. Before you make your army, decide what colors the uniforms will be. It will look more realistic if you have all your soldiers wearing the same outfit. Color a hat and face on the top part of each spoon. Cut out hats from construction paper, and glue them on. Color the uniforms onto each spoon handle. Don't forget to color the backs of your spoons, too. Make tiny badges of honor from foil and bits of ribbon, and glue them onto your bravest soldiers. When the glue dries—1, 2, 3, march!

Veteran's Day (November 11)

MARCHING SONGS

346

Get everybody marching to your tune!

What You'll Need: Drum, tambourine, other percussive instruments

Everyone loves marching songs. If you have ever marched to *Yankee Doodle Dandy* or *When the Saints Go Marching In* you know how much fun these songs add to a parade. You can make up your own Veteran's Day marching songs. Think of themes that go with the holiday, and make up titles such as *Peace Forever* or *War No More*. Then write the lyrics to your song. These songs work well if the phrases rhyme. When you sing the marching songs, call out the lyrics in a loud, clear voice. Use a drum, tambourine, or other instrument to keep the beat while you sing. To get yourself started, sing these lyrics while you pound your drum: "Today's the day when we all say: No more war! War go away! All our soldiers are home to stay!"

347

Veteran's Day (November 11)

PATRIOTIC RAINDROPS

Here's some raindrops you'll want to let right in the house!

What You'll Need: ½ cup white grape juice, 1 package unflavored gelatin, red and blue food coloring, mini marshmallows, saucepan, spoon, 2 bowls, cookie sheet, waxed paper

If the parade's rained out, you can still be patriotic. Make a batch of red and blue raindrops, and serve them up with white marshmallows. Put the grape juice in a small saucepan, and have an adult cook it on medium heat until it boils. Sprinkle the gelatin on the fruit juice, and mix it until the gelatin dissolves. Be careful, this mixture is hot. Have an adult pour the mixture into 2 bowls. Put a few drops of red food coloring in one bowl and a few drops of blue in the other. Spoon 1-inch raindrop shapes onto the waxed paper. Let them cool for about 20 minutes, then peel them off the paper. Put them on a plate with some mini marshmallows for a victorious Veteran's Day dessert!

Thanksgiving Day

ORANGEY POPCORN BALLS

348

This snack is a pretty centerpiece when piled into a pyramid.

What You'll Need: 1½ cups popcorn kernels, cooking oil, 1 package orange gelatin, 1 cup sugar, 1 cup corn syrup, orange food coloring, saucepan, large bowl or serving platter, butter, honey, cranberries

Get the whole gang involved in making this edible centerpiece. Everyone loves the sound of popcorn pinging away in the pan while it pops. Have an adult help you pop the popcorn. After the corn is popped, mix the gelatin, sugar, corn syrup, and a few drops of food coloring together in a saucepan. Have the adult heat and stir until the mix reaches a full boil. The adult should pour the syrup over the popcorn. Stir it well to thoroughly coat all the kernels. Let the popcorn cool a few minutes. Now for the really fun part! Butter your hands, and shape the popcorn into orange-sized balls. Arrange the balls in a stacked pyramid shape on a serving platter or in a large bowl. If you have trouble balancing the popcorn balls, use a little dab of honey as "glue." Dot your pyramid with fresh cranberries to add even more Thanksgiving color. Don't forget to eat this centerpiece for dessert!

Thanksgiving Day

STAND-UP PILGRIMS

Put these pilgrims all around the house in surprising places.

What You'll Need: Stiff cardboard, pencil, scissors, markers, felt, glue

Who's that standing on top of the television? Who's hiding behind the sugar bowl? Is there someone standing next to the faucet of the kitchen sink? Why, it's the pilgrims! And they seem to be standing around all over the house! Make lots of these cutout figures, and place them in your home to create a thankful Thanksgiving mood. For each pilgrim, draw a 6- to 8-inch-high person. At the bottom of each figure, draw a rectangular base a little wider than the person's body. Draw on hats, breeches, buckled shoes, and long dresses such as the pilgrims wore. You could also cut out the pilgrims' clothes from felt and glue them onto your figure. Then cut out your pilgrim with its rectangular base attached. Cut a vertical slit in the bottom center of the rectangular base. Then cut out another same-sized rectangle from cardboard, make a vertical slit in the middle of the top, and insert it into the other slit to make a cross-shaped base. Now, who's that standing around? Why, it's Miles Standish!

Thanksgiving Day

YAM VINES

Save the tops from your Thanksgiving yams, and watch them grow!

What You'll Need: Yam (or sweet potato), knife, vegetable brush, toothpicks, jar, water

This is such a pretty Thanksgiving plant, and so easy to grow. The top of a long, skinny yam will work best for this. Cut off the bottom third of the yam (have an adult help you). Scrub the top well with warm water and a brush. Then stick 4 toothpicks into the center of the yam top so that it will sit in a jar full of water with half of it poking out the top. The cut part should be fully in the water. Place the jar in bright light, but not direct sun. Check your yam every day to make sure that the water always covers the cut part. Turn your yam so that all sides get even light. After about a week, you will see stringy white roots growing out of the cut part. Soon, purplish leaves will sprout from the top. If your water gets cloudy, pour it out and refill the jar. The yam vine will grow fast, and soon the leaves will be bright green. Transfer the plant to larger and larger jars as the vine grows and grows and grows.

Thanksgiving Day

TURKEY BLOW-UPS

351

These turkeys are full of hot air!

What You'll Need: Round balloons, poster board, glue, markers, scissors

These turkeys come in all the colors of the rainbow. Blow up lots of different-colored round or oval balloons. Then cut strips of poster board to make stands for the balloons to rest on. Cut some strips 3 inches wide and 6 inches long. Cut other strips 1½ inches wide and 10 inches long. This will give the height and look of your turkeys more variety. Glue the ends of each strip together. Draw a line of glue around the top edge of each stand, and gently press a balloon onto it. Draw turkey heads and tails, and cut them out of the poster board. Add a little extra flap at the bottom of the neck and the base of the tail. These flaps can be bent and glued onto each end of the balloon to form the turkey. Make a whole flock of these terrific party decorations! (Balloons are choking hazards—keep them away from small children!)

352

Thanksgiving Day

"THANKFUL" MESSAGE BOX

Help the family get into the Thanksgiving spirit with this message box.

What You'll Need: Shoe box, tissue box, paints, paintbrush, assorted decorative art supplies, pencil, string, tape, small slips of notepaper

When the pilgrims first harvested crops in their new country, they held a big party to celebrate and give thanks. When your family sits down to a big Thanksgiving dinner, everyone's stomach is probably very grateful for all that delicious food. But what else are people thankful for? The week before Thanksgiving, paint and decorate an empty shoe box and tissue box. Tie one end of a string around a pencil, and tape the other end to the tissue box. Set a stack of notepaper next to the pencil. Invite family and friends to write down what they are thankful for, and put the slips inside the tissue box. On Thanksgiving Day, take turns reading the slips aloud. The shoe box can be used to store the slips, adding a new bunch of "thankful messages" each year. You may want to paint traditional Thanksgiving symbols on your boxes, such as turkeys, pilgrims, Native Americans, and harvest foods, such as corn, pumpkin, squash, and apples. You can print the words "Give Thanks" around the opening of the tissue box and the words "Our Thanks" on top.

Thanksgiving Day

HARVEST CANDLEHOLDERS

353

Can a fruit be a candleholder? You bet!

What You'll Need: Apple, orange, grapefruit, apple corer or knife, candles, raisins, toothpicks, cloves

Choose the right fruit for these candleholders by making sure the fruit can sit securely on a plate. Use an apple, orange, or grapefruit. Have an adult help you make a hole in your fruit that is large enough for a taper candle to fit snugly inside. The hole should go almost to the bottom of the fruit. Have the adult light a match and drip some warm wax into the hole. Press the candle into the wax before it cools. This will keep your candle from falling over. Now make pretty designs on your fruit by sticking raisins on toothpicks or cloves into the flesh. (Break the toothpicks in half). You may want to alternate stripes of cloves with stripes of raisins. When you are done, ask an adult to light your candle, and use it for a festive, flickering centerpiece for your holiday meal.

354

Thanksgiving Day

PILGRIM SEED PICTURES

It will take patient hands to make this 3-D picture.

What You'll Need: Poster board, markers, glue, sunflower and pumpkin seeds, lentils, uncooked spaghetti

From tiny seeds grow mighty trees—and mighty pilgrims, too! Draw a large outline of a pilgrim on a piece of poster board. Give him a hat, knee breeches, a shirt with a collar or a short jacket, a belt, long stockings, and shoes. Glue the seeds one at a time to fill in the outline. Overlap the seeds to fill in all the gaps. Use sunflower seeds for the black hat, shoes, and belt. You can color pumpkin seeds with markers to fill in other areas. Lentils can be used for the eyes, nose, and mouth. Break pieces of uncooked spaghetti to glue on for the hair. You will have to work carefully to make this picture, but you'll have the patience of a pilgrim when you are through!

Thanksgiving Day

YUMMY YAMMY MUFFINS

355

Everyone at the breakfast table will be thanking you for these yummy treats!

What You'll Need: 4 tablespoons sweet butter, 1 cup canned yams, 1¾ cups whole wheat flour, ½ teaspoon salt, ½ cup brown sugar, 2 teaspoons baking powder, 2 eggs, 4 tablespoons sweet butter, ¾ cup milk, 1 teaspoon cinnamon, 1 teaspoon nutmeg, measuring cups and spoons, saucepan, fork, mixing bowl, muffin tin and cups, honey or jam

These muffins are a snap to make. Have an adult preheat the oven to 350 degrees and melt the butter over low heat. Mash the yams in a bowl. Combine all the ingredients, and mix well. Pour the batter into muffin cups in a muffin tin. Bake for about 20 minutes. Let cool a little before serving with honey or jam. Breakfast has never been so yummy, or so yammy!

Thanksgiving Day

TURKEY COSTUME

Entertain the Thanksgiving crowd at your house by turning into a giant turkey!

What You'll Need: Box, paint, paintbrushes, scissors, glue, tissue paper, cardboard, craft feathers, T-shirt, tights

There will be 2 turkeys in the house this Thanksgiving: one on the dinner table and one dancing through the house! Turn yourself into a festive holiday turkey! Make a turkey head by painting a cardboard box (large enough to fit your head inside) red. Cut out holes for the eyes. Tear off yellow, orange, and red tissue paper feathers, and glue them all over the front of the box, leaving the eye holes free. Cut a triangle-shaped beak from cardboard, paint it yellow, and glue it underneath the eyes on the front of the box. You can also cut the turkey wattle from cardboard, paint it red, and attach it to the bottom front of the box. Glue craft feathers onto an old red T-shirt, and put on some red tights to complete the costume. Now, practice your gobble and start talking turkey!

PILGRIMS REMEMBERED

The Pilgrim monument was built to commemorate the pilgrims' historic landing on Plymouth Rock. The monument was dedicated in 1910, and it is the tallest granite structure in the United States! It is 253 feet high.

357

Thanksgiving Day

MOSAIC PLANTERS

The fall harvest can decorate your spring planters!

What You'll Need: Paper, crayons, assortment of dried beans, empty can, sandpaper, white glue, small paintbrush, shellac or clear nail polish, dried flowers

Before you begin to make these planters, sketch out pattern ideas on paper first. Look at your beans and arrange them on a table, then copy the design you like on paper, using a different colored crayon for each of the colored beans. Refer to your sketch as you glue the beans onto the can. Make sure that your can really is clean and that all the paper labels are removed before you start. Sandpaper the can so that the beans will stick better. Paint a thin layer of glue on one area at a time, and glue the beans on in your chosen design. Cover the can so little metal shows through. Protect your design with 1 or 2 coats of shellac or clear nail polish. Fill the can with dried flowers for a harvest theme decoration. Or use the can in a few months when you start your spring seedlings.

Thanksgiving Day

TINY TURKEY PILLOWS

Place these tiny pillows on the couch or an easy chair for a soft, turkey touch.

What You'll Need: Old knit glove, cotton balls, glue, clothespins, craft feathers, yellow and red felt, scissors, 2 wiggle eyes, fabric paint

These soft little pillows are just the thing to brighten up the furniture during the Thanksgiving season. To make your turkey pillow, stuff an old knit glove with cotton balls until it is entirely full. Turn the bottom edges inside, and glue them together. Hold the edges shut with clothespins until the glue dries. Glue colorful craft feathers between and around the fingers of the glove. Cut a beak from yellow felt and a wattle (the turkey's red throat) from red felt. Glue them on the side of the thumb. Decorate your bird by gluing on wiggle eyes. You can also paint details on the turkey's body with fabric paint. You might want to paint a name on your turkey. How about Tillie? Terwilliger? Thomasina?

359

Thanksgiving Day

PIN THE TAIL ON THE TURKEY

Help the Thanksgiving turkey get a tail!

What You'll Need: Large poster board, crayons, construction paper, double-sided tape, scissors, bandanna

Here's a great game for everyone to play after that big Thanksgiving meal. It's guaranteed to get everyone giggling! Draw a large, silly-looking turkey without any tail feathers on a piece of poster board. Hang it on the back of a door or on a wall. Draw lots of turkey tail feathers on construction paper, and cut them out. Put a small piece of double-sided tape on the end of each feather. To play pin the tail on the turkey, use a bandanna to blindfold players one at a time. Twirl them around 3 times, and point them in the direction of the turkey. Who can pin the tail on the turkey? Perhaps the prize will be a big slice of pumpkin pie!

PILGRIM CLOTHING

Much of what we believe the pilgrims wore is incorrect. They did not wear those large buckles or tall hats—those weren't around for another hundred years! They only wore black on Sunday—red, green, brown, gray, and lavender earthtones were for everyday wear. And boys usually wore dresses until they were 8 years old!

360

Thanksgiving Day

HEADDRESS NAPKIN RINGS

These napkin rings will help your holiday table honor the people who made Thanksgiving possible.

What You'll Need: Cardboard paper towel tube, scissors, markers, construction paper, craft feathers, glue

The Native American people helped the pilgrims survive by teaching them about the different foods that grew in this land. The holiday of Thanksgiving started with a big dinner that celebrated the first harvest as well as the new friendship between the Native Americans and the pilgrims. Remember the role of the Native Americans of long ago at your dinner this holiday with these pretty napkin rings. First cut a ¾-inch-wide ring from the cardboard tube for each napkin ring you want to make. Use markers to color the rings, and draw Native American designs all around them. Draw and cut tiny feathers from construction paper, and fringe their edges with your scissors to make them look more featherlike. You can also use craft feathers or a combination of both. Glue the feathers inside the napkin ring. When the glue dries, slip the rings over rolled napkins and lay one across each person's dinner plate.

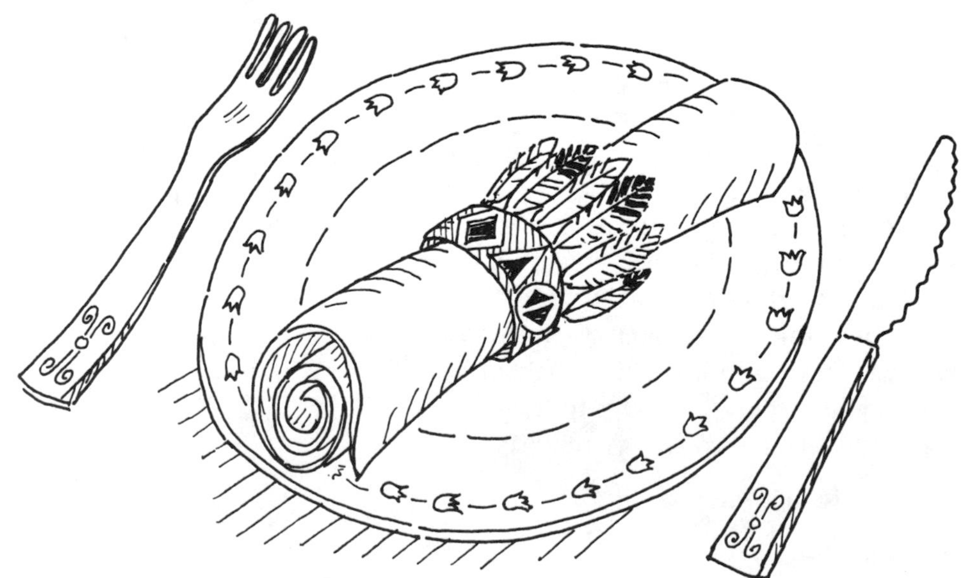

Thanksgiving Day

SALT AND PEPPER PILGRIMS

Now you'll always have pilgrims at your holiday table!

What You'll Need: 2 clean, empty spice jars with shaker tops, paints, paintbrushes, salt, pepper

At the very first Thanksgiving there were no salt and pepper shakers. But there were pilgrims! Now you can have pilgrims at your Thanksgiving with these nifty shakers that you make from spice jars. Make sure that each jar is well washed and dried. Paint a male pilgrim on one and a female pilgrim on the other. Label one jar "Salt" and one jar "Pepper." Now fill them up to decorate your Thanksgiving table!

Thanksgiving Day

TURKEY FEATHERS GAME

362

Know your feathered friends—or lose the game!

Gather together 5 or more players for this fast-paced game. One person is the leader, who will say "Turkey Feathers, Turkey Feathers" while flapping his or her arms. Other players should flap their arms, too. The leader keeps calling out, "Turkey Feathers" again and again, sometimes naming other creatures—some that have feathers and some that do not. For example, the leader may say, "Chicken Feathers, Pig Feathers, Dog Feathers, Turkey Feathers, Turkey Feathers, Mouse Feathers, Robin Feathers" while flapping and flapping his or her arms. Any other player who flaps her or his arms when a non-feathered creature, such as pig or dog or mouse, is called is out. The last person still playing when everyone else is out gets to be the leader for the next round.

363

Thanksgiving Day

FRUITY TURKEYS

These gobblers will be gobbled up in a hurry!

What You'll Need: Oranges, knife, spoon, fresh or frozen cranberries, honey, measuring cup, blender, small carrot sticks, cherry tomatoes or radishes, toothpicks, raisins or currants, small plate, leafy lettuce

Is there a vegetarian in your family? A vegetarian is someone who doesn't eat meat. Even a vegetarian will enjoy this special turkey! Cut an orange in half and scoop out the insides. You might need an adult to help you do this. Put the pulp, 1 cup cranberries, and ¼ cup honey into the blender. Mix well. Spoon the mixture into the orange halves. Use small carrot sticks to form the turkey's tail feathers. Stick a cherry tomato or a radish on a toothpick for the turkey's head. Raisins or currants stuck on bits of broken toothpick can be poked into the tomato or radish for the turkey's eyes. Two bits of broken toothpick can be used for the turkey's beak. Set your turkey on a plate, and surround it with lots of leafy lettuce. Everyone will agree that this turkey is gobble-gobblin' good!

Thanksgiving Day

BALLOON PARADE

364

Hold your own Thanksgiving Day Parade!

What You'll Need: Balloons in assorted sizes, shapes, and colors; glue; permanent markers; string

Blow up lots of different-colored and shaped balloons. You may need an adult to help you do this. Glue several balloons together to make animals and your favorite cartoon characters. Draw on faces and clothes. Tie a long string to each animal or character, and march your balloony creations outside in a neighborhood Thanksgiving Day Parade. Make a big turkey and a pilgrim. Make your family dog. Is that Superwoman flying so high in the sky?! (Caution: Balloons are choking hazards. Keep them away from small children and pick up all broken pieces immediately!)

Thanksgiving Day

BIRDIE'S THANKSGIVING HOUSE

Give your local birds something to be thankful for.

What You'll Need: Milk carton, waterproof paint, wooden dowel or craft stick, glue, string, scissors, bird seed

Everyone loves a Thanksgiving feast—even birds! Wash and dry a large milk carton. On one side, trace and cut out a round hole big enough for a bird to pop through. Glue a dowel or craft stick below the hole so the birds will have a place to sit outside their house. Now paint the birdhouse in pretty colors. Write the words "Thanksgiving House" on the sides if you want. Fill the bottom of the bird-house with bird seed. Then have an adult poke a hole in the top. Thread the hole with strong string, and tie it to a tree branch that is easy to see from your window. Watch the birds come and celebrate!

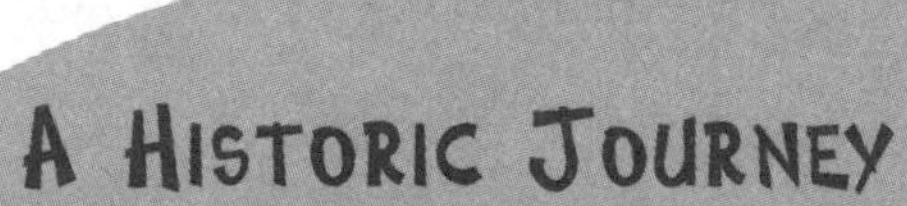

The voyage from Plymouth, England, to Plymouth Harbor took the Mayflower 66 days, but the Mayflower was never used again as a passenger ship. There were 51 men, 22 boys, 20 women, and 11 girls on board the ship. The oldest passenger to participate in the first Thanksgiving was William Brewster, who was 54 years old.

CALENDAR

Christmas

Winter

Hannukah—End of November to early December (determined by Jewish calendar)

St. Nicholas Day—December 6

Christmas Card Day—December 9

Winter Solstice—About December 22 (determined by solar calendar)

Kwanza—December 26 to January 1

Christmas—December 25

Trivia Day—January 4

Epiphany—January 6

Thank You Day—January 11

Martin Luther King, Jr., Day—Third Monday in January

Chinese New Year—Late January to early February (determined by Chinese calendar)

Groundhog Day—February 2

National Inventor's Day—February 11

Abraham Lincoln's Birthday—February 12

Valentine's Day—February 14

George Washington's Birthday—February 22

Mardi Gras—Pré-Lent (Late February to early March)

Spring

Hinamatsuri—March 3

Purim—in March (determined by Jewish calendar)

St. Patrick's Day—March 17

Vernal Equinox—About March 21 (determined by solar calendar)

Easter—Late March to early April

Passover—Late March to early April (determined by Jewish calendar)

April Fool's Day—April 1

Children's Book Day—April 2

Flower Festival—April 8

Earth Day—April 22

Arbor Day—April 22

May Day—May 1

Cinco de Mayo—May 5

Mother's Day—Second Sunday in May

Memorial Day—Last Monday in May

Easter

Summer Solstice

Summer

Flag Day—June 14

Children's Day—Second Sunday in June

Friendship Day—June 15

Juneteenth—June 19

Summer Solstice—About June 22 (determined by solar calendar)

Father's Day—Third Sunday in June

Canada Day—July 1

Independence Day—July 4

Bastille Day—July 14

Ice Cream Day—Third Sunday in July

Moon Day—July 20

Family Day—Second Sunday in August

Night of the Falling Stars—August 11

National Aviation Day—August 19

Fall

Labor Day—First Monday in September

Grandparent's Day—First Sunday after Labor Day

Back to School—Late August to mid-September (determined by school district)

Rosh Hoshanah—Early to late September (determined by Jewish calendar)

Yom Kippur—Early to late September (determined by Jewish calendar)

Citizenship Day—September 17

World Gratitude Day—September 21

Autumnal Equinox—About September 22 (determined by solar calendar)

Native American Day—Fourth Friday in September

Oktoberfest—Late September to early October

Columbus Day—Second Monday in October

Sweetest Day—Third Saturday in October

United Nations Day—October 24

UNICEF Day—October 31

Halloween—October 31

All Saints' Day—November 1

Veteran's Day—November 11

Thanksgiving Day—Fourth Thursday in November

Sweetest Day

INDEX